Tír na n Óg

Moving to Lisdoonvarna

By

Nancy Chambers

Editing & Maps

By Philip Ward

Cover image: The Meadow at Rockville

Gradually I became aware of the softness of the grass. The meadow had been cut in July and the new grass felt soft and cool at the end of the day. The edges were never cut, and the flowers continued to grow and offer up their sweet scent, which was always stronger in the evening.

ACKNOWLEDGEMENTS

I thank Joe, my first-born Grandchild, who in his early years unwittingly planted the seeds. Liam is the Gaelic name for William, his second name.

I must thank Claire Considine, who read the first chapters and encouraged me to continue.

I wish to pay tribute to Liz Perrott, Judy Evans, Gabriel Marshall, Sr. Mary O'Callaghan, David McGhee and Antoinette Lythgoe, who took the time to read the early draft. Their comments were challenging, but spurred me on.

I would like to thank Delyth Williams for giving me permission to print the poem which her husband Les wrote for me when he tutored me in the Welsh language.

My grateful thanks to Eileen Clark for reading the final manuscript; correcting and commenting where she thought fit.

Heartfelt thanks to Carrie for her thoughtful appraisal of the author's note, and her observations regarding the maps.

Special thanks to Alan, Sarah and Jessica Heal, and Chris, Katie and Matt Cooper for being the special people they are; always ready to listen, and provide thought-provoking answers.

My everlasting gratitude to Jack Flannagan of Kilshanny who contacted me after reading a copy of Tír na nÓg – Áine's Diary, which I had published in 2009. Jack kindly supplied me with a paper which he had written concerning the Phosphate Mines, particularly the Doolin mine, where he remembered my Father having worked as Paymaster. The importance of those mines, when the supply from Africa ceased during the emergency, as well as the family history, made fascinating reading. It also supplied me with many missing details regarding that period. My regret is that I didn't have more time to spend in his company. May he rest in peace.

I am particularly indebted to Philip Ward who has travelled with me on what has sometimes been a laborious six-year journey; editing, commenting rigorously, and map-making.

Finally, I pay tribute to the inhabitants of my local community in Bryncrug where I have spent the past thirty years, for allowing me 'to be' in the heart of the beautiful Snowdonia Valley, which has many similarities to the Fertile Crescent, called The Burren.

DEDICATION

I dedicate this book to my Grandchildren

MOVING TO LISDOONVARNA
CONTENTS

FOREWORD

Nine-year-old Áine becomes rebellious when she learns that she is to move from her idyllic surroundings at Rockville, in County Clare. Living halfway up a mountain in the Burren has given her an affinity with the earliest inhabitants of that place - the Celts, which will be with her throughout her life

Áine's grandfather, a retired headmaster, concerned about her reaction to the forthcoming move, decides to prepare her, not merely for the change which is due to take place, but also for life's journey. For Áine his story became a fascinating, frustrating, rollercoaster of emotions, which relied on her unbounded love and admiration for him, to keep her steadfast throughout. It was to be a story for which she learned to be truly grateful as she journeyed onwards: one which helped to explain why he had chosen that out-of-the-way place to spend his life, helping others to get the best out of theirs.

This is the story that Áine shares with her grandson, as they spend time in her favourite place: the place of her childhood, believing that this will prepare him, as it did her, for whatever is to come.

Nancy Chambers

Long, long ago, beyond the misty space
Of twice a thousand years,
In Erin old there dwelt a mighty race,
Taller than Roman spears;
Like oaks and towers
They had a giant grace,
Were fleet as deers,
With winds and waves they made their 'biding place,
These western shepherd seers.

Thomas D'Arcy McGee, 'The Celts'

CHAPTER I

MOVING TO LISDOONVARNA

"Why are you crying, Nan?"

"Oh Liam, I am just being a bit silly really, remembering how it was all those years ago. You know I can't stand here looking down to the sea, with the Aran Islands in the distance, without feeling emotional."

"Well, you have told me often that it isn't wrong to cry occasionally, but you've been sad for some time and you didn't even notice when I tugged your sleeve earlier, and I don't know what I can do to help."

Nan puts her arm round Liam's shoulders and says reassuringly, "You are here with me: that's all the help I need. You see, despite all those stories I have shared with you about the first ten years here, I have never been able to think about the day I left this place, well not until now, and then only because you asked the question, "How did you feel when you moved to Lisdoonvarna?" Nobody has ever asked me that question before, and perhaps it's as well, considering my behaviour just now. Oh! Imagine if anyone saw me, they would surely say, what a silly old woman. Heavens, I have to laugh at the very thought."

Liam seems very relieved at the sound of Nan's laughter, but he is still quite serious as he says, "Well I won't laugh, and if it doesn't upset you too much, I really would like to hear what happened after your Grandma died, and why you moved from here?"

"That could be a long story," Nan replies, looking closely at the young man before her; how much he has changed, even in the brief time since they last met. And lad she can no longer call him, for here is someone on the threshold of manhood; a young man whose shyness at times threatens to drown those gifts he needs to explore – a delightful disposition, with a need to care for others and yet a wish to tease also. Now in the grips of the teenage challenge to go forward, be happy, be aware, make decisions, be responsible for his actions and be kind and sociable to all both within and without the family home. What a tall order, when as yet he doesn't know what being really means. But it is a challenge which faces him, and all teenagers. During the time they have been here it has been possible to see how this somersault has been affecting him, and the pendulum keeps moving; happy one moment, then thoughtful; angry then remorseful; needing answers yet wanting to challenge them – the thought processes perpetually challenging all that has gone before, and the questions about the future railroading at every bend on this very tricky journey. It could almost be compared to a train journey without a known destination. It's almost as though he has a ticket which is only valid as far as the first main station, where the trains depart in many directions to their appointed destinations. There are many seasoned travellers there, but there are the first timers too. The overhead rolling screens display the names of the main stopping places along the route. Anyone needing to leave the train at these stations will need to be ready to exit as soon as the train stops. The on board announcements aren't always very clear, and the assistant isn't always readily available when in doubt. At the main station there is the constant noise of trains coming and going; people alighting or boarding – sometimes scrambling to catch the next train on their planned route. All this is accompanied by the constant sound of the loudspeaker regarding the incoming and outgoing trains, with reminders of what to do and not to do next. Even for the seasoned travellers, who normally look relaxed, almost bored at times, a last minute announcement regarding a platform change or cancellation can cause temporary chaos; there is anger and frustration because of the disruption, and worry about how this change will affect the remainder of their schedules. Meanwhile the first timer, trying to make sense of all the confusion, has to believe that he is heading in the right direction. And we all know how that feels.

Now, confronted by this deeply thoughtful first timer, Nan realises that there would be many questions to come but, hopefully, not too many arguments. Remembering Granddad's thoughtful answers to her own questions she hopes that she may, in some way, be able to emulate him. That too seemed to be a very tall order but, after all, Granddad and Grandma were the reason for her being here as an evacuee, all those years ago and Granddad, with his interest in teaching others, was the link between the present and the past. Despite her reluctance to revisit some of the past, now in her twilight years, she believes that the past should be a legacy for the future, not because of anything she has achieved personally, but in an attempt to convey to the hearts and minds of others that the end usually justifies the means. Looking back she has so often been reminded of Erik Erikson's *Eight Ages of Man*, where in infancy there is a battle between trust and mistrust, through to old age, where integrity is at war with despair. Liam, as a young adult, would definitely be able to identify with the sixth age where intimacy strives against isolation. But Nan, now in that eighth stage herself, realises with a wry smile, that *time waits for no man*.

Liam isn't too concerned about the silence this time, especially when he sees the smile. Then Nan chuckles and says, "I was just thinking about how much you have grown and that I will have to watch my p's and q's from now on."

Liam finds this highly amusing and laughingly says, "I thought I was supposed to be the one to do that!"

Nan still chuckling replies, "I will tell you as much as I can remember about my story, even though the early part may not be easy, and you can give yourself permission to ask questions wherever and whenever you like. Actually Liam, it is a story which might amaze you: not so much my part because I was simply a child who didn't really know where she was going. All I knew at the outset was that I didn't want to leave my haven in the Burren in order to move to Lisdoonvarna which, as you know is only three miles from here, but to me it seemed like another world. I didn't realise then, how fortunate I was in spending my formative years here. Nor did I appreciate the benefit of having two teachers in the house, but more especially my Granddad, who became my mentor at such an early age. The breadth of his knowledge, wisdom and patience, enabled me to find my real self and find the best way to manage that person. He was someone who had fulfilled his ambition in this out-of-the-way place, and he seemed at peace with himself. I could easily feel embarrassed when I think about my endless questions, and my need to know. Grandma refused to be harassed and invariably told me gently that I should wait until I was older, but she was not physically well and probably didn't need any extra challenges. Granddad took a different stance and later on you will hear how he managed to take me to the Middle East and back again in a very circuitous manner, as he outlined his story…a turbulent story for a turbulent pupil.

It is a perfect summer's day; bright and sunny with a gentle breeze. Finding two large stones with flat surfaces, which have been warmed by the sun, they make themselves comfortable. Seated as they are, it is possible for them to allow their gaze to wander down the slope and out over the sea to the distant horizon. To the left are the Aran Islands and on the right is Galway Bay. The sea looks magical with the sun dancing on the waves. All around them the butterflies and insects are hovering over the tall grasses and flowers. As always, it is an idyllic scene and it is difficult for Nan to take her thoughts back to those times which Liam is waiting to hear about. But do it she must and the sooner the better.

Turning to him she smiles and says, "You are asking why I moved from here and on such a glorious day it's difficult to imagine being anywhere else. I believe that there were a number of practical reasons for the move, at least from Mum and Dad's point of view, but I wasn't an adult then and practical reasons for doing things I didn't wish to do fell way short of my expectations. My parents didn't have time to consider my emotions as well as all the other problems which they needed to cope with. It's quite possible that the weather might have played a part in their decision too. The winter of 1946/1947 was to become one which no one was likely to forget, and few would wish to remember the worst blizzard to hit Ireland since 1917.

The summer of 1946 was described as miserable and wet. I was only seven years old at the time, and really excited at the thought of Uncle Ben and Aunt Alice coming from Dublin to stay in the Queen's (now Hydro) Hotel, in Lisdoonvarna, for their annual summer trip. Of course, I wasn't the only one to await their visit with such pleasure. Grandma used to say: "They are like a breath of fresh air and the motor car will make a nice change from our pony and trap." It was the highlight of the year for her because they came to lunch each day and took her out for a drive in the afternoon. Being quite little then, even though there may have been a car full of adults, it was still possible for me to join them, sitting on somebody's knee. That year though, it was a bit of a disaster because there were days when no one wished to go out in the rain; there were other days when we went out to Doolin and just sat in the car looking through the rain spattered windows at the waves crashing on the rocks. It was difficult being in such a confined space and not being able to ask a lot of questions, but this was Grandma's special time and interruptions from me would not have been appreciated.

The weather was causing problems for the farmers too. Ours was a small farm, which some people occasionally described as a sideline or hobby for Granddad, because it provided food rather than a living. Nevertheless our few animals did graze the fields, and the meadows provided some of their winter food. Like the majority of families, we had a crop of vegetables, which needed to be lifted and stored. However, it was the bigger farms on low-lying areas which fared worst. There was still a scarcity of food following the war, and tales of the devastation caused by the famine a hundred years earlier still gave rise to a real sense of unease. Eventually the army was enlisted to help to save the harvest. But it couldn't be all doom and gloom; fortunately, in our house, everyone liked mushrooms and we children loved picking them. After so much rain, September arrived; the weather was bright and sunny and the misty mornings provided ideal growing conditions for the mushrooms. My brothers and I went out early, and before the adults had time to enjoy the peace, we were back with our buckets full. We were allowed to sprinkle salt on some and place them on the range to cook. It was fascinating to watch the droplets develop as the grains of salt melted and we were always impatient to taste the first few. Because there were lots of them, and provided we didn't cause too many ructions, we could cook as many as we wished. Mum was able to prepare them in many different ways but they never tasted as good as those we cooked ourselves on the top of the range.

During August we youngsters had created a shallow lake in a field near the house by blocking the water running down into a gulley and creating a dam. It provided us with hours of fun, and some challenges too. There was no shortage of small stones for skimming and there were lots of sticks and feathers for floating; but that wasn't quite enough for my younger brother Patrick, who on one occasion disappeared into the barn to search for the redundant baby bath, and wasn't happy until he had assistance in carrying it to the lake. Whereupon he climbed into the bath, leaving his legs dangling over the side and successfully propelled himself out to the centre. Great, I thought, it will be my turn next. But then he tried to move within the bath and the inevitable happened. Tom, my eldest brother, was standing nearby and soon hauled the bath and its little captain onto dry land, but who would present the dripping victim to Mum? On that occasion we had to remain united and share the punishment. Alas, there would be no more trips to the lake for some considerable time."

Nan stops suddenly and, looking at Liam, realises that he needs to ask a question, but he laughs and says, "This wasn't one of your fields, was it?"

Nan knows what he is hinting at and replies, "No it wasn't but we weren't really trespassing because apart from cutting the hay which had to be done with a scythe, it had no other use. It wasn't possible to allow animals to graze there; the area was fenced off from the remainder of the field. The farmer was a friend of the family and knew what we were up to. However, we were strictly forbidden to go there until after the grass had been cut; when we waited patiently for a few weeks for the new grass to come through and provide a soft base as we tumbled down the hill. Of course, we couldn't do that once we dammed the gulley, but it was one of our play areas; we had to make a choice and, as the adults were always telling us, we should respect the boundaries beyond which we shouldn't go."

Liam seems happy and Nan continues, "The remainder of that autumn was uneventful; we managed to collect a bumper crop of blackberries, apples and hazelnuts, and were well prepared for Halloween and Christmas. The temperature was mild and this made such a difference when we set out in the dark to attend Mass on Christmas morning. Everyone prepared for the cold spell which usually followed Christmas, and when the wind changed direction in the middle of January, Grandma, who spent most of her days seated near the fire with a rug over her knees, began to recite her seasonal poem:"

The north wind doth blow and we shall have snow,
And what will the robin do then, poor thing?
He'll sit in the barn and keep himself warm
And hide his head under his wing, poor thing!

The north wind doth blow and we shall have snow,
And what will the swallow do then, poor thing?
Oh, do you not know? He's gone long ago
To a land that is warmer than ours, poor thing!

The north wind doth blow and we shall have snow,
And what will the children do then, poor things?
When lessons are done they'll jump, skip and run,
And play till they keep themselves warm, poor things.

"The snow didn't arrive immediately but the arctic wind did. Granddad said it must have come from Siberia, when the temperature dropped to below freezing. The adults seemed to be permanently gathered up."

A sudden laugh brings Nan's attention back to Liam who probably notices the smile as she was speaking and remembering.
"I haven't heard that expression before" he says.
"Well! I haven't heard it for many years either, but to us youngsters at the time it seemed funny. Now I know full well what it means. When you feel really cold you gather into yourself, in an attempt to keep the cold out, and people look very pinched when that happens."
"I don't think I have felt that. Will I have to wait until I reach your age to know that sensation?" Liam asks.

"I hope so, but if you were ill and cold I think you may

understand what I mean." Nan smiles and continues, "as I said, the adults were suffering, but for a time we youngsters, who didn't feel the cold as much, found immense pleasure in being out-of-doors. There was a large notice on the inside of the back door which read: 'Close the door', and underneath that, 'all those under twelve leave it open at their peril.' The lake had frozen over, and once it had been checked by Dad, we were able to skate there. But it was always good to be back indoors where peat fires burned in all the rooms. The snow didn't arrive until the beginning of February, when we had an overnight blizzard. Although the drifts were very deep it was still possible to build snowmen – without their noses, because the carrots were too valuable to waste. Within a few days the snow had melted, apart from the drifts in the hedgerows and by the roadside. Although the temperature dropped again, the wind had also dropped, and as the days went by, and despite the fact that the snow still remained where it had drifted, everyone began to look forward to spring. People didn't seem to be too concerned with the intermittent snowfalls, which continued well in to February.

Perhaps it's just as well we can't see into the future; hope, we are told, is a marvellous lifeline. Indeed we were hopeful, at least until the 24th February, when we awoke to a complete whiteout. We had heard the weather forecast on the radio the previous evening, which warned of more snow to come, but nothing could have prepared us for the blizzard, which had crept in during the night. It had only seemed like one more night of very high wind, and facing the Atlantic Ocean as we did, there didn't seem anything unusual in that - or so we thought, until the following morning!

There was no feeling of excitement this time, as we surveyed the windows which were almost completely covered by the snow banked up outside; this wasn't just drifting as it had been at the beginning of the month; this was deep all over snow, and it was still snowing. When we eventually found a window, with a small space at the top free of snow, we looked out at an unbelievable scene. There was a sense of unreality both outside and inside our house: a feeling of stillness, which seemed quite eerie. All those indoors were wondering how it was going to be possible to access the buildings outside because we were completely marooned. Granddad was hoping for a weather report when he switched the radio on. The radio spluttered and crackled for a while, with odd snatches of news, but finally gave up. The odd snatches of news that we were able to hear were sufficient to convey that this blizzard was one of the worst; it was countrywide but worse in some areas than others; it had to be bad to bring the cables down. The cables didn't affect us because, being so far up this mountain, there weren't any erected at that time. In some respects that was an advantage just then, because we weren't relying on any outside services.

It was to be some time before we heard who had been most severely affected, which was just as well, because we couldn't have done anything about it. Our immediate problem was how to reach the out-buildings, because although we had sufficient supplies of peat and vegetables for up to two days, no one expected the snow to have disappeared in that time and the store was on the other side of the back yard. As the house was situated part way up Knockauns Mountain, we had never suffered in the same way as those people who lived in the valleys. However Rockville was built into a high bank with a yard and high garden at the back. Fortunately, there was always a spade in the back porch which was used to dig out the stored potatoes and turnips; this would now be a lifeline. Opening the back door slightly Dad remarked: 'That's not going to be the way out. Let's hope and pray that it's better at the front door'.

The front door was at the side of the property, and thankfully the snow only came half way up the door. Dad was able to start moving it by working round the front towards the other side, and eventually to the back, where the real problem was. The snow at this point was shoulder high, and it was difficult for him to shovel it at that height. When he came indoors for a hot drink he asked Mum whether she and Tom, who was twelve years old at the time, could find some pails and help him to transport the snow round to the front. This was one occasion when the younger members tried to be on their best behaviour. Our new role was to help Granddad and Grandma to keep the hot drinks coming. By evening a narrow channel had been created to the storehouse in the yard, and the steps leading to the top garden had been cleared. The frustration for Dad was the build-up of snow on the cleared area, because the snow continued even though the wind had dropped. Night fell early because the sky was so laden, and he needed to resort to using oil lamps, which we called tilley lamps; ours were portable paraffin lamps in which air pressure was used to supply the burner with fuel. We all took turns in carrying the lamp as we followed Dad, even though there were lights burning in each of the windows. We discovered later that if we had had an electricity supply it would have been useless because so many of the cables were down. When Dad was able to survey the extent of the wider problem, his main concern was for the animals, which were kept in the cowshed and stable, but these were two fields away from our house. He knew it would be quite impossible for him to reach them that day. At least they were indoors and it would be the first task in the morning. Our prayers that evening were for those who would have suffered more hardship than us, and that there would be no more snow during the night.

When eventually we learned the full extent of the damage, with the loss of animal and human life, we had to count our blessings. But the freeze lasted for about three weeks and during that time everyone in our house was to be tested to the limit. There we were four energetic children and four adults, confined to our quarters. It was Granddad who, after the first few days, decided that there needed to be some order and discipline: the youngsters were to have lessons each morning.

Since we couldn't possibly go out to play and we couldn't even trap the birds because they were nowhere to be seen – this was our harmless competitive pastime as the birds were released immediately. We had a large box in which we had made lots of little holes; the front having a moveable flap which we propped open with a stick to which we attached a long piece of string. It was possible to open the kitchen window very slightly to allow the string to feed through and whoever was on duty quickly scattered the crumbs and then dashed indoors to join the others, where we could all watch unnoticed. It was exciting to watch the birds appear as if from nowhere and then proceed to squabble over the crumbs. We had to name the species and the number of each and then wait patiently, watching carefully until one decided to explore the inside of the box. The adults thought it one of the best occupations declaring that nothing else could keep us so quiet and for so long. Deprived of that particular pleasure we were happy to be organised and felt very fortunate to have a headmaster and teacher in the house, because they knew how to go about it. If Granddad thought we were flagging, he resorted to his favourite poem for reluctant pupils, as he presented us with our workbooks:"

'Drive the nail aright boys, hit it on the head;
Strike with all your might, boys, while the iron's red.
When you've work to do, boys, do it with a will;
They who reach the top, boys, first must climb the hill.
Standing at the foot, boys, gazing at the sky,
How can you get up, boys, if you never try?
Though you stumble oft, boys, never be down-cast;
Try, and try again, boys – you'll succeed at last.'

"Being the only girl around I sometimes took a dim view of all the boy stuff, but it was a case of three against one and I thought it best to keep my thoughts to myself! Anyway I felt much happier when the lessons were over and Grandma presented her own challenge – we were to practice improving our deportment. It was especially funny because I knew how the lads regarded this exercise, since it meant placing a book on our heads, and being reminded that we must keep our heads up, chins in, chests out and stomachs in. Tom, the eldest, usually became very red in the face: Joe was quietly tolerant: I quite liked it but our younger brother Patrick fell foul of the whole procedure because he couldn't control his giggles and the book kept falling off, causing Grandma to banish him to the next room. When we had finished Tom usually beat a hasty retreat as he muttered, 'What a waste of time.' His comment usually included a few words which didn't sound very appropriate to me; ones which I didn't feel that I could repeat to the elders in order to clarify them, even though they thought I was a tomboy. As I said some things are best kept to oneself!

What was a complete nightmare for the adults became, at times, a lot of fun for the children. The road outside our house was on a steep incline, which initially provided the ideal site for tobogganing, and later as an ice rink, until the adults decided that it was turning the main road into a potential disaster zone, which meant that a new location had to be found. I did join them on a few occasions but it wasn't my favourite pastime, because I spent too much time on my rear when I should really have been upright and keeping up with them; plus the problem of my chilblains which always seemed more annoying when I spent too much time out of doors. I couldn't understand why the boys didn't appear to have that problem. In any case there was always a need for my help indoors.

Attending school was out of the question for a few weeks, and when it did re-open, it was only possible for those children who lived closest to it to attend. Although there were two classrooms, and because on occasions we had only one teacher, we all gathered in one room. When that occurred we were spoilt, because the teacher lit a large fire in the classroom and the children were allowed to sit round it. We were given hot cocoa which seemed to taste much better than it did at home, but I think that was because it had more sugar in it. The teacher told us funny stories as we sipped our hot drinks and it felt more like a party, but we still had do some school work, and homework. When we delivered our usual report on arriving home, Grandma never missed the opportunity to remind us that we were lucky we didn't need to attend hedge schools."

"What are hedge schools Nan?"
"Well they are as the name implies, schools which sometimes took place behind hedges."

Noticing the smile which Liam couldn't seem to suppress, Nan laughs and says, "It does seem unbelievable now, doesn't it, that anyone would ever need to hide behind a hedge in order to learn how to read, write and do their sums and I will tell you more about that another time."

It was Liam's turn to laugh as he said. "I guess that wouldn't have been a problem for the Celts."

Seeing the surprised look on Nan's face, he added, "Well everyone knows how their creativity has inspired you, but I think you once said that they had left no written legacy. Could that be because they couldn't read or write?"

"Oops, now you really have interrupted my train of thought, but I am very happy that you have remembered what I said about the Celts, and we can return to the question of the move at another time. I know that I go on about the Celts but that's really because I see myself as a Celt, and my early years, living here, helped me to connect with the spirit of those ancient people. Even though approximately two thousand three hundred years separates the arrival of the Celts and the problem of the hedge schools. We couldn't have chosen a better spot for me to give you a glimpse into the Christian and historical background of this area which is so alive with evidence of their presence, and what imaginative reading their own records would have made. We are fortunate though that we do have evidence of their creativeness all around us, but it has been left to others to write about them. Whenever I return here I can sense their spirit, and each time I learn a little more about them, because archaeological excavations and research are proving that these early settlers were not only aware of and inspired by this beautiful lunar landscape, with its incredible flora, but they used their creativity to produce the artefacts which became their legacy. You know, for me, the Celts came to life the first time I stood in the grounds of Kilfenora Cathedral with Aunt Alice all those years ago, and in many ways I now realise that what I learned that day was to remain precious throughout my life. They weren't wishing to write about how they were feeling and what they were seeing. Theirs was a different approach; their gifts of imagination and creativity were combined with their learned skills to produce signs and symbols, which were manifested in so many ways in wood, stone and metal. They used all of nature's provision to communicate their inner appreciation of all that was available to them. They were a people who remained in touch with their spirit, and their legacy is an outward expression of their inner world: a means of self-expression whilst using their creative energy. They had many other attributes but these can wait. Whatever may have caused the sea bed to erupt millions of years ago we have to be thankful for all it provided us with and thankful also for the creative energy of those enlightened people."

Seeing the look of interest on Liam's face, Nan felt inclined to continue, but had become aware that the stone she was sitting on was very unforgiving and maybe, before launching into history and facts, it would be good to have a break. Liam sensed the change in her mood as she said, "My bones will cry out long before yours, but I do believe this could be a good opportunity for me to give you a background picture, which hopefully will help you to understand why the problem of hedge schools arose in the first place. Heavens! What a leap from the Celts who emerged in Europe in approximately 700 B.C. to the Penal Laws and the hedge schools in 1695 A.D. Now that is going to be my challenge because, in order to give you a proper picture, it will be necessary to go back long before 700 B.C." Liam couldn't help asking how long that might take and Nan laughs and says, "Well, we are not measuring time, and it would be difficult for me to estimate, but first things first! It's time for our drink and for me to part company with this stone whilst you collect my flask as well as your own drink, and can you bring my cushion too."

Within seconds Liam had the car boot open. "Didn't we pack something to eat," as he surveyed the hamper; knowing very well that it contained some of his favourite treats?

"Oh, very well," Nan laughs, "bring it all, we can have some now and save the remainder for later; at least it will ward off the pangs and help us to concentrate better."

"Well, you say that growing youngsters should eat, and may I say that you also tell me that old people need to eat a little and often."

"I do indeed," Nan replies, "but you missed some words didn't you?"

"You mean like healthy food," he laughs whilst his eyes are resting on the chocolate biscuits."

"Ah yes! The biscuits are for afterwards, and you should relish the thought that there would not have been any such treats for our forbears, since they had to struggle just to survive." They had re-seated themselves as she continued, "However, before we look at the distant past, and the implications it has had for us, I want to finish telling you about the period following that unforgettable winter; remembering, as I do, that everyone in Ireland suffered much hardship during that dreadful spell.

For days on end we appeared to be living in an isolated planet, but it didn't feel like living because we seemed to merely exist from one day to the next. Dad had managed to plough his way through to the cattle shed and feed the animals, but the milk yield was low. Fortunately we always had a stock of condensed milk; not that it was anyone's favourite choice and no matter that the porridge had an obnoxious taste, we were reminded that we must get it inside us – not pass it on to the dogs - because we must keep our strength up since we weren't to know what lay ahead.

The radio, our only source of outside communication, continued to crackle for three or four days, but finally Granddad's efforts paid off and we began to hear the countrywide reports, but they were very depressing stories from all over the country. The electricity supply had failed; there was a shortage of peat, and many Dubliners, who relied on electricity, resorted to chopping up their furniture for firewood: Uncle Ben and Aunt Alice gave us a detailed account of those problems when they came to visit us later in the year. Oil lamps and candles became a major necessity once more, but we were very fortunate in that respect because they were our main source of light, especially when the wind charger failed, which was quite often. In many respects we fared better because we had learned to be self-sufficient, but no one was happy to be so isolated. The main hardship was caused by the frost which followed the snow, and which made the ground rock hard, freezing the rivers, ponds, and our water butts.

It seemed inevitable that many homes were hit by the flu virus and ours was no exception; it was almost an annual occurrence. Thankfully Mum was, as always, a veritable tower of strength – Granddad and Grandma said so – but she became exhausted as she endeavoured to cope with so many invalids. It seemed that eating our porridge did give us young ones strength, and it wasn't long before we recovered. Unfortunately Grandma became a major source of worry, because she developed pneumonia which entailed a few visits by the doctor, who said that it would take considerable time before she was likely to return to fitness. Sadly it was to mark the beginning of her deterioration.

There was little change until the end of March; the thaw started round the time of St. Patrick's Day, accompanied by heavy rain which, we were told, made it the wettest spring for 300 years, and with so much frozen snow about it also seemed to be one of the sludgiest. We were all accustomed to the expression, 'Nothing lasts for ever', and that was true; gradually the sun became warmer and the March winds a little less bitter.

The only place people seemed to gather en masse was at Church, and there was that unforgettable day in April, when we gathered as usual for the mid-morning Service. Everyone emerged from the Church to brilliant sunshine; people were smiling and happy to stand about and chat. Even the old folk seemed to have a spring in their step. On our journey home we could see that the daffodils had fought their way through, and from then on it seemed that spring couldn't wait to fulfil its natural function: speeding up the whole process of regeneration and reminding us again of the beauty of creation.

Of course it wasn't only nature which appeared to be working overtime: there seemed to be a sense of urgency everywhere and in everything, which seemed to have been dormant for far too long. There were waterfalls and rivulets where we had not previously seen them. They glistened in the sun as they rushed to join the rivers which, in turn, became overfull and overflowed their banks in places, as they tumbled onwards towards the sea. The farmers worked long hours repairing the damage which had been caused by the storms, and preparing the soil for planting. The housewives, who took pride in their homes, were desperate to open the windows and get on with the spring-cleaning. There was such a flurry of activity, but what impacted most directly on the children was the need on the part of our teachers to catch up with our schoolwork. Of course they knew that, in our house, we would have had tuition and wouldn't have fallen behind; they reminded us that we should be prepared to help those who had not been so fortunate.

That was the year I became aware of the abundance of yellow spring flowers, probably because they all appeared to arrive at once. The daffodils were first, then came the primroses, marsh marigolds, irises, celandine, dandelions, cowslips, buttercups, and my favourites, the daisies. What a feast of yellow, but why yellow, when throughout the year there was such a wonderful variety of colour. Botany was one of Granddad's hobbies and he was delighted to be able to tell me about nature's cycle and colours. He took me through all the primary colours, but explained that yellow was the most luminous colour of the spectrum and could be seen from a considerable distance. I told him that I was already aware of that because it was possible to see the daffodils from afar. When I told him he said, 'Good, and if you can see them so can all the bees, as they unfurl themselves from their winter hibernation, and theirs is one of the first and most important springtime chores, to cross pollinate the plants and ensure that the cycle continues.' For me it was obvious that spring had indeed sprung, and with that thought came the question, why was it called spring? I suppose the answer lay in all I was witnessing, but I wanted to know who named the seasons. The answers had to wait because everyone was too busy, then.

It was a glorious summer, when all the crops flourished and people were able to forget what had gone before. Grandma was happy to sit out in the sunshine but, as I said earlier, she had remained feeble. Uncle Ben and Aunt Alice had made two visits from Dublin, and on those occasions had managed to take her out for a few drives, which lifted her spirits enormously: so she said. Shortly after their departure a letter arrived from another uncle called Tom, who apparently hadn't been home for a number of years. He was coming home and bringing his wife Dorothy with him. None of the family had met Dorothy previously, because Uncle Tom had married in England, and it was her first visit to Ireland. All the adults seemed to be full of anticipation and excitement at the prospect. Granddad and Grandma were particularly happy because Tom was their youngest son, whom they hadn't seen for some years, although they corresponded regularly. Although, like Uncle Ben and Aunt Alice, they stayed at the Queen's hotel in Lisdoonvarna, they spent their days with us, and took Granddad and Grandma for drives, except for one day when Grandma didn't feel up to the journey. That provided Uncle Tom with an opportunity to take Dorothy further afield and he said, 'Where better than the Galway Races.' Of course Granddad wouldn't leave Grandma: everyone else was busy, and Uncle Tom asked for Mum's permission to take me. It was a lovely warm summer's day, and my chores were completed before the visitors arrived, so Mum was happy to agree. The races had no particular appeal for me, but I felt that there would certainly be lots to see on the journey, and it would be interesting to see Galway city. Feeling hesitant with the new visitors, I didn't think that I would be asking lots of questions, but they seemed completely unaware of that and were in a very exuberant and talkative frame of mind.

The journey took just over an hour, although it didn't seem that long because Uncle Tom was talking about various interesting sites along the way. However, as we entered the racecourse a sense of indignation overwhelmed me, as I said, 'But this is not Galway. I thought we were going to Galway.'

My indignation increased when I realised that they appeared to be laughing at me, but Uncle Tom seemed to sense my disappointment and replied, 'Oh, I see what you mean: we are in Galway County but not the city, and you mustn't fret because when the races are over, we will be having a quick tour round the city.'

Having parked the car, we joined the masses of people, keeping in mind what Uncle Tom had told us about remaining close to him. The only racing I did was making sure that I didn't lose sight of him, whilst he dodged between the stand and the bookies, which happened a number of times during the course of the afternoon. Being small didn't really help: it isn't easy trying to see around people when one is in a crowd, and there were so many people too who, like Uncle Tom, spent so much time on the move. They only settled down when each race was taking place, and then it became bedlam as they cheered on their favourite horse.

There didn't appear to be any other little people present; if there were they must have been swallowed up, like me. I had overheard Uncle Tom explain to Dorothy earlier, that the Galway Races was a celebrated event, lasting two days and occurring annually at the end of July or beginning of August, with racing enthusiasts travelling from all over Ireland and England. There was a very festive atmosphere, which apparently started before and continued long after the racing events themselves. It was fun to share Uncle Tom and Dorothy's excitemen,t when a few of their chosen horses came in first, but I couldn't help but breathe a sigh of relief when it was all over, and we were making our way back to the car. The first stop was the nearest hotel where we had a lovely meal, but according to all accounts the hotels were well prepared for the influx of the racing enthusiasts, where once again the atmosphere was very jovial. Being allowed to choose my favourite dessert was one of the highlights of the trip: fresh cream trifle was normally a Christmas treat, and it wasn't even my birthday!

During the course of the meal Dorothy and I became very attentive listeners as Uncle provided some interesting historical details about Galway. Apparently a man named Richard de Burgh took the city of Galway in 1232 and made it his home, it became a prosperous Anglo-Norman colony having, among its settlers, a number of families whose descendants were to become known as the Twelve Tribes of Galway. Although there were fourteen tribes altogether, the description had apparently been used by one of Cromwell's team and it stuck. Unfortunately the settlers were at pains to avoid any contact with the native Irish people, who were Gaelic speaking, which didn't seem to me to be a recipe for peace. There followed a lot of interesting detail, at the end of which, although it was all very interesting and informative, I was left wondering why it seemed so difficult for tribes to live in harmony with one another. However Uncle Tom said that their legacy was still apparent in the form of architecture and many unusual features, including stone plaques dotted about the city. They were a tangible reminder of the Twelve Tribes of Galway, and he told me that I should try to see them for myself one day. The other legacy was the determination of those early natives to protect their culture, as well as the Irish language. Western Connemara and the Aran Islands are known as the Gaeltacht where the tradition is upheld to this day.

At last we were in the car and setting off on our excursion. The weather had remained beautiful throughout the day and it promised to be a heavenly evening. According to our navigator the journey was to be a feast for our eyes, with a commentary on one or two of the more interesting sites, and he continued as he winked at me and said, 'There is one particular place which I want you to see because I think it may have a special meaning for you.' That wink did the trick and from there on I became his ardent admirer, but it was impossible to suppress the giggle as I asked for more information; it wasn't forthcoming. Before long we had arrived in Salthill where we stopped briefly. I already knew that it was one of the most important Irish seaside resorts, with the longest promenade, because Uncle Ben and Aunt Alice sometimes made it their next destination after their visit to us. Unlike Doolin and Fanore which were our favourite haunts, the promenade in Salthill was ideal for long gentle strolls, so we were told. It was possible to look to the south and see the Burren across the bay, and to the southwest where the Aran Islands appeared to guard the entrance to Galway Bay.

Shortly after we resumed our journey we turned off the coast road and travelled inland for a few minutes, before arriving at the little village called Claddagh, which is known to be the oldest fishing village in Ireland. It was a *look and see* before we returned to the coast road, and I guessed that it was going to be one of those places about which we would hear more on our journey home. That wasn't a cause for concern because I already knew the whole romantic story of the Claddagh ring, which is shaped with two hands holding a heart over which there is a crown, and it symbolises everlasting love and friendship. I suspected that it would have to be a story for Dorothy later.

Along our route we passed through Barna, Spiddal, and many little hamlets whose names I couldn't remember, with the exception of one which was called Ballynahown; this was very familiar to me since we had an area by that name just up the road from our house. It was indeed a beautiful drive enhanced by the evening sun which cast a magical glow over all. The enchantment and the effects of the meal earlier were inclined to take their toll, and my eyelids were feeling very heavy, but suddenly the road forked to the right and we began to travel round Cashla Bay, where the scenery changed dramatically. There were so many indentations or sea inlets, and numerous craggy islands. Just before arriving at the head of the bay we turned left to Rossaveal, where we had our second stop. The pier was similar to the one in Doolin, but whilst Doolin had only one safe pier Galway and the Connemara region boasted many safe bays where sailors could harbour their boats. Apparently one of the larger boats was called the Galway Hooker, which made regular trips to the Aran Islands. The Hooker (Bád Mór) was the name used for the largest of this type of boat, and there were three smaller grades but all had sails, whereas it was necessary to use oars for the currach.

Whether the currach would have been used to row to the Islands from Galway, or not, it was still used to travel from Doolin. Although I didn't know much about Galway City I was able to tell my companions about the Aran Islands, because we had covered that subject at school, and we knew that the people living there had a very austere existence. In the same way that the very early dwellers in the Burren needed to clear the forest, the Islanders needed to do likewise, but unfortunately they mistakenly removed the roots of the trees and the harsh winds blew the soil away. They were known to have created their own soil by using sand and seaweed from the beach, which was mixed with fishmeal and manure. They managed to produce fertile soil which allowed them to grow potatoes. Since there was no shortage of stones they built high walls round small enclosures, which protected the crops and also the animals from the ferocious Atlantic gales. Over time they built up a trade with Connemara, Galway and Clare. Turf was one of the main imports, with Aran sweaters for which they became renowned being one of the main exports. They spun and knitted or wove their garments, and every man was known to possess a *bawneen* – a white homespun coat which is weather resistant and long lasting. Sea fishing remained one of the main activities but the sea claimed many lives.

We were on the move again, through Cashla and on to Screeb, where we turned left off the main road and travelled down the other side of the bay to Kilkieran, which was so called after Saint Kieran of Clonmacnoise, who was reputed to have stopped there after visiting the Aran Islands. As Uncle Tom was giving us that information, I noticed that he had begun to drive faster. Very shortly we turned left again onto a *boreen,* which was very narrow and not well maintained. It was a bumpy ride and I was intrigued because we were still travelling faster than we had been on the main road. Dorothy must have been perplexed too, although she was laughing as she said, 'What's the hurry,' as she hung on to her seat. We made yet another left turn and it became necessary to slow down and navigate with care, because that lane wasn't really suitable for cars. Fortunately it was a short drive and we quickly arrived at the shore of a little place called Ard, which was at the tip of the Peninsula. Uncle, who hadn't uttered a word since we passed Kilkieran, switched off the engine and took a deep breath, followed by a long sigh. As quick as a flash he was out of the car, opened the rear door and said to me, 'Now young lady your parents and grandparents have been telling me what an inquisitive busybody you are, and I am hoping you will be happy when I tell you a story about this place, which happens to be very special to me.'

As far as I was concerned there didn't seem to be anything exciting there. We had driven through an area of unimaginable beauty, with crags, islands, lakes and flat boggy areas, all bathed in the soft glow of the evening sun, in order to arrive at a spot which, by comparison, seemed very drab. Dorothy didn't appear to be very excited by the changed surroundings and made no attempt to get out of the car. However, Uncle Tom had already extended his hand to me, and I had no choice but to alight and scamper over the rocky ground until we reached the water's edge. Having located a flat stone on which he perched himself, he invited me to join him.

In stark contrast to the gentle waves, which were lapping near our feet, my feelings and emotions were very turbulent. What on earth had induced him to go there and take me with him, but turning to me he said, 'I know that your imagination will help you to fill in the gaps as I give you the bare details. Now look out to sea and tell me what you can see.' 'Well! Just more islands and there are so many.' I replied. He seemed intense, but not impatient with me as he agreed, whilst indicating one of the islands, which looked very small indeed. 'That one is Saint MacDara's Island!' Oh! So that was the reason for his quietness and my mental turmoil; Saint MacDara, had given his name to the valley where my brothers and I spent many happy hours. Inevitably, Uncle Tom, my Dad and the other uncles would have done likewise. Oughtdarra was our hunting and feasting ground.

As I grew up I came to realise that there is no accounting for human emotions in any given circumstances. I knew that the information I had been given was real, and not fiction or myth, as many of our earlier stories had been. However the emotion I happened to be wrestling with at that moment was not due to excitement regarding the news he had given me, but rather to the knowledge that I was seated next to someone who had been where I was; had grown up in the Burren and visited all those places which I loved, but who had subsequently become an exile. It had obviously caused him considerable heartache and homesickness. At that moment I realised why he had wanted me to share his journey, knowing that I could empathise with him.

Throughout the day there had been so much laughter and merry-making; it seemed strange to hear the gentle laugh, so tinged with sadness as he said, 'They didn't warn me that you could be so quiet and for so long.' Could I be bold enough to share my thoughts with him, and tell him that I was trying to understand what being an exile really felt like? Why not! I didn't need to ask if the name MacDara evoked the same sentiment in him as it always did in me: he had already demonstrated that it did.

Everyone knew that Saint Patrick was the Patron Saint of Ireland, and even though he was reputed to have paid a visit to Connemara, he still appeared very remote from us, whereas Saint MacDara, who was of the same era (5th century) was much closer to home. He was reputed to have been on the Aran Islands with Saint Enda, but they had had a disagreement and Saint MacDara had made his way to Oughtdarra, which is the valley near our home, and where my brothers and I went nut-picking and apple-scrumping. It was easy to imagine how he would have accomplished his journey by using a currach or even more primitive boat, and island hopped from Inishmore to Inishmaan, and on to Inisheer, where a final hop would have taken him to Doolin. From there he would have travelled on foot to Oughtdarra, which was a very sheltered and secluded valley. We were told that he was followed by other monks, but it is also likely that one or two may have joined him on his initial journey. He had built a church in the valley and the ruins are still there, as proof of his presence; so too is the graveyard which was supposed to have been for the burial of infants under the age of seven. However, we had also been told the sad story of the mother, who during the famine period in 1845-1849, had carried her dead grown-up son's body down the mountain in order to bury him there. She had done so because she had hoped that by concealing his death for just a few days, she would have been able to claim his ration of meal – oats roughly ground. Unfortunately someone reported having seen her, and she was only allowed to claim her own ration. I had been upset and indignant when I first heard the story, because the mother so obviously needed the food but Grandma, who told the story, reminded me that starving people become desperate, and there were many of them.

Uncle Tom had said that he would give me the facts about Saint MacDara and his island, but there were two questions which I really wanted to ask him before we returned to the car, where Dorothy was waiting patiently. My brothers and I had explored the Oughtdarra valley and had seen what looked like a number of cave openings, and I asked if he and my others uncles, and Dad had done any exploration of the caves. Apparently they had but not to any depth because they weren't equipped with any means of lighting their way forward. I was particularly interested because I believed that all the early settlers would have used caves, where they were available, as their first place of shelter. So too with Saint MacDara, and as the valley was surrounded on two sides by high cliffs, which were part of the Knockauns mountain, there was ample choice. There was no time for the second question because Uncle had looked at his watch and remarked, 'When we set out this morning I hadn't intended travelling this far, but I am very glad that I did and you will have more background to our local saint. We don't actually know how long he spent in Oughtdarra but it is believed that he ministered to a wide area, and there would have been many more families living there long ago. Since there are a number of old churches dotted about the area he must have enticed others to follow him. Would he have left another monk in charge when he departed and made his way to Connemara, where he sought the seclusion of the little island? Would he have been on his own or had company with him on his journey? We do not know the answers to these questions but he would not have made a beeline for the island, and must have spent time in Moyrus, near Carna, where there is a church dedicated to him. Regardless of his movements we do know that he has been adopted by the Connemara people living on the western shores as their local

Saint, and many make pilgrimages to the island twice a year. On the island he built a one-roomed chapel which has a dirt floor. Apparently the original chapel was made of wood, but the present structure is one of large stones with a stone roof, although only part of that remains. The island also has another building which presumably was living accommodation, and it is the final resting place of the Saint. He was known to be the Patron Saint of fishermen and sailors in that area; there are many tales, and some superstitions, which abound. Regardless of the truth of the stories it remains a fact that boatmen always dip their sails three times in honour of the Saint.

As I said there was no time for the second question, because Uncle Tom declared that it was time to take me back home in case my parents started to worry. We didn't return via the coast road but took a more direct inland route in order to join the main Galway road.

After our sojourn on the peninsula, Uncle Tom was more subdued and spoke quietly to Dorothy, leaving me to pursue my own thoughts, and my goodness how many there were. The overriding thought was the question, which I hadn't asked earlier, concerning Saint Enda and his association with Saint MacDara. With my thoughts still in a state of turmoil, I knew that I needed to resist the drowsiness which had returned again, and be remote from all about me. That wasn't usually a problem for me, and Uncle Tom and Dorothy would hopefully assume that I had finally succumbed to sleep. Uncle had said earlier that it would take us approximately two hours to arrive home, and by that time I hoped to have a proper skeleton for my story. As I battled with the desire for sleep I seemed to hear again the words of Granddad's favourite poem for reluctant pupils,

'Standing at the foot, boys, gazing at the sky,
How can you get up, boys, if you never try?
Though you stumble oft, boys, never be down-cast;

Try, and try again, boys – you'll succeed at last.'

I guess that was the impetus which fired me, and as I chuckled to myself, I decided that I didn't need to be a boy, or even a tomboy in order to prove that I could at least try! But where could I begin? That was the problem!

There were actually three issues to wrestle with: St. Enda and the Uí Neill Dynasty: the Celtic Saints on the Aran Islands, and why did Saint MacDara fall out with Saint Enda. There is no record of Saint MacDara having been on the Islands, and he may not have had a falling out with Saint Enda at all. His stay might have been a very temporary one before he was sent out to work in unknown territory. Since there was no record, I decided that I could use my own imagination as well as listening to other people's stories, and somehow try to make sense of it all. I put those three problems into my framework."

CHAPTER II

REVELATION

"Whenever I stood outside Rockville, looking across to the Aran Islands, I began to think about Saint Enda. What had attracted him to that place. We know that at one time those islands had been an extension of the Burren, and had it still been the case I guessed that history would have told a different story. On one occasion I imagined what it could have been like to venture there on foot, but having travelled there by currach with Dad, I realised that it would have been more of the same, just an extension of where I was living. Time and the Atlantic Ocean had separated them from us, and enabled them to become a very important part of history, and apparently very inviting, since it was Saint Enda's choice to go there. So, who was he? Where did he come from? What were his beginnings? Why the Aran Islands? There are so many islands off the coast of Erin.

Those were many of the thoughts which had been on my mind as we began to learn about Niall Noígiallach (Niall of the Nine Hostages), who was the Head of the Uí Néill Dynasty in Ireland: a subject of great interest to Granddad. It was more interesting because Niall appeared to be the bridge between the mythical stories, which we had been accustomed to hearing, and recorded history. It became easier to identify with the time scale. I wasn't too concerned with Niall's ancestry but could relate to him as King of Meath. Previously there had been four provinces in Ireland, namely: Ulster, Leinster, Munster and Connacht, with each province having its own King, but when Niall and his sons conquered Meath and much of the area surrounding it, he established himself as King of that Province, eventually becoming High King or *ard ri* of Ireland. We knew that he was a Celt and a pagan, who carried out many raids on England and Wales, taking booty and slaves back with him. It was on one of these raids on South Wales that he is reputed to have taken about two hundred slaves: men, women and children. Among his captives was a sixteen-year-old boy named Patricius, whose family was of noble birth; his father being a deacon and a local magistrate. The boy, who was later to become known as Patrick, was taken from what was believed to be a life of luxury to one of slavery. He was sold to a chieftain named Milchu, a Druid Priest who owned the territory around Slemish mountain in County Antrim. It was there that Patrick became a shepherd learning to speak the Irish language, and learning all he could about the pagan practices of the druids. It was said that during his enslavement over a period of six years, he used frequent prayer to help him to cope with his loneliness. On one such prayerful occasion he had heard a voice which told him to leave that place and return home. According to his own *Confession*, he travelled over two hundred miles to the ship, discovering after it had sailed, that it wasn't travelling to England but to Gaul. His confession includes, among other interesting details, the hardship that he and the other sailors suffered after they landed, and whilst they travelled on foot for twenty-eight days through very desolate country. That journey must have led him to Auxerre, because we know that it was there that he was trained for the priesthood by Saint Germanus, who was Bishop at that time. The whole of his story was very familiar to all school children, but I was more concerned with what happened when he returned to Ireland. As I said earlier we had been learning about Patrick's captor, Niall and I was caught up in the mystery of Niall, his sons, and their conversion.

Niall is reputed to have had twelve sons and at least two daughters, but by the law of averages I always suspected that there were other daughters too. Apart from the first four sons, I didn't focus on the others, but the four were called Lóegaire (Leary), Eógan, Conall(Gulban) and Enda, who followed in their father's footsteps taking other people's lands and possessions. I could imagine them building their clans and tribes, since we had been told that they and their descendants became the tribal Kings who ruled most of our island. There was a difference between King and High King. I had guessed that King actually meant overlord, because there was only one *ard ri* or High King, who ruled from Tara in County Meath, but they were all Pagan Celts.

When Niall died the Kingship passed to Lóegaire, who happened to be reigning when Patrick returned to Ireland after his ordination in Rome. There are many enlightening stories regarding Patrick's movements following his return, two of which were favourites of mine. The first was the conversion of Lóegaire after Patrick's encounter with the Druids on the Hill of Slane, County Meath.

Patrick had arrived on the Hill of Slane in time to light the first Easter Paschal candle, which he did without realising that King Lóegaire had given orders that all fires should be extinguished before the druid's fire was lit. The King and the druids were positioned on the Hill of Tara, about twenty miles away as the crow flies from Slane, and they were about to light their fire to celebrate the Beltaine Festival (Spring Equinox). The King suddenly noticed the fire on the Hill of Slane, and asked who the culprit was. The Druids were very fearful of Patrick, and wanting him killed they were happy to enlighten the King, who summoned Patrick to appear before him. The ensuing contest required that Patrick and the Druids demonstrate their supreme power in front of him. It seemed to be a contest between good and evil, or the godly versus the ungodly, with the outcome being the conversion of the Pagan King to Christianity.

The second story involved the conversion of Lóegaire's brother-in-law Óengus, who was King of Munster, and that story was told to me by Aunt Alice, who had a wonderful sense of humour. Apparently Patrick always carried his crozier, with a spear like tip, which made it easier to penetrate the soil when he needed both hands to be free. That was the case as he stood before king Óengus at the time of his conversion, but in the process of setting the Crozier down, he accidentally put it through the King's foot. Being full of remorse when he noticed what he had done he asked the king why he hadn't cried out, but the king told him that he had thought it to be part of the ceremony. I smiled again as I remembered laughing and hopping around on one foot as Aunt Alice told the story. Sadly though, Saint Enda's conversion was very different and quite sad.

Enda was a prince who was determined to prove that he could be a king, and to that end he followed in his father Niall's marauding footsteps. However, returning from one of his warring excursions he decided to pay a visit to his sister, Fanchea, who was the Abbess of a Convent in Rossary, Enniskillen in County Fermanagh. She was horrified when she saw his bloodied state, and told him that he should give up his barbarous way of life, settle down and get married. He had replied that he would do so if she would let him have one of the pretty young girls in the Convent. She tricked him into believing that she had agreed, knowing that the girl she had chosen didn't have very long to live. When Enda later saw the corpse of his beautiful bride-to-be he immediately regretted his previous life style and became very despondent. It was then that Fanchea persuaded him to become a priest. Accepting her advice he allowed her to send him to Candida Casa, in Rosnat (Galloway), which we know as Whithorn, and where St. Ninian had his monastery. When his training was completed he went on to Rome where he was ordained. On his return to Ireland he built a church at Drogheda and a monastery in the Boyne valley. Then he persuaded his brother-in-law Óengus to give him the Aran Islands, which came under the province of Munster. Óengus reluctantly agreed but he would have preferred him to have had more fertile land in order to make his life easier. However, Enda chose a wild desolate area in order to develop the fruits of his training and belief. Those fruits must have been very apparent because the Islands came to be recognised as the home of Irish monasticism. Indeed there is a long list of saints who spent time on the Islands including Saint Columba (Saint Colmcille) who, on leaving the Islands, had built an oratory at Crumlin , which is situated near Fanore – one of our local haunts - and opposite the Aran Islands. He had later become known as the Apostle of the Outer Hebrides. So, there were two saints who had built churches virtually on our doorstep: one recorded in history, and the other in folklore.

Prior to my memorable and enlightening trip with Uncle Tom and Dorothy, my knowledge of Saint MacDara was confined to the fact that he had probably lived in one of the caves in Oughtdarra when he had first arrived. Although he may have lived like a hermit, he must have gone out into the community, otherwise there would not be evidence in the form of a church and cemetery. Trying to imagine a community of that type wasn't easy, because we lived in a house. Whereas, up the mountain in Ballynahown, and out towards Ballyryan, near the sea, there is evidence of numerous forts, which would have been the dwelling places of many of those early people. I don't suppose Saint MacDara's existence would have seemed particularly unusual to fort dwellers. His first oratory would probably have been constructed from wood, or clay and wattle, as many others had been, but the stone building, - what remained of it, - was supposed to have been built in the fifteenth century. Sadly the church was covered in ivy, and had brambles growing through it. Granddad once said that it had been measured, and that the inside was approximately eighteen feet by thirty-six feet, but the walls were about three feet thick which made it look bigger from the outside. We were told that there was a well, which was called the wine well, but we hadn't been able to locate it. Of course there were lots of spring wells in the area, including the two spring wells near home, where I often went to collect water, because the tea always tasted so much better when made with spring water, so they said. Once a year the wells needed to be treated with lime in order to purify them, but they couldn't both be done at the same time, because it wasn't possible to use the water until it became completely clear, when the lime had settled. They quickly became overgrown if they weren't maintained properly, which we believed had been the fate of the wine well.

As Uncle had said there are also a number of church ruins in our locality, and I was sure that there had been a connection between Saint MacDara and the founders of some of those churches. I was particularly intrigued by Saint MacDara's Church and its proximity to Saint Columba's Oratory in Crumlin. For people who thought nothing of walking over, as well as living in, rough terrain, it was such a short distance to travel; they may even have travelled on their initial journey together, each one choosing where best to site his new church. It remains an interesting mystery. As children we might not have been aware of the church, had we not ventured down the hill as we collected hazel nuts. That was the journey which took us to the huge orchard, which sat alongside the ruins, and where we went scrumping. Fortunately the landowner, Nora Kelliher, was a friend of the family, and invariably observed from a distance until our bags were full, when she would invite us into her thatched cottage for tea and scones. Her presence and the orchard kept the valley alive, in one sense, but I also felt that the spirit of Saint MacDara lived on after he finally left to go to Connemara, and onwards to his island, which is also his final resting place.

We weren't far from home, when I finally nodded off. Mum had obviously heard the car when we arrived, because she had come out to meet us. I heard Uncle Tom apologise for being so late, adding that I was fine, and had slept all the way home.

Nevertheless it had to be a quick drink and then bed, but I wasn't arguing!'

'That seemed to be a mental marathon,' Liam commented, 'and a worthwhile story but you haven't taken me down to the valley.'
'No sooner said than done' Nan quipped, 'Lets put all our bits and pieces in the car, and we'll be there before you can say Jack Robinson. You can identify more easily with the story if you see where the inspiration came from'. The car was parked outside Rockville and it didn't take many minutes to drive down into Oughtdarra valley, re-park the car, and wander across to the ruins of the old church. Nan stood for some time surveying the scene before commenting, 'Of course I haven't been down here since I left Rockville, and even if I hadn't told you that story, I think it would have come flooding back, because nothing has changed. I remained grateful to Uncle Tom for our journey, because it enabled me to understand a little more of our heritage.' Without warning Nan started to laugh as she said, 'And guess what? All those saints were Celts, and they are reputed to have been the first educators, because they had been trained to read and write.'

Liam found the reference to the Celts amusing, but as they climbed into the car he said, 'I am grateful to you for bringing me here.' As we drove back up the hill he continued, 'Did you ever do as Uncle Tom advised, and go to see the sights in Galway?' Nan was still chuckling as she replied, 'Actually I did and it happened much sooner than I might have anticipated.' They had re-parked at their original location, looking across to the islands, and she continued, 'When I awoke on the morning following that eventful trip, I had a very clear picture to put in the frame, which was remarkable really, because I had had a very confused dream about saints warring with the Úi Neill family, where all the saints had croziers which had very sharp spears on them. They were all dressed like Saint Patrick with mitres and vestments, which billowed out behind them as they charged. Then one of them was wounded, and handed me his crozier, telling me to go after the enemy.' Liam was laughing helplessly as he said, 'And what did you do then?' Nan replied, 'Well I didn't wish to be like Queen Meave, the fighting Queen, who wished to be as powerful, and have as much wealth as her husband. I didn't like battles where people were hurt or killed, and in that instance I couldn't even manage the crozier, which was long enough to reach a man's shoulder, and it was heavy. The best I could do was to drag it, not charge with it. I became very scared and the dream seemed to have become a nightmare, and thankfully, I woke up. Unfortunately I couldn't tell anyone about the dream because I knew the answer would have been, 'Well that's what comes of being a tomboy.' Nor was there an opportunity to recount the previous day's events, because Uncle Tom and Dorothy were due to depart on the following day, and they wished to spend the whole of that day with us. Mum was hard pressed to keep up with the cooking arrangements, and I sensed that she had something worrying her, because despite being busy, she usually managed to be jovial. In any case she really needed all the help that I could give her. I wasn't to know then that within a few days we would both be in Galway together.

Grandma wasn't the only person whose health was deteriorating. There was also Mum's stepmother, who had remained living and working in the family homestead, and with whom Mum had remained in touch. Mum's brothers and sisters were among those who had emigrated to the United States, when they were young, but Mum, being the youngest, remained at home and inherited the farm when her father passed away. There was a covenant in her father's will, which stipulated that her stepmother would remain as limited owner for her lifetime, and be supported in the dwelling. That had been Mum's responsibility since 1940, and it remained her concern throughout that dreadful winter, but with Grandma's health deteriorating, and a very busy spring and summer on the farm, it hadn't been possible for her to make the journey. However it had become an urgent necessity, and fortunately she was able to call on the lady who used to help Grandma in the house before we descended on them; the lady's name was Nora who happened to be the same person who owned the orchard in Oughtdarra. Mum was very relieved to be able to hand over the domestic reins for a few days. Had we owned a car it would have been possible to make frequent visits, because the distance from Ballinalacken to Carrownageeha, near Milltown, was approximately seventy miles - today that would be in kilometres – and it would have been possible to make a return journey in a day, but that is nowadays and not as we knew it then. It was a complicated journey involving the pony and trap, two buses and a hackney cab, and I remember it well. I must have become too excited, since Grandma decided that she needed to lecture me on what I should be doing on the journey, so that I didn't make a nuisance of myself. I was to take a notebook and make a note of all the interesting sites I saw. I endeavoured to understand her reasons, but we children had been reminded that we must be very patient with her, because she was not always *in good form*; it gave her something to think about instead of her own problems. I left her with a smile and a promise to do as she had asked. Granddad must have overheard because later, when I was preparing for bed, he had whispered, 'I wouldn't worry too much about Grandma's request, just do what you can. Of course I know Mum has a long list of bibs and bobs which she hopes to buy, and she doesn't often manage to visit a city these days, but see if you can persuade her to take you to see Lynch's castle in the centre.'

'Oh! What a beautiful morning, and I will have my mum all to myself.' That was my first thought on leaping out of bed, as the sun was streaming through the window, but I needed to contain my excitement, and try not to exasperate any one. It wasn't a problem though, because there was only Dad, who disappeared after breakfast in order to collect the pony and prepare the trap. The boys had already gone outside to complete a task, which Dad had asked them to do in order to keep them out of mischief, *so he said*, but not, I gathered, before Mum had reminded them to be on their best behaviour whilst she was away. She had packed our suitcases, and was waiting for Nora to arrive, so that they could have a chat about what needed to be done, and in particular, about Grandma's needs. It wasn't necessary to disturb Granddad and Grandma, because I had heard them discussing the arrangements before Grandma had retired early the previous evening. Then we were on our way, and Dad was taking us down the road to the Castle crossroads, where we were to wait for the bus, which arrived just after 9.00 a.m. I wondered why we needed the pony and trap for such a short journey. It was a ten minute walk, and it was the first landmark we usually passed on Sunday as we walked to Church; a journey which took an hour. Of course I didn't have to carry the big suitcase, and mine seemed suspiciously light, but Dad wished to talk with the bus driver about the return time four days later, so that he could be waiting for us. Mum and I sat on the front seat opposite the driver, and with a quick wave to Dad, we set off. I heard Mum sigh as she settled down to enjoy a brief respite from all her cares, and on such a glorious morning it was easy to relax. I don't think she had any idea of how I felt, having her all to myself: no chores and no neighbours popping in for a quick chat.

'You will remember to take note of all you see, so that you can tell me all on your return.' Grandma's voice echoed in my head, and I supposed that she really knew how it was going to be. After all she had been a nine year-old herself at one time, and we all knew, that even though she was in physical decline, there was nothing whatsoever wrong with her memory. I had already endeavoured to make a note in my book as we set out, but the bus was vibrating as it sped along, which made legible writing impossible. I quickly decided that the writing would need to wait until later:

short notes to prompt me would have to do, as I hoped to rely on memory and imagination, when I recounted the details. Besides we were rapidly approaching Poulsallagh, and all my thoughts were focused there.

Travelling on a bus was a new experience for me, and I couldn't have anticipated the feeling of space and freedom. I didn't have that sensation in Uncle Ben's car, or when I travelled with Uncle Tom, because the car windows were high and it made the car feel rather claustrophobic, but then I was usually on the back seat. Of course I had been accustomed to travelling in the pony and trap, where there were no visual barriers. The bus had one huge advantage over the cars or the trap, since it was so much higher off the ground, and it was possible to look over many of the hedges and into the fields beyond. The first part of the journey was very familiar to all in our house, because we often travelled it on our way to the seaside at Fanore. Being elevated I had a much better view of the hazel bushes, where the road appeared to have been carved through what was a hazel grove. My excitement grew as I caught sight of all the hazel nuts waiting to be picked; it wouldn't be long before I set out with my brothers on our annual nut-picking expedition. There was no time to dwell on that because we had arrived at Poulsallagh, where you and I will shortly be having our lunch. From there it was possible to look back up the mountain and identify our house, which was partly surrounded by an escallonia hedge, protected as it was from the Atlantic gales. Granddad had often said, as we stood outside our house and looked down to the sea, 'No words are adequate to describe this place, one has to be here,' and how right he was.

With the exception of the driver, Mum and I were the only passengers, so it was quite easy for me, on that particular stretch of coastline, which extended for about four miles, to imagine that the bus was our space craft and we were the aliens who had just popped in from the planet earth, arriving on what looked like a chaotic lunar limestone wilderness. Nor was it difficult to accept that it had erupted from the seabed over 300 million years earlier; there probably wasn't much order down there either. The eruption had given us stones, rocks, boulders, eratics, limestone pavements, interspersed with karst areas, crisscrossed with fizzures and grykes, where the tropical plants found a home. There were cliffs which looked like layered sandwiches, and the most awesome sight, when they came into view, mountains which looked like giant grey mushrooms, to which someone had taken an enormous paintbrush in order to create the fascinating swirls, but no human artist had had a hand in that incredible scene. Travelling at sea level made it possible to feel totally integrated. On our right were the cliffs and various plateaux, and on our left further rocks and boulders which extended to the ocean. Not far out to the west were the Aran Islands, which as I said earlier were at one time a natural extension of this area, with many of the natural features; and to the northeast there was Connemara. Being a bright sunny morning the views were crystal clear; the sun danced on the blue water – Mum called it azure – as it reflected the colour of the sky, but it was the limestone assortment which had captured me.

The word Burren is taken from the Gaelic word Bhoireann, which means a stony or rocky place, and no wonder since it extends over such a vast area. It isn't all rock, being interspersed in different areas with masses of scrubland and hazel groves, and elsewhere lush green fields, where the limestone covering is deeper.

Summer trips to Fanore were the usual exciting Sunday afternoon excursions for the whole family, but on most of those occasions the children needed to walk whilst the adults travelled in the pony and trap. Travelling by foot down the steep hill we needed to weave our way through the scrubland in order to arrive at Poulsallagh well ahead of the pony and trap, which had to follow the circuitous route of the coast road. We were reminded to walk on the road for the remainder of our journey and not venture near the sea. The elders usually found us at Ballyryan near the cliff which towered above us; there we could marvel at how many shrubs and plants could make a home in the horizontal and vertical cracks and fizzures, which seemed to have such a sparsity of soil. At different times during the summer we were asked to report on the progress of the plants.

I would have been happy to remain in my reverie, but we had arrived in Crumlin and, as we rounded the bend, Mum claimed my attention, as she pointed out the ruin which was situated half-way up the hill. It was mostly covered by ivy but she told me that it was an oratory, and reputed to have been built by Saint Columba, adding that I should make it the first item in my notebook; I didn't and as I told her why I made a mental note to tell her, at some stage of the journey, about my expedition with Uncle Tom and Dorothy. With so many arrangements needing to be made over the previous days, there definitely hadn't been any time for storytelling. The main task was to identify fairy mounds, wedge tombs, ring forts, cahers or any other evidence of Celtic or pre-historic habitation. I didn't realise, at that stage, that there would be less of that evidence as our journey progressed, and that I had taken for granted all that lay around and about me at Rockville where, in the heart of the Burren, I merely needed to walk up the mountain or cross over the short stretch of karst, and on to the limestone plateau in order to find it.

All too soon we had passed Fanore, which was flat with more vegetation, and we were speeding towards Black Head, where the road had been carved at the base of Gleninagh Mountain. Once round the bend the scene opened out into Galway Bay, and we were on our way to Ballyvaughan, a little fishing village. I had made quite a few mental notes, because we had passed some very interesting places, which I had heard the family talk about, but I realised that we had left my dream scene behind, and the terrain had become very ordinary. Our next village was Kinvara, and I was quite glad when the bus stopped because it provided an opportunity to make a few notes.

It was customary for the driver to make a prolonged stop in some of the larger villages and towns, which allowed him to stretch his legs, and chat to the passengers. Mum was keen to know more about Kinvara which is a very pretty fishing village, with a small harbour, and on the outskirts situated on a promontory stood a Castle. I had noticed the Castle immediately because it looked similar in shape to Ballinalacken Castle, where my brothers and I often played, and I couldn't wait to know more about it. I thought they would never get round to the subject. The driver must have sensed my impatience, because he eventually looked at me teasingly as he said, "And would you be interested in the Castle then?" He had laughed when I nodded eagerly, but continued, "Well fancy that because so am I, and I pass this way regularly, so I have time to think about how it used to be in these places. So, let's see now what I can remember. It was built in 1520, but in the 17th century it was given to a man named Martyn – you know that was a popular name among the gentry in these parts – who had another castle near Gort, which isn't far from here. He lived in the castle until 1642, but then moved to his main residence and this castle became neglected. And so it remained until the Martyns had died out. A man called Gogarty bought it in 1922 and began to restore it. It became a popular meeting place for Irish writers who set up the Celtic Revival. If my memory serves me well, they were George Bernard Shaw, John Millington Synge, Lady Gregory and W.B. Yeats and, of course Gogarty himself." Suddenly looking at his watch he declared, "Oh! My goodness, sure I must be off," as he closed the little window of his cab. That was unfortunate but he had already fired my imagination, and hopefully when I told Grandma she would fill in more of the detail. I didn't know anything about George Bernard Shaw, John Millington Synge, or Lady Gregory but one poem by W.B. Yeats happened to be popular at school and at home, although I'm not too sure about home, but that's where we did our practice, and we children were all supposed to know it.

> *I will arise and go now, and go to Inisfree,*
> *And a small cabin build there, of clay and wattles made;*
> *Nine bean-rows will I have there, a hive for the honey bee,*
> *And live alone in the bee-loud glade.*
>
> *And I shall have some peace there, for peace comes dropping slow,*
> *Dropping from the veils of the morning to where the cricket sings;*
> *There midnight's all a glimmer, and noon a purple glow,*
> *And evening full of the linnet's wings.*
>
> *I will arise and go now, for always night and day*
> *I hear lake water lapping with low sounds by the shore:*
> *While I stand on the roadway, or on the pavements grey,*
> *I hear it in the deep heart's core.*

The Lake Isle of Inisfree: W.B Yeats

I could imagine the pre-historic people building clay and wattle cabins round that area, where there weren't many stones: unlike Ballinalacken where they would have used stones or alternatively lived in caves. We had passed a little village named Kilcolgan, and were about to arrive in Oranmore, where there was another castle, and a boulder dolmen or megalithic stone tomb. Perhaps that too would be a question for the driver on our return. Mum had said that we would be arriving in Galway in ten minutes, where she was looking forward to having a cup of tea: that would provide me with an opportunity to make a few notes. The journey to Galway had cost five shillings and three pence or, as it was spoken, five and thrippence, which would be approximately twenty-six pence in today's currency. We had arrived in Galway at 10.56 a.m. but our bus to Dunmore wasn't due to leave until 4.35 p.m. which gave us nearly four and a half hours in Galway. Fortunately there was a left luggage room at the station, where we were able to deposit our luggage before setting out for the city centre.

Mum knew Galway very well because she had grown up in Carrownageeha, and the distance from there to Galway wasn't as far as Ballinalacken to Galway. She was really looking forward to spending some time in the shops, and had a list of items which she needed to buy. The problem for me was that I had a notebook and pencil in my pocket, but I suspected that Grandma wouldn't be interested in what we had bought.

I was a bit bowled over by all that was to be seen, and Mum needed to stop at intervals, because I lagged behind so often, until she almost lost me, at which point she ran out of patience. Eventually she declared that her legs needed a rest, and having found a restaurant she was relieved to temporarily off load her purchases. After lunch it was time for me to pass on Granddad's request, and I was thankful when she said that she had done well with her shopping, and we weren't too far from Lynch's castle. Offering to relieve her of some of the bags, we set off jauntily, and I was in my element. As we walked she was able to tell me about the castle because, as she said, her class had covered the history of Galway when she had been at school. It was wonderful to listen to her comments on the various interesting sites, and her knowledge was very extensive. Of course we had never had the occasion to talk about those things, as she settled us down for the night at home, when invariably she simply read stories to us. I felt saddened when I realised that she had revealed an aspect of herself, which I hadn't known existed, because caring for such a large family didn't leave her much time for leisure, or herself. In fact she had so much information to impart that my brain refused to accept it all, and of course, I hadn't yet told her about my previous journey, and my effort to come to terms with it. I listened intently to some of her comments, but let many go over my head, until we arrived at Lynch's Castle. That was what I really wanted to learn about because Granddad had suggested it.

I wasn't sure what to expect, but it certainly wasn't what I was faced with. I had formed my own image of what a castle looked like, because we had one quite close to home, and we had passed Kinvarra Castle earlier. I had seen many pictures of castles, and mostly they were surrounded by green fields and moats, or on promontories facing the sea. Mum had noticed my quizzical expression, because she laughed and said, "It's different isn't it?" I replied that it was very different, being in the centre of the town, and on the corner of two narrow streets surrounded by shops; and it looked more like an enormous square mansion house with four storeys. I knew that it was from the medieval period, and it fitted in well with all the other high stone buildings, but to me as a castle it still seemed a bit strange. Mum went on to describe its background, and said that it was a Gothic limestone building, which dated from 1320 and, although it had been converted to a bank, it had originally been the residence of the Lynch family. Of course the Lynch's were not only one of the Tribes of Galway, they were the most powerful family, with many descendants becoming mayor. The windows of the building had highly decorated surroundings and carved gargoyles, or water spouts, which looked very fierce, and I wouldn't wish to be thinking about them when I went to bed. At the front of the building we saw the Lynch coat-of-arms. Mum said that it would always be remembered, because of a heart-rending story concerning the son of one of the owners. The man's name was James Lynch Fitzstephen, and he was a chief magistrate at the time. Apparently his son had murdered a Spanish man, who had become too involved with a female member of his family; he was subsequently ordered to be hanged. Since no one would agree to carry out the execution the father had to do it himself. Mum had begun to walk away from the building as she talked, and having walked to the end of the street and into the next road, she indicated the site of the Old Jail where only one wall still stood. There was a window and a closed-up Gothic door, and set in the wall we were able to see the block of black marble with an inscription which read,

"This memorial of the stern and unbending justice of the chief magistrate of this City, James Lynch Fitzstephen, elected mayor A.D. 1493, who condemned and executed his own guilty son, Walter, on this spot."

Before I had a chance to become too morose, Mum was moving on again to the end of that street and into another, where she was able to show me the Church of St. Nicholas. My mood lightened immediately because it was such an imposing building, and more as I expected the Castle to have been. It was another medieval building from the period around 1320, but it had suffered considerable damage when it was taken over by the Cromwellians, as they apparently stabled their horses there. Hastily Mum went on to add that Columbus was supposed to have prayed there before setting out for America, and that a Galway man called Rice de Culvey had accompanied Columbus on his major voyage of discovery. I would have loved to spend more time inside the church, but we needed to make our way back to the Bus Station.

Having reclaimed our luggage, I was to learn why the suitcase, which I had carried in the morning, was so light, it was actually empty. Mum had brought it along in order to fill it with her purchases, saying as she did so, 'That will help to keep them tidy, and don't worry because I have packed enough clothes for you.'

Then there was time to sit and wait for our bus to arrive, and we chatted about what we had achieved, and the places we had visited. I produced my notebook so that I could jot a few items down. I had written the word Columba in the morning to remind me to tell her about my visit with Uncle Tom and Dorothy. She was delighted to hear the news, but as always, looked sad when I mentioned the mother who had carried her son's corpse down the mountain. Unfortunately it reminded her of her own two daughters, Mary and Bríde, who had died in infancy. I was relieved to be able to tell her, for the first time, that I really missed not having two older sisters to play with.

On boarding the bus we were happy again to have a front seat, which allowed us a much better view. Unfortunately it wasn't long before I had to confess to Mum that I was feeling tired, and would it be alright if I left my observation of any more interesting sites until our return journey. She responded that it would be much better to relax and close our eyes, because we would need to be rested when we finally arrived at her old home. The bus didn't pass close to Carrownageeha, and it was necessary for us to get a hackney cab in Dunmore for the remainder of the journey. By that time I was wide awake again, and full of curiosity. There wasn't really time to talk about Dunmore, which looked very interesting, with a castle which had been built on a big fort. I wondered if that was where the name of the town had stemmed from: in Gaelic it was known as Dún Mór, which meant big fort. Mum had said that I would see a number of forts in that area. I already knew that Saint Patrick was reputed to have built a monastery there, although that had later been replaced by an Augustian Friary. I hoped that, on the return journey, I would be able to learn much more. Mum hadn't taken long to find a cab, and soon we were on our way again.

I had become very conscious of Mum, as we had covered the last stage of the journey, because I realised that, although I was merely visiting, she was going home to where she had been born.

Growing up in the midst of such a large family, which covered three generations, I needed to take account of the feelings of others, and we were often reminded of that. Instinct was a wonderful guide when deciding what, and what not to do or say. On that occasion, I sensed that she was remembering, and I hoped that later she would be able to share some of those memories with me.

Whatever Mum's thoughts were, I knew they would not have been anything like mine. Although I had slept through most of the journey from Galway, the last stage by cab, had enabled me to survey the countryside; and I couldn't help comparing it with the morning journey. Apart from the houses and buildings, the area seemed very flat, with fields everywhere, and it didn't really excite me. For some reason that thought made me feel guilty, and I realised that it was probably a very productive farming district, which was evident from the number of cattle I saw. There were lots of fields where the hay had been cut and saved, with the haycocks ready to be taken into the barns, or made into an enormous hayrick, which would then be covered with a tarpaulin and weighted down; I had been involved in the hay-making and saving process on our farm, but it was on a mini-scale compared to very large farms. Alongside the cottages and houses, it was possible to see the mounds of peat which had been saved, and as always there were fields of crops waiting to be harvested. I could see that the summer had also been kind to all those who lived there. Stones had been used to build the walls around the fields, and like our walls at home, they seemed to wander around the fields in a wobbly fashion: very rarely in a straight line. But my eyes longed to see the vista of stone which surrounded our home. I couldn't have shared that thought with Mum, and anyway we had arrived, and she had paid the cab driver. Then I heard her take a deep breath, as she approached what had been her own front door. In fact, it still was, because she was the owner of the cottage: a lovely, old, white, single-storey, thatched cottage with small windows, and roses round the front door; so different to Rockville, which was modern.

I hadn't consciously thought of what the meeting between step-mother and step-daughter was going to be like. I was standing slightly behind Mum, but able to observe the lady who opened the door, and had eyes only for her stepdaughter. There were two ladies – one young and one elderly – who hadn't met for a number of years. I could only observe the face of the lady in the doorway whose name was Mary: a lady who had the gentlest face I had ever seen, even though it was deeply lined. I could see the mixture of joy, pain and love which flashed across her countenance, as she looked at Mum, and I loved her for that. She had obviously loved Mum as though she were her own daughter. As she hugged her, her eyes alighted on me, and as she looked I noticed the twinkle, and knew that despite any sadness, there would be an abundance of humour and love in the following days. It began on the doorstep as Mary said to me, "And what would you like to call me, then: you already have a Grandma?" That really tickled me, because I too have a wicked sense of humour, and I already felt very much at home with her. I had quipped that I would love to call her Gammie, because it suited her and sounded friendly. Smiling broadly, she stood back in order to allow Mum to enter, and extending her hand to me she whispered, "This is where she grew up." Oh boy! Like stepping back in time: everything was so different, and I couldn't wait to have a closer look.

Our visit must have been anticipated, because the table was laid for tea. The preparation hadn't been done by Gammie, but rather by one of her relatives who lived nearby, and who went in each day to look after the meals and do the chores. It had been a very welcome sight, and all that remained for Mum to do was to make the tea. The strangest feeling stole over me, as I watched Mum moving about, as though she had never left. There was much happy chatter as we ate, first concerning our journey and later the more serious business concerning the farm, which was being managed by a local man. It didn't include me, and I was happy to allow my gaze to wander round the kitchen and wait.

I had visited many cottages near home, some of which had been updated, but it was the first time I had had an opportunity to explore one. It seemed that there had been no modernisation in Mum's old home, and apart from freshly lime-washed walls, and beautifully polished furniture, it remained as Mum had left it, a picture of time gone by. There were two bedrooms, a parlour and a huge kitchen, and I guessed that the parlour had been an additional bedroom when Mum had been growing up there. It had a small table, some chairs and what looked like a cupboard or press , which Mum later told me was a press-bed, which could be used for visitors: also pictures, some of which were of family members. The bedrooms were very plain with no decoration, apart from very pretty floral curtains and bedspread. The kitchen was a different matter altogether.

I knew from home that the kitchen was the central hub of the family, mostly doubling as a reception, cooking and dining area. In fact, it was where all the domestic activity took place. When the meals were over and everything restored, it was ideal for the occasional ceilidh, provided that someone was available with a musical instrument: our kitchen would not have been sufficiently large for that, but as I said it was more modern, with a range for cooking. However I was very happy to survey the old scene and imagine what life might have been like when Mum had lived there. The open hearth was the main feature, being a large inglenook, which had a crane suspended from the back. The crane had a series of nicks on the top edge, and a hook at the end for hanging the kettle or griddle. There were some trivets which were used for resting the pots or kettle on when removed from the heat. There were hooks of different lengths hanging on the side wall, which could be used on the crane hook in order to lower the kettle or griddle further into the fire. On the same side there were a few niches, and the salt was always kept in one of these, because when it became damp, it was impossible to distribute it properly. The pots, which were of different sizes, had lids and three legs, which allowed the coals to be placed underneath and on top, depending on what was in them: both they, the kettle, and the griddle, were jet black. I wondered if that was where the expression, *as black as the pot,* had come from. There was a hob on either side of the fire, which was the perfect place for children to sit, and I made full use of it. On either side of the hearth there were two very deep cupboards, which provided much needed storage space. Of course the older cottages had to rely on the hearth as the main source of heat - the bedrooms didn't have fireplaces - and the fire also helped to illuminate the kitchen in the evening. The other source of light would have been the tilley lamp or candles. It was the type of light, which always seemed conducive to reminiscing and story-telling, and for me it had a very mystical quality, but of course it wasn't very good for needlework, or reading, unless one happened to be very near the lamp.

As I said, the hearth was the focal point, but the kitchen contained all the necessary pieces of furniture. There was a large oak table and four chairs, which were placed in front of the window, and tucked underneath the table were two three-legged stools; on either side of the fireplace, stood two very comfortable wooden, high-backed armchairs, which had soft cushions, with one chair having a rug on the arm rest. Working my way round the room, I could see the old pine dresser, which Mum said had been in the family for a very long time. It was a very functional piece of furniture, and every part was used for storage; the top half contained three shelves, at different heights: the top shelf was used for two large upright platters, with space for a milk jug in the middle. The next shelf contained dinner plates, and the one beneath, tea plates. Below that, on the base itself, there was room for tureens, small jugs and sugar bowl. On the fronts of each of the shelves there were lots of hooks for hanging mugs. The base contained two large drawers: one for cutlery, and the other for bits and pieces. The cupboard beneath contained the best china, which was only used for special guests. There were more hooks on the outside of the top portion, where ladles and other cooking utensils were hung. Close to the dresser there was a tall pine cupboard where the food was stored. Then there was the settle: a fascinating piece of old oak which had a long seat, a high back and two wooden arms, providing seating during the day, but which could be opened out at night, to provide a bed for the occasional visitor. Being in the kitchen, where the fire was, I felt that it would be very cosy indeed, but I didn't think that Mum would appreciate my request to sleep there. The kitchen had very dark beams with hooks, which would normally be used to hang the salted bacon joints, in order to allow them to cure. Somehow the beams seemed to compliment the stone floor, giving the whole area a very cosy appearance. The cottage would not have been complete without a spinning wheel, but it was tucked into the corner with a dust cover placed over it.

I was happy to complete my tour by which time Mum was ready to wash the dishes and I was able to make myself useful. Afterwards she and Gammie seated themselves on the armchairs, and continued to share their news. Mum had taken along the letters, which she had received from her brothers and sister, who were in the United States. Having never met those relatives, I was unable to feel part of the conversation, but as I perched on the hob, I could try to imagine how Gammie might be feeling about them. Remembering the expressions which I had seen on her face when we arrived, and knowing that she would have cared for them as she had obviously done for Mum, I concluded that it must be very difficult for her to accept that she may not see them again. I also remembered how excited Mum was whenever the postman arrived with letters from them, nor could I forget the urgent trips to the meadow to collect the shamrock.

Saint Patrick's Day is a national holiday, Church Feast Day, and a day of celebration in Ireland; it is also a day when the majority of Irish immigrants celebrate the wearing of the green. As children we were particularly happy on those occasions, because we were allowed to relax our Lenten fast, and indulge ourselves in any of the sweets, which we had been saving since the beginning of Lent. There was music, song, a special meal, and lots of storytelling. Finding and wearing a sprig of shamrock was crucial to the meaning of the celebration, because we had been told that Saint Patrick had used the shamrock as a symbol of the Church's teaching on the Trinity. It was possible to confine the search for our own shamrock to the days prior to the event, but for those relatives who lived overseas, the annual search began weeks in advance, with a request from Mum for volunteers to go to the meadow. One year my younger brother Patrick and I were the only two available, and as he accompanied me, he declared, 'This won't take long because I saw loads when I was there the other day.' He had seen loads too, but it wasn't shamrock; what he had seen was clover which has three leaves, as does the shamrock, but the clover leaf has white markings and grows vigorously; whereas the shamrock is completely plain, smaller, much more delicate, and not at all easy to find. It took concentrated peering and searching before we managed to collect enough bunches for Mum's needs. She re-arranged the shamrock into sprigs, wrapped the stems in moist cotton wool, and placed them in specially prepared boxes which had a waxed interior. The boxes were purchased in good time, and needed to be on their way, so that they reached their recipients on time for Saint Patrick's Day.

I was content with my own memories, as I gazed into the fire, whilst listening to the hum of their voices nearby; it was as I had thought when we arrived: there was love and humour, and occasionally I was able to steal a glance at their faces, and watch the reflection of the flames from the fire. At length, Gammie announced that it was her bedtime, and because she was quite feeble Mum went along to help her. When she emerged from the bedroom, she was using her handkerchief and I could see that she had been crying. Trying to conceal her distress she announced that, since it had been a very long day for both of us, we should have cocoa and retire ourselves.

The following two days were full of the usual domestic bustle, because the lady who attended regularly didn't wish to intrude; although she called a few times, firstly to welcome us, and later to have a long chat with Mum about future arrangements. Mum made bread and, much to my delight, she also made griddle scones, allowing me to help prepare them and keep an eye on them as they cooked. Gammie remained in bed each day until after lunch, with Mum popping in to see her at intervals, but on our second day, after one such visit, she suggested that we go for a walk along the lane, and that was music to my ears. On our arrival I had noticed and been fascinated by the front door, because it was a stable door made in two parts, and was a very practical invention. When the weather was suitable, it was possible to have the top half open to let in light and air. The bottom half remained closed, preventing the children from escaping, or any animals from wandering in. When it rained, on our first afternoon, I was able to lean out without getting wet, because the thatch extended beyond the building, creating a canopy. I had ventured out on a number of occasions, but Mum had said not to wander off, and I didn't, well not too far, although I loved to be out-of-doors. We hadn't walked very far when we met a farmer coming towards us, and Mum stopped to chat; she later told me that he was the man who managed the farm, and she was pleased to have met him because it saved her making a visit to his home that evening. They seemed to chat for a long time and, as they parted, I heard him say that he would drop the papers in to her that evening. We continued our walk in silence until we came to a farm gate where Mum stopped, and leaning on the gate, began to survey the fields which belonged to her. Because she seemed content to rest awhile, I climbed the gate and sat facing her. My sudden movement had distracted her and, as she planted a kiss on my cheek, she said, "Oh, you are such a tomboy."

I was completely unprepared for what followed, although I knew that I wasn't responsible. As she gazed about her the tears began to flow, and then she began to sob until I felt I wanted to join her, but I didn't have any tears: only an ache which said I want to help her, and I felt so helpless. I put my hand out to stroke her face, as she had so often done with me, but she took it and held it until eventually the sobs subsided. Finding her hankie, she had a good blow and said, "Oh, that is so much better, and please don't let it upset you. I think you appreciate that Gammie is gravely ill, and I know that I won't see her alive again, but she is in so much pain: I wouldn't wish her to continue like that. I know you won't tell her about this: you see I am trying to be strong for her." I did see what she meant, and knew that I must be strong too, even though I couldn't possibly know what they were going through. I couldn't even compare it to when I lost my favourite dog, which had followed me everywhere I went, or to the times when Mum chose my special hen for the pot. Mum couldn't remember losing her own Mother, because that happened when she was born, but she would remember losing her Dad, and her own two daughters. I wondered if she had chosen the name Mary for her first daughter as a tribute to Gammie. I would ask her at some stage in the future, but it would not have been appropriate right then. However, at that moment, I ached to be back in Rockville, where I could have stood and looked down to the tumbling waves on the shore, or even taken myself to the meadow. Those were the places where I could make sense of things: of course I would be there on the following evening, but a lot would happen before then.

The remainder of that day disappeared very quickly. After lunch Gammie joined us and spent time talking to me; asking me what I wanted to be when I grew up, and when Mum was out of earshot, reminding me to take care of her, because she was a very special person. I knew they needed more time together, and I slipped out quietly to stand and survey the kitchen garden and the wild flowers, which were growing round the edge. How well it had served the family and how wonderful it would have been to have had Mum out there too, so that she could tell me more about being little, but I tried to imagine it.

After tea it was time for a final tidy up, and Mum needed to prepare the suitcase for an early morning departure. She had made arrangements with the cab driver to collect us and take us to Dunmore. Taking our leave was distressing for everyone; Gammie had remained in bed and I had gone to her room to say goodbye, and to tell her that I thought she was a lovely, special person, and I loved her. Mum had appeared then, and I walked away. We waited outside for the cab to arrive, which gave Mum time to compose herself, and once he arrived, we needed to project a happier image.

Mum knew that before long she would need to make a return journey to Carrownageeha, but on that occasion it would be for Gammie's funeral, when Dad would hire a car in Lisdoonvarna and take her.

So much had happened during those days that I forgot about Grandma's request, and concentrated more on Mum, as we made our return journey. By the time we arrived in Galway she was much brighter and planning the week ahead.

I had been excited at the thought of going away, but nothing could compare with the joy I felt as Dad met us at the crossroads. When we arrived at the bottom of the hill near our home, I asked if I could walk the remainder of the journey. As soon as the pony stopped I opened the trap door and jumped down. I didn't notice the trap moving off as I stood, surveying the scene before me. Even now, at my advanced age, it makes me want to sing and dance, and yet, despite its vast rugged appearance, there is such an incredible feeling of peace. It was easy to see why Granddad wanted to be here, and how could I ever leave!

Now, why, oh why are we sitting in the car when we could be out there, once more? Let's make the most of every moment, and seat ourselves outside for a little while longer, before going down to the beach." With what seemed like a rather impatient move, Nan extricated herself from the car, and drawing herself up to her full height, took a few very deep breaths, as she surveyed the timeless scene before her.

CHAPTER III

WHY MOVE

What is this life if, full of care,
We have no time to stand and stare.
No time to stand beneath the boughs
And stare as long as sheep or cows.
No time to see, when woods we pass,
Where squirrels hide their nuts in grass.
No time to see, in broad daylight,
Streams full of stars, like skies at night.
No time to turn at Beauty's glance,
And watch her feet, how they can dance.
No time to wait till her mouth can
Enrich that smile her eyes began.
A poor life this if, full of care,
We have no time to stand and stare.

Leisure by William Henry Davies (1871-1940)

Nan, who had remained standing by the car, lost in her own thoughts, was endeavouring not to lose sight of what she wished to convey to Liam, whilst they were on this particular vacation. Meanwhile, Liam was looking back on all that she had shared with him. This was a story, which had begun to create a sense of urgency in him, with a need to know more. Yet he was aware of what those deeper emotions, and level of thinking was costing her, but he hadn't forgotten that she had given him permission to ask questions; like her, he had a need to know and understand, so he ventured to ask, "Are you able to tell me why you thought that being here would have helped you to make more sense of all the emotions you encountered, when you spent those days with Gammie in Carrownageeha?"

They had crossed the road and climbed through the fence, in order to seat themselves once more, before Nan continued with a smile, "That's a bit tricky to answer, because I have just realised that, in some respects, my thinking hasn't changed one iota since I lived here all those years ago: its rather like brick-building in that we can build on what we already know. I know, for instance, that I have a turbulent spirit and Granddad explained that type of restlessness to me, when we sat out here to watch a particularly beautiful sunset. The weather had been very stormy over the preceding twenty-four hours, with heavy downpours of rain, high winds and thunder. In the morning I had waited until there was a break in showers, before going outside to be blown about by the wind, which was so exhilarating, and then to stand transfixed as I watched the mountainous waves thundering on the shore. The power of the sea, as it moves turbulently towards the shore, carrying a selection of stones, weed, driftwood and sand, is awesome to behold and, on occasions, when Dad took us children down to the shore after a similar storm, we were amazed at what the tide had brought in, and how far inshore it travelled to deposit its load. You and I are aware of the movement of the tides, and what causes them: that is nature at its most powerful, but I couldn't help but think of human nature, and human beings in the almighty scheme of things. I could say that the turbulence of those waves was sometimes a perfect match for my spirit, especially when life was out of sync. Merely looking at those scenes helped me to realise that I was very small indeed: no more than a speck of sand, even though I was a complete and important being in my own right, as we all are. Even so, the sight of the thunderous waves helped to give me a perspective, whilst I examined my problems, and the sunset which followed was rather like balm over what had been troubled thoughts. I couldn't possibly have realised how much that theory was going to be tested!

One day during the week following our trip to Carrownageeha,

Mum was preparing for my eldest brother Tom's birthday. She had seemed very light-hearted over the previous few days, and I thought it was because she looked forward to making it a special occasion for everyone, and I wanted to do all I could to help her. The chocolate blancmange needed to be made the evening before, in order to allow it to set. On that occasion she said we would use cream, which would taste so much better than condensed milk. It would indeed be a treat because the cream was usually reserved for making butter. Next day she decided that the occasion provided the perfect opportunity to use the whiskey sponge recipe, which Aunt Alice had brought with her on her last visit from Dublin, and she could do with a spare pair of hands to beat the sugar and butter. I was in my element because I had read the recipe, and noticed that although it was a sponge, we needed to use raisins, which had to be simmered for a time, and then allowed to cool before being used. She normally used those raisins when she made a boiled fruit cake for main feasts, and whereas my eldest brother couldn't resist surreptitiously helping himself to a small piece of fruit cake now and then, I couldn't resist helping myself to the prepared juicy fruit before it reached the cake mix. Mum knew me well, and said that we should add extra raisins to allow for sticky fingers, and she didn't think that the men would miss a few tablespoons of whiskey. Of course, it wouldn't have been a high tea without scones, and I was allowed to make those, with a lot of supervision. The lettuce was set aside in water to allow it to become crisper. The kitchen was a hive of activity, and the smell of cooking scones had drifted round the house, and through the open kitchen window, titillating the appetite of all those within its range.

No one was late for tea that day, and everyone was in very high spirits. It was a very happy occasion, particularly as we were able to eat out of doors. Even Grandma was able to join us, with a rug over her knees.

Much later, when order was restored, Mum declared that it was time for a leisurely cup of tea. Grandma had retired, Dad and Granddad were keen to listen to the radio, and the boys, who were never known to sit still for long, had disappeared to have a game of football. Mum decided to take her tea outside and enjoy the late evening sunshine; I collected my drink and found a seat close to her. Chatting contentedly she must have noticed that my gaze was fixed on the sun, which had been changing colour for some time, and was beginning to set out in the west; the exquisite range of colours would never cease to fascinate me, but before I had an opportunity to commence my usual animated chatter she dropped her clanger. *'You know that by this time next year we will be living in Lisdoonvarna.'* I continued to gaze at the sunset, becoming aware that my body was beginning to feel very strange; like pins and needles creeping up from my feet; my head wasn't feeling or thinking either. I could hear Mum's concerned voice asking if I was alright. Maybe it was that word alright that did it, because my brain was suddenly finding the right gear. I could could still hear the word alright, but the scream inside my head was saying no, no, no, it's all wrong. We had been taught that we must never, ever shout at our elders; at that time I wanted to shout never, ever. But there were no words and it wasn't even as Granddad had said, 'When you can't find words to describe something beautiful, you just learn *to be.*' That thought simply made matters worse, because this was where I wanted to be, and I couldn't imagine why anyone would want me to be anywhere else. I couldn't answer Mum when she asked again if I was feeling alright. Could it be too much blancmange, or cake, or perhaps too much excitement? Blancmange or cake my foot I thought, and leaving her looking very puzzled, I ran from the garden, through the top garden, across the road, into my meadow, and in case anyone should dare to come after me, I kept running until I reached the far end, when my legs just crumbled. There are moments which remain crystal clear throughout our lifetime, and this was one of those - my first big crisis. I do not know how long I remained there: the tears were silent because I didn't wish to be found. I remembered all the beautiful moments when I had been able to lie in the grass: to think, and dream, and wonder.

You know how I feel about the skylark, and my invisible friend who is always with me. Where was he now, and couldn't he ease this pain I felt each time Mum's words echoed in my brain, 'you know that by this time next year we will be living in Lisdoonvarna;' a statement which, right then, I could neither accept nor understand. But how could Mum understand: she hadn't been able to spend all that time in the field, listening to the skylark, and all the other beautiful sounds as I did, and she had been too busy looking after everyone else to listen to my daydreams. Once again I thought about my invisible friend, feeling that, yes he was there with me, but was I listening to him. Gradually I became aware of the softness of the grass. The meadow had been cut in July and the new grass felt soft and cool at the end of the day. The edges were never cut, and the flowers continued to grow and offer up their sweet scent, which was always stronger in the evening. Suddenly the skylark, which was nesting nearby, decided that it was time for one more heavenly offering before the sun set, but that one time it failed to have the desired effect. How could my heart soar with the lark when it felt as though it was in my boots; the tears started again.

The moon was full and bright when Granddad found me; they had known where I should be, but not that I had gone to the far end of the meadow. I learned later that Mum had told them I had disappeared, after she told me about moving. Granddad had said that he would like to go and find me. I could hear the gentle rustle as he moved round the meadow, and his body was silhouetted by the moon, but I made no attempt to move; when he reached me he sat down quietly and continued to smoke his pipe for a few moments without speaking. I hoped he hadn't noticed my messy face, which by then, must have been very crumpled. I knew why he had come, and I knew also that he was the one person who would have known how I felt. Although I hadn't looked at him, I could smell the sweetness of the tobacco he used, and I knew that he was gathering his thoughts before he spoke. When he stopped puffing his pipe, I sensed that he was looking at me, as he said that Mum was very upset when I ran off, and she couldn't understand why the thought of moving would make me so miserable. He also explained that she couldn't feel the same as I did, because she had been accustomed to having all the facilities, which people had in towns and cities before coming to Ballinalacken, and she would be grateful to have those conveniences once more. Gradually he helped me to understand, and that was fine, until I said that at least we would be able to talk about it after we moved. 'Oh dear,' he said, 'has she not told you that Joe and I will be remaining here and your Dad will come most days.' Well, that was just too much in one day; he must have known what my next move would be, because he suddenly grasped my hand very firmly and said, 'but you will be able to come often.' Deep in the pit of my stomach I knew that would not happen; there were no more tears left and I couldn't even think about it.

When we arrived indoors everyone was happy that I was *safe and sound,* but I couldn't share their feelings, and I felt that they couldn't understand or share mine at that moment; they were too deep and I hadn't yet come to terms with them myself. But Granddad understood, and must have realised that he and I had a lot of ground to cover, before I was ready to leave Ballinalacken. He understood all about my inner and outer journey; or my dual journey as he was wont to call it.

Good manners were all important in our house and regardless of how I felt, and without looking at Mum, I said goodnight to everyone, and prepared to leave the room, being aware that Mum had attempted to follow me. Dad had put his hand on her arm, and I heard him whisper, 'Let her be and she will find a way.' So he too must have understood, but then he had grown up here, which meant that in similar circumstances he may have felt the same way. Well, that felt like balm in my moment of torment, but I couldn't reason further that evening. As I lay in bed I remembered that I hadn't knelt to say my prayers. I started with the first line, 'O Angel of God, my Guardian dear,' but couldn't carry on because it was all too familiar, and my new state was too alien. Living here I was very familiar with all weather conditions: the fog – sometimes so dense it was difficult to see anything: the mist – which seemed like thick fog but left one feeling cold and wet, and the rain which sent us scuttling for cover at the earliest opportunity. Just then it felt like all three, but it was all inside me, and I couldn't escape it. I hoped though that my invisible friend was still with me, and understanding why I couldn't pray or even think. Then there seemed to be a feeling of peace somewhere in the depth of my being, and I thought of the words I had heard in church, 'I am The Way.' I knew that next day I would need to go to that inner place, and as always Granddad wouldn't be too far away.

Next morning I awoke with a very heavy heart, and having washed and dressed, I tried to pretend that I was still full of bounce when I appeared in the kitchen for breakfast, but I fooled no one, least of all myself; I couldn't magic up that feeling: I didn't wish to be a burden to my parents, but at that moment I felt that I was a burden to myself. There was no rebuke when I couldn't finish my porridge.

It was a bright, clear, sunny morning and there was only one place I wanted to be, and one thing I wished with all my heart; that I could pretend that last evening had never happened. Granddad had not yet arisen and I knew that, when we met, he would not want a repeat of the previous evening, but how could I prepare myself. Mum seemed sad because I was so unhappy, but

I couldn't make her feel better until I had time to come to terms with it myself, and anyway, trying to pretend that everything was fine wouldn't work, because she knew me well; but only in some respects, it seemed – she hadn't been prepared for my reaction to her news.

Journeying to the far side of the meadow, once more, it was possible to manage a wry smile; thank heavens the meadow grass had been cut, for I would almost certainly not have noticed the previous evening. My brothers and I had been given strict instructions not to flatten the grass, before it was due for cutting, because it was almost impossible to cut flattened grass, which was a pity because it always looked so inviting just before it was cut. When, on one occasion we had forgotten the warning, and gambolled on the lawn, we were duly punished. Somehow, I felt that in my particular circumstances no one would have mentioned the grass, but I would have realised later and felt very guilty. I didn't need to feel guilty about what had happened, but how, oh how could I come to terms with it.

The grass was still long at the edge, and still wet after the heavy dew, but the area, which I had flattened the previous evening, appeared to have dried off quickly in the early morning sun; it was there that I attempted to find a way to face what seemed to be inevitable.

Sometimes I had heard the adults say, 'Well it's up to you.' Now it seemed that it was up to me, but it seemed a very adult thing to have to do by myself. I remember clearly that I was beginning to feel quite adult for my nine years – and wouldn't they be pleased if only they knew - but if the skylark had sensed my feelings, it couldn't have chosen a worse moment to start its journey upwards. As soon as the notes touched my heart my adult moment vanished, and I found myself, once more, in the depth of my own misery. How would it be possible to leave here; the tears wouldn't stop flowing. Then I recalled other comments I had heard, such as, *laughter is always better than tears* and *isn't she brave*. Oh, if only they could have seen me then, wallowing in my own misery. The very thought was like a challenge; they shouldn't find me like that, especially Granddad, and for the second time.

As the tall grass was still wet, it was possible to run my hands through it until they were quite wet, and then wipe my tear-stained face with them. The moisture reminded me of the fresh fragrance of the dew-covered flowers. Washing away the tears and drying my face had a very positive affect, and the cotton petticoat proved very useful on that occasion; it reminded me that Mum was always busy making garments for us children. It was time to look at the options. I could continue to be miserable every time I thought of moving: be thankful that it would be at least twelve months before it would happen: plan to use the intervening time to prepare myself. Being miserable wasn't really an option, and it was not my way of being, but if I didn't get my bounce back they wouldn't really know me at all.

The meadow had always yielded a good crop of hay and, before cutting, was full of daisies and buttercups. It saddened me to see them disappear, although I knew they would grow again. They were all around me then, as I sat contemplating my problem. One of my favourite pastimes, whilst dreaming in the meadow, had been plucking the daisies to make bangles and necklaces; often using some buttercups because the colour matched the centre of the daisy. On that occasion, I remember plucking a handful, but with no intention of making anything - they looked so beautiful and delicate. My thoughts, however, were focussed on the feelings I had before drifting into sleep the previous evening, and now was the right time to go on that inward journey. Having just made a decision regarding my options, I knew that all that reasoning had taken place in my head. I felt that my elders would be very pleased that I *had come to my senses.* They could only see the outer me; they couldn't know that deep inside I had not even come to terms with my own decision; that I couldn't be certain about being brave, if it all crept up on me, when I wasn't really thinking about it. That was the part I really needed to cope with, because I had a strange feeling that when the hype, which overtook me as I made my mature decision, finally deserted me, I might feel as bad, if not worse, than I had done the previous evening. This was the moment to leave the hype behind and go into that saddest place, hoping that my invisible friend, who was with me when the bull had been hot on Dad's heels, and with my younger brother and myself, when we had had our moment of terror at the crossroads with the dead goose, was still there and able to help me to find a way.

For just a moment I surveyed the scene before me; a scene, which filled me with a sense of wonder; a scene which had remained unchanged for as long as anyone could remember, but with reminders of past inhabitants, who would have struggled to survive in such austere conditions, yet had seemed to exist thousands of years before. What was this incredible quality, which held them and me here? Even the birds and the bees seemed to be in harmony with their existence. Whilst gazing at the scene before me, I was conscious again of the last words which had been on my mind before drifting into sleep the previous evening; they had returned again. I wondered what they meant, but concentrating on all the beauty around me seemed to increase the need to find a way to resolve my sadness, because I seemed to be the one who was out of harmony. The beauty was a temporary distraction, yet I knew that I couldn't dismiss it as I had dismissed the feeling of hype earlier, but rather take it on my inward journey to meet the turmoil there. As I did so, the words seemed to be waiting for me again – *I am the Way.* Even though I didn't really understand, I knew that this was my invisible friend, just waiting for me. This was a new way of *being* for me, no adults to question: no imaginative thoughts: not any desire to do anything, but to remain in that peaceful moment, as the turmoil subsided and the pain began to ease. There was no inclination to move; no thought of time, but gradually I became aware of a sweet tobacco scent, and looked up to see Granddad smiling down at me. Being so engrossed, his approach had gone completely unnoticed, but there was no guilt, just acceptance that he and I knew that my journey had been fruitful.

Oh yes, there were to be a lot of questions in the next twelve months, and I knew that I would need to store the answers to last me for the rest of my life. The first question would have to be why, if he understood Mum's reason for wishing to move, he had chosen to spend most of his adult life in this place, without all the convenient amenities. I sensed that his attachment had a big part to play, but I also felt that there was so much more to learn. And yes, as we walked back across the meadow, the weight of my sadness seemed to have lifted and it wasn't too long before the bounce returned too. Despite that fact, and regardless of all the questions, which I felt he would be able to answer, there was one question, which I knew he couldn't answer, and that was because I couldn't ask it.

During the dialogue, which had taken place since Mum's announcement, nobody had mentioned Grandma. Granddad had said that he and Joe would remain in Rockville, with Dad visiting daily, but he hadn't said that Grandma would be there, or that she would be moving with us: I knew he would never agree to that. I also knew that it would be impossible for him to look after her himself, even with help from Joe. Of course there was another possibility, namely that Nora would visit regularly, but she wouldn't be in a position to be there all the time, because she had her own home to look after. I didn't know what to think, except that, for reasons which I couldn't understand then, nobody wished to enlighten me. Not for the first time, I decided that it was very frustrating being considered too young to be told and, on that occasion, it left me with a very uneasy feeling.'

Liam, who has been listening very intently, and looking at Nan, says, "Thank you Nan. I'm sure that was probably the most difficult part of your story."
Nan is looking at this very discerning young man, and grateful that he is such an attentive listener, as he continues, "And I know that you have been lost in that particular time too because..."
He couldn't continue, and as Nan looked more closely, she could see that his eyes were beginning to dance. Neither could he contain the laughter, which had started to bubble up, as his gaze rested on her hands.
"Oh shucks," said Nan, surveying the collection of daisies in her hand, "I guess I must have been transported, but thankfully, I haven't damaged any of them. I can take them back to the house and put them in water, just for old time's sake. I am so glad that we have shared the beginning of that journey, because it was never going to be easy.

I had always been very interested in the words that the adults used to describe me. Grandma had often said that I was too inquisitive. I hadn't been too sure about that, but she wasn't always feeling very well when she said it. Granddad said I was thoughtful, and I thought that was ok, because I knew he was thoughtful too. Mum thought I was a bit of a wanderer, and I did sometimes wander off, when I knew she needed me to do something, then I really needed to be doing something else; and Dad thought I was imaginative and a bit of a day-dreamer, because he said I didn't always seem to hear him ask me to do something. That was fine because there were times when I asked him a question but he didn't seem to hear me either. Yet they all knew when I was determined to do something, because they said that I stuck my chin out, and I often wondered if anyone had noticed on that particular morning, when I returned indoors with Granddad, that I was feeling very determined indeed. Whether they noticed or not, no one was going to comment that time. I was about to make a list of all the questions I could think of, and doing so helped me to be positive, and probably mischievous too."

"Why was that? Was it a long list?" Liam asked.

"No", Nan replied. "But it was a positive beginning: it would remain open ended, and all the grown-ups knew what I was doing and why. I think I must have felt that because they had caused the crisis, and hopefully felt a little guilty, I had the right to ask questions and, after all, the only thing they needed to do was to reply to them.

I didn't really need to include Granddad in my scheming, because later that day, when we were sitting in the garden, he told me that whilst we had been returning home across the meadow he had read my thoughts; he had indicated that after the move life would be very different for both of us. As he explained: my brother Joe - who is a year older than I - would remain in Rockville, and continue to attend school in Ballinalacken, but he had his own friends, and liked to spend much of his time out of doors. Dad would be carrying on with the usual work on the farm, and bringing them food each day, but he wouldn't be there in the evenings, and of course Mum wouldn't be there to reprimand him when she thought he was neglecting himself. She was a wonderful homemaker. I remember thinking, he is talking about each of them in turn, but what will he say when he gets to me, but he didn't say anything and merely continued to fix his gaze on his pipe, which he seemed to carry everywhere in those days. As I studied his face, whilst waiting, I had the same uncomfortable feeling, which I had experienced during the morning: why hadn't he mentioned Grandma? Perhaps he couldn't: perhaps he knew that she wouldn't be with us then! We all knew she was ill, but I hadn't realised how ill she really was, and I needed to understand. I had to be strong when Mum told me about Gammie, and I had to make some adult decisions when

I was in the meadow, so I needed to be brave again, as I looked into his face, and asked him gently if we were going to lose Grandma. He simply nodded.

Guilt is a very unpleasant feeling, and I experienced deep pangs at that moment; I had been so engrossed in my own feelings and reactions, that I had only considered him in the light of his ability to understand what I was going through, and how he could make me feel better. As the tears started to prickle again, I just put my arm round his neck and whispered, 'I am so sorry Granddad, I feel so mean thinking only of myself.' Maybe it was the realisation that we each had our own ache to contend with, in our own manner, which helped us; but sharing our feelings appeared to make the load slightly easier to bear, and there was a hint of a smile as he said, 'Well it's no use moping and I have seen the list you were compiling, so where shall we begin.' It was my turn to be down to earth, as I reminded him that I liked to know about the beginning of things, because everything had to have a beginning. I must have hit the right note, because suddenly he laughed aloud – which hadn't happened for some time – and I realised that he would have known about the move long before I was told, and it would have been weighing on his mind. It was a joy to hear him laugh, as he said, 'Well we had better get started then, and it is likely to be a very interesting and rewarding journey for both of us.'

I knew he was looking at me with a sort of quizzical expression, which often happened when he was wondering what I was going to say next; and I began to giggle and needed to wait for a few moments in order to control myself, and think about how best to ask the first and the most important question. Very often, when we children seemed hesitant about asking or saying something, the adults would say, well out with it, but that sometimes seemed to put pressure on us. I was very happy that Granddad didn't say that. I really needed to decide whether to ask the question first, at the risk of being told that I wasn't really old enough to understand. I wanted to reassure him about the thought in my head, and I told him that nobody had put it there – just in case he said, as the other adults often did, "Who put that thought in your head." I simply said that seeing the chickens and the hens had set me thinking. That made him laugh even louder, and it was his turn to find some self-control, because when he laughed I couldn't help but join him, and then he said, 'Well that is a new beginning and I can't wait to hear more.' That laughter seemed to make up my mind for me; I decided to tell the story first and ask the question at the end.

He was never with Mum and me when we went to feed the fowl, that chore being part of Mum's domain. Quite often she would send one of us children to do it for her, but she usually said that it took me much longer than my brothers to accomplish the task. I didn't tell her that I liked to talk to the birds, especially when they were nesting, and not too preoccupied with scratching the ground for food. Speaking very softly didn't frighten them, and they had a habit of turning their heads from side to side whilst maintaining firm eye contact; so far and no further, the look seemed to say. On one such occasion I was lucky enough to be just on time to see the first stage of a chick trying to find a way out of the shell. Being very quiet, it was possible to hear the persistent tapping inside one of the eggs, which sat at the outer edge of the clutch, and hadn't been completely covered by the nesting hen. Realising that something exciting was about to happen, I rushed indoors to tell Mum, only to be told that it would be some time before there would be anything to see, and meanwhile my dinner was ready and everyone else was waiting for me. Then there would be the dishes to collect before I needed to think about going out to check the progress. All that seemed to take an eternity, and I felt sure that the chick would have arrived in my absence, but of course Mum had been right. When I finally got there I could see that a hole had appeared in the shell and within minutes a large crack developed, accompanied by a loud cheeping. What next I wondered, as I waited! It seemed to be ages, but in fact it was probably only about ten minutes before the shell divided and the cheeping became louder, as the chick struggled to emerge. I felt bewildered, because what I could see inside the shell didn't look anything like the chicks which ran round the yard with their mothers. When it finally appeared, I took one look at it and flew indoors to tell Mum that a chick had arrived, but it looked so wet and scrawny that I felt sure it was about to die. By that time Mum had washed up and was sitting quietly, knitting and listening to the radio. Surveying my worried look she asked what had happened. When I told her she laughed, and said that I mustn't worry, but go back and inspect the chick in an hour, by which time she felt sure I would be happily surprised by the change in its appearance. Once again she was right, for by then it had managed to stand on its spindly legs, which topped what looked like enormous feet with big claws that seemed out of proportion to the rest of its body. Thankfully its lovely soft down had dried off and it looked like a soft yellow ball, with a small head which had two sparkling eyes, more like the chicks I was used to seeing. I longed to pick it up, but I could tell by the look in its mother's eyes that it was too soon.

It was always interesting to watch the chickens' development, knowing that some of them would be destined for the pot, but hoping that it wouldn't be any of my favourites. It was easy to see which of the birds were more aggressive, and liked to control the others by pecking at them; these were the ones which I hoped that Mum would choose. She had earmarked a few when I had been with her, and a few days later, when she was very busy, she asked me to go and see if I could catch one. I had a sneaking feeling that I must have been *getting under her feet,* because she was smiling as she spoke, but she was still able to hear my reply as I left the kitchen, "Well, if I do manage to catch it, that's all I will do."

To which she replied, 'Don't worry, you can leave the next stage to me.'

I didn't worry about that. Indeed I had enough to worry about trying to work out what my best tactics would be, because in the past I had merely been Mum's helper. What followed was a battle of will and wits, because on my way, I had decided which hen I wouldn't loose any sleep over. When I finally approached it, and looked into its eyes, they seemed to say that it knew what my intentions were, almost as though it had known that whenever a bird disappeared from the yard, it didn't return, and it definitely didn't wish to join that queue. As I moved, whilst speaking softly, it also moved squawking loudly, and each time I lunged the squawking became more persistent. It spread its wings in an attempt to fly, but collapsed on the ground instead, because it was one of those birds which had never mastered the art of flying, even a short distance. However, its efforts were enough to give it some temporary space. It wasn't the first time I had wished that Mum would have allowed me to wear trousers – like the boys – because the struggle would have been so much easier if my skirt wasn't getting in the way. I needed to stop and take stock of the situation. Would the hen tire before I did, would I need to go and ask Mum for help, or would I have one more determined attempt?

Another attempt it had to be, even though I could see from the bird's stance, that it seemed ready to cope with any move I might make. I reminded myself that it was destined for the pot, with or without Mum's assistance. I propelled myself forward, managing to grasp a fistful of feathers, but not the bird; and found myself lying in a heap on the ground with blood on my knee. The thought of going indoors with a damaged knee but no bird, tucked safely under my arm, wasn't worth considering. Whilst sorting myself out, I noticed that my target had made its way through the open door of the shed, and was resting in the corner. No way, I thought, are you leaving there by yourself. Having closed the door it was still possible to see it in the dim light, and my task was complete. It was strange though, because at that moment, and despite its aggressive behaviour towards the other hens, and my own injury, I didn't want it to be a victim, and I definitely didn't want to see Mum wring its neck.

Looking relieved and a little surprised Granddad said, 'Well, that was a beginning, because you saw the chicken arrive, and you helped to catch the hen, but I don't remember seeing that on the list you made."

I told him that there was nothing about the chick or the hen, or the follow-up question on the list, because I hadn't been sure how to word it. But I had also been worried that it might get me into trouble.

'Then tell me what is bothering you,' he said.

He already knew that I helped Mum to pluck the hens, which was easier to do when the birds were still warm. Then it was back to Mum to remove the organs. She normally discarded everything with the exception of the neck, the gizzard and the heart, these were usually boiled and the liquid was used for gravy. When the cleaning operation was complete, it was possible for me to inspect them more closely. My fascination had always been with the heart. Grandma had shown me pictures of a heart, and I could feel my own as it beat inside my chest, it felt like the rhythm of our clock going tick-tock. But what, I asked him, had started the heart beating in the first instance: it stopped when life was ended but how did it start when life began.

It was something which had been on my mind for a long time, and finding an answer had become very important to me, because I was interested in living things; being able to share it with Granddad was a tremendous relief. His reply was very simple, 'You know the answer to that already, because you have learned your catechism and you know that God created all things.'

And of course I did know, but that wasn't the crux of the matter. Having watched the clock being repaired a few times, I understood how it was constructed and what made it tick. I really needed him to tell me if a heart could ever be jump started in the same manner. 'Never, ever,' was his immediate reply, but I could see that the question had startled him, and I had to wait patiently whilst he thought carefully about his answer. He seemed to take a long time to load his pipe, find his matches and then wait until it was properly lit, but all the while I knew he was deep in thought. Finally he said, 'I feel inclined to say let's leave it until you are older, but I know that won't satisfy you. I can only add that occasionally when, say an older person has had a bad shock to his system his heart could stop, but if there is someone available who knows how to do it, it can be jump started, and it resumes its normal rhythm. However that cannot be compared to the creation of an organ, which is the central part of one's being, and without which all the other organs would refuse to operate. It's probably a bit like the mechanics of the clock, as you said, without the finely tuned spring the cogs wouldn't work. But the clock is only similar to a heart in its motion, being merely a mechanical thing. The function of the heart is vastly different as you know to your cost.'

He had stopped talking, and had turned to study my face for a few moments, but it was a sad look and I wondered what he was going to say next. I had begun to feel a little uneasy inside, and had to remind myself that I had instigated the conversation and should be equal to the answer. He took a deep breath, but his voice was a little shaky as he continued, "I am reluctant to remind you about the move to Lisdoonvarna, even though I know that it is probably the best way to try to explain what I mean.' That was a shock because I had tried so hard to put it at the back of my mind, and having promised myself that I would always be honest with him I told him so, but he already knew that and understood. He continued, 'Take yourself back to the moment when your Mum told you about the move, and tell me how you felt before you took off to the meadow.'

I remember saying that I wasn't sure that I could, because the memory was still painful, but he took my hand, squeezed it and said, 'It's because of that painful memory that you are more likely to understand what I am trying to tell you. Yes it's a difficult discussion for us, but you will always remember that it took place. So let's start with your first feeling and take it from there.'
'Oh dear,' I said, 'do you mean the numbness: the pins and needles in my feet, the agitation in my brain, the anger towards Mum, not being able to speak, the need to be on my own, all that happened before I went to the meadow. It was in the meadow that I really felt the pain. It had crept in slowly because my brain couldn't give me an answer. When the lark began to sing I thought my heart would break, but it had been so different to those previous occasions. I know I cried a lot and that seemed to ease the pain a little, but it felt as though it had settled in my heart. Is that what you wanted me to tell you?'

He replied, 'Exactly that! You had a shock, which upset your normal pattern, but it was only when you tuned into your heart that you came face to face with the feeling of pain. Of course you needed to use your brain to reason with, but it was your heart which felt those deep emotions and helped you to understand later. Despite what we all say when we tease you, your parents and I know that you think and feel deeply. Had it not been for that reason I wouldn't be here talking with you now. You see there are many occasions when we need to combine our thinking and our feeling in order to understand. More importantly it is only when we experience a situation that we can fully understand the important part that our heart plays in our *being.* In answer to your question then, I know that a shock could cause the heart to stop in extreme circumstances, and properly administered shock treatment can help it to restart, but I also feel that the function of the heart, merely as a mechanical means of keeping all the other body organs working, is just unthinkable. Without all the sensations with which it provides us, we would simply be like mechanical dummies. We can create all manner of things and enable them to become operational, but no man can create something, which can feel deep emotions. We will leave that for now and maybe look at it again on another occasion. Let us just sit here for a moment and enjoy the beauty around us, as we listen to the skylark singing its heart out.'

The hand which had been holding mine very firmly suddenly became quite limp, and I sensed that he had found that a difficult discussion, particularly towards the end when he sounded almost angry. I would need to think carefully about what he had said. Meanwhile I was happy to do as he bid and simply just *be*."

Liam was laughing as he said, "I'm trying to imagine you rushing about after the hen. That would have been great fun." Although she couldn't help laughing along with him, that comment had touched a sensitive spot and Nan replied, "Well, had you been there you wouldn't have been a spectator, I can assure you. It would have been two against one. I was feeling just a little peeved, because I thought that Mum should have waited for the boys to return, at least the two older ones – the younger one would have considered the whole episode one hilarious joke, so he wouldn't have been much help."
Nan was about to say more on the subject, but noticing that Liam had become quiet and thoughtful, decided to remain silent. He had obviously been imagining that scene, but she was still unprepared when he said, "I know you are painting a picture of that time for me and I wondered, before you go any further, if you could describe your granddad to me, so that I can see him in

the story."

"Oh dear, that isn't going to be easy." Nan replied. "And, before I venture down that road, I need to explain what I meant earlier, when I said that I wasn't to know how my theory concerning the therapeutic benefits of living at Rockville, was to help my powers of reasoning and faith.

The initial shock for me was Mum's bombshell regarding our move, which resulted in the list of questions, which I thought was a practical way of dealing with the problem: it was supposed to be a preparation, and much better than being miserable. As well as my list though, I had made another resolution, which was to note and store up all the changes I could see taking place about me, as we headed into autumn, then winter and on to spring. By that I meant that I would notice again, as if for the first and last time, all the natural changes which accompanied the changing seasons. That, together with Granddad's input, would help to strengthen my inner journey. My outer journey would continue, as expected by all those who knew me. As it happened, after that last major discussion with Granddad regarding the hen, it was to be some time before he could really focus in any depth on my questions or problems.

Grandma's deterioration became rapid, and she needed to spend more time in bed, when naturally Granddad wished to be in their bedroom, and he looked so weary and pensive afterwards. There had been one occasion at the beginning of that period, when Grandma must have awakened to bright sunshine in her room, because she informed Granddad that, if she needed to spend more time confined to her bed, she wished, before autumn really set in, to have one last trip to Fanore. He had emerged from their room with a rather comical look on his face, as he announced that she must be feeling much better because she had expressed a wish to visit Fanore. It had caused a flurry of activity since Dad had already gone to the main garden to continue harvesting the potatoes, and Mum had asked me to run and find him. We had set off after lunch, but I have already told you about that very moving visit, which was to be her last outing.

After that event, it seemed that I needed to mature at an alarming speed, both mentally and emotionally. I didn't harass anyone with unnecessary questions; there wasn't time, because with the exception of school attendance and homework, I spent all my spare time helping Mum to cope, when the role of full time nurse was added to her domestic and maternal roles. There were a few occasions when I felt, rather guiltily, that I would have loved to disappear with the boys and join in their pursuits. Instead I took myself out of doors whenever I could, and immersed myself in the timeless beauty which was available to me, and I learned to be thankful for that.

Standing outside I tried to focus on what it felt like to be losing two grandparents; what that would mean for me, but more importantly, how it would affect those who were closest to them. In particular I thought about Mum who had lost two of her children when they were babies, and the pain she must have endured at that time. I began to wonder if there were different levels of pain, but decided that, at that particular time, it wasn't really a wise road for me to travel down. I wasn't where they were in years, having lived their lives: only where I was. They would have been able to look back, and hopefully feel happy with their achievements, whereas I didn't have much to build on, except what they had told me, and my own limited experience and beliefs. I was thankful that there was to be no physical change to my circumstances until the following year. So I tried to become very aware of and sensitive to the needs of my elders. Sometimes, when the weather permitted, Granddad would go outside and sit or stand and gaze beyond the rushing tide into the distance. I wondered what his thoughts were on those occasions: was he thinking about different levels of pain, and would he think about our conversation concerning the chicken; when I was more concerned with beginnings, but didn't consider until afterwards, that he might also have been thinking about endings. Sometimes I let him be, and on other occasions I went out to be with him, in comfortable, loving silence. I wondered if he too was thankful for our belief in the higher order of our being. Maybe one day I could talk to him about that, but not then, it was all too deep for words.

The time sped by, with the normal daily activities merging with the extra responsibilities. Of course, as children we needed to be ever conscious of Grandma, particularly when we were trying to celebrate Halloween and Christmas. The noise level had to be muted and we weren't allowed to rush past the bedroom door at any time. I was happy to comply with Granddad's wish for me to spend short spells with Grandma, and he gave me some of her favourite poems and prayers to read to her quietly. Occasionally she would hold my hand as we prayed together, and she seemed very comfortable with that, but more importantly for me, I was no longer in awe of her.

Christmas came and went very quietly, and it was no longer possible for me to pop in to be with Grandma, because there was no longer any response from her: Granddad and Mum decided that it could be too distressing for me, and I was happy to agree with them. However, there were a few occasions when I needed to make a quick visit, just to reassure myself that she was still breathing.
We were all glad to welcome the New Year in, but there was no merry-making, or mummers calling to dance, sing and of course raise a toast to the New Year. Many people did call, and following the usual custom which abounded in country areas, simply said, "God Bless all here, and how is Jennie?" The doctor was making a daily visit, and preparing Granddad for the inevitable, which occurred on the 4th January. Then we became a

family in mourning, with many people calling to offer their condolences, and help if we needed it. The traditional mourning period for many families in Ireland used to be called the wake, which commenced as soon as somebody died, and continued until after the funeral. I suppose it could be seen as a company-keeping process, not merely for the bereaved, but also for the deceased, who were not to be abandoned on their demise. Members of the family took turns in spending prayer time with the departed, and those visitors who felt able to do so offered to share in the watching process. It was seen as support time for the nearest and dearest, and in our situation was very beneficial for Granddad, because as Mum said, 'It took him out of himself.' For Mum though, it proved to be an exhausting period, since the house became like a hotel, from late morning until late in the evening, when even Granddad looked all in. As Mum had said, there were always a few who liked a pint too many, and didn't know how to stop talking. There was her favourite, who she said, was still talking as she eased him out through the door. His last comment was, 'See you tomorrow,' but fortunately he didn't hear her reply, as she closed the door, 'Perhaps not. You would think he hadn't got a home to go to, poor man.' Poor Mum! I thought, as I fell into bed and went out like a light.

Throughout those chaotic days, I did sneak outside occasionally, but I also wanted to spend my own minutes with Grandma. On my first visit to her, my brothers came along too, but Patrick was rather giggly, and I put that down to nervousness. None of us knew what to expect, there was a sort of eeriness in the room. Grandma had been properly laid out, with two of the neighbours helping Mum. Everything on the bed was white: pillowcases, sheets and counterpane, with Grandma in a white garment. I think it was the whiteness which created the eeriness, because Grandma's hair was snow white, and her face looked like alabaster. None of us wished to stay very long, but before leaving the room I had begun to focus on the two candles which were alight, one on either side of the bed, and I resolved to return again by myself, because the candles had been very comforting. Later that day, when everyone was at the table having finished eating, I excused myself and returned to be with Grandma. I knew that nothing would have changed, but I stole a quick, uneasy look at her face, just in case. It wasn't going to be easy: even though I was accustomed to seeing animals, and fowl in a lifeless state, but the candles had drawn me back and I hoped that they would give me an inkling of what it was all about. I know how important candles were in the running of our house: it was that, the tilley lamp or the torch, because we couldn't often rely on the wind charger. Candles were a source of light or illumination, as well as being mystical."

A sudden movement nearby distracted Nan, and she looked at Liam, realising that he was eager to say something. "Go ahead, Liam. I am not sure if you will understand, because I didn't find it easy then: only life and time can confirm, or strengthen what we feel and believe." "I am struggling?" Liam replied, "That word mysticism has really foxed me, what does it mean?" Nan began to laugh so suddenly and loudly that Liam was really taken aback, but the laughter continued, until she saw a look of consternation on his face, and became concerned for him. However, she had had a flashback herself to those occasions when she had put Granddad on the spot: realising just how difficult it must have been for him, as he tried to give her some real foundational meaning for her existence: how hard he had tried, and she must continue. "Forgive my outburst, Liam. I now know exactly what I was putting my Granddad through, and he was older then than I am now. He was old and determined, with an incredible spirit: his knowledge was truly inspirational, and woven into all the stories and experiences he passed on to me, like a tapestry. To fully answer your question about mysticism would be impossible to achieve in five minutes, but I would like you to ask again before we leave this place, when I hope to have recounted the best of what he said. You know from the books you read, that only certain aspects or passages remain with you. The same could be said about all I pass on to you: the gems passed down to me, which feed my spirit, provide the highlights for my own tapestry: the brightest gem was, and remains, spirit. If you hang on to that word, I know our journey will be much easier.

Meanwhile, back then, my own journey continued before the candles, in Grandma's presence, as I tried to accept what her passing meant. We had been told that when we die we go to our eternal rest, but she was still with us. I had fully understood when Granddad had explained about the heart, which kept us alive. Of course I knew that her heart had stopped, and then I remembered Granddad's words, 'But the clock is only similar to a heart in its motion, being merely a mechanical thing. The function of the heart is vastly different as you know to your cost.' As I gazed at the candle I began to realise that to be a being I needed to have a heart and a spirit: one kept me ticking and feeling, the other had to be my spirit, or guiding force which motivated me. So, one answer to your question about mysticism, and remember it is only one of many, is that focussing on the candlelight enabled me to think deeply about my subject, until I felt some enlightenment. Also, the candles had reminded me of being in Church, where we always had candles; and I remembered hearing the Priest reading some of Jesus's words, 'I am the light of the world. Whoever follows me will not walk in darkness, but will have the light of life.' Only then was it possible for me to look at Grandma without wanting to tear my eyes away: when I observed a very peaceful old lady, at rest. By the time I left the bedroom it was dark out of doors, but there remained the candles to light my way."

Realising that the stone she had been sitting on for some time had begun to make its presence felt, and that she had been talking at some length, she said, "Yes, I'm sure you wish to know more about Granddad and some of that will reveal itself, but first things first. I didn't intend sitting here for so long and my old bones are now objecting. I am also very thirsty, so let's collect our picnic bag from the boot of the car, and a cushion this time, and head down to the beach. It should only take twenty minutes on foot if we cut down across the fields. I have noticed you looking longingly at the sun sparkling on the water." Without more ado Liam opened the car boot, collected the necessary items, and after a quick drink of water from their bottles, they set off. It wasn't a journey which would allow them to concentrate on any particular topic, if they were to avoid all the obstacles in their path. The fields, which were rough grazing pasture for the animals, had a mass of boulders, stones, rushes, hawthorn bushes and potholes and, as always in the summer, a lot of nettles. Liam enjoyed circumnavigating the obstacles but Nan, whilst remembering being just as light footed, was quite relieved to draw breath when they finally climbed over the last wall: a few moments away from their destination at Poulsallagh. Even so, they rested for a short while, Liam quite elated after his excursion, and Nan laughing in relief as she recalled childhood journeys, when girls were not allowed to wear trousers. Trousers were a must for this terrain.

Addressing Liam, Nan laughs as she tells him that she is now older than Grandma was when she left them, and it is no longer a problem to bear; the real, and annoying problem, is accepting that she cannot sit around on hard stones as she used to, nor is she as nimble. Liam's sense of humour is spontaneous as he replies, "Well, I guarantee that you couldn't catch me in a race, but sure you didn't do too badly cutting through the fields just now; at least for your age, ha, ha"

CHAPTER IV

WHY

Where there is a why,
There is a wherefore.

William Shakespeare: A comedy of errors.

The sand was soft and warm, and Nan was content to remove her shoes and socks, but chose a suitable boulder on which to place her cushion. Liam, having remembered to put a towel in his sack, spread it on the ground and unpacked their picnic. They sat and ate in companionable silence, contentedly enjoying the scene before them. Meanwhile, Nan's thoughts were concentrated on how she would create a lasting picture of Granddad for her young companion, as with a wry smile, she thought of all those occasions when she had put her elders on the spot. Liam, having surreptitiously helped himself to a second cake, noticed the smile, and thought at first that it was directed at him. Not wishing him to feel guilty Nan said, "I have been thinking carefully about how to portray Granddad as he was, and not just as I saw him. I often heard adults speaking when he was out of earshot, and I feel that, in order to give you a rounded picture, I should look at the period before I was born in 1939. Dad had three brothers, two of whom were married with families, as was Dad, and they all lived and worked in Dublin. At the beginning of the war, which started in September 1939, those families who could leave were advised to vacate Dublin, although Ireland remained neutral throughout the war.

I often wondered, as I grew older, why Granddad and Grandma decided to invite Dad and his family to join them in

Ballinalacken. From the little I heard over the years, I believed that it was due to Dad's state of health, since he suffered with rheumatism. The disease could affect the whole body, attacking joints, muscles or fibrous structures. The name is less common today, because medical science has discovered that many of the individual complaints had other causes, and rheumatism was a sort of collective or blanket name for them. Nevertheless it was a condition which had crippled Dad by the time he was thirteen years of age. I often heard the elders singing the praises of a Doctor Ball, an expert in this field, who worked in Dublin and who treated Dad for the condition. However I know that he still had recurrent bouts of the symptoms throughout his life.

I was born in Dublin, and immediately afterwards we moved to Ballinalacken. Thirteen months later my younger brother Patrick was born. When I was old enough to understand, Mum told me, that Granddad had wished for a daughter when he had his own family, but it hadn't happened and my being there with three brothers probably meant that I was singled out for some extra attention. Being the only girl around wasn't always much fun, because the boys took off when they had free time, but my place was at home with the ladies, doing domestic chores for Mum, and learning to knit and sew in my free time, when I would have really preferred to be out with the lads. Consequently I was nicknamed a tomboy. There were some advantages though, because I was often able to eavesdrop on adult conversations, and study the speakers at the same time. There were times when I didn't understand the conversation, and there were other occasions when I understood but didn't agree, and this gave me a lot of food for thought. At no time were children allowed to ask an adult any personal questions, and this proved to be very frustrating, until I learned that studying people could be fun, provided they weren't discussing me!

Granddad had already retired as headmaster of the local school, and was happy to spend time with his grandchildren. This was a tremendous help for Mum, particularly when Grandma was ill, and I never considered going out to play, if I knew that he was going to be available. He was a tall upright person: bald and clean-shaven, although in some early photographs I noticed that he had a very bushy moustache. I was glad that he had shaved it off, because I think it would have detracted from his very soft-looking face. He had a gentle good humour, but he could be very strict when the occasion demanded. He believed that deportment was very important and, like Grandma, would have my brothers and I stand in a line as he quoted one of his favourite sayings, *'Chin up, chest out, shoulders back, stomach in'*. As I said earlier, my eldest brother, Tom, merely waited until he was out of earshot before saying, 'Can't be doing with that!' It did however stand them in good stead, because they grew to be quite tall, and maintained good deportment.

If we were confined to the house for any length of time, Granddad would give us a new copybook, and provide us with exercises. He never demanded that we finish them, but said that the first person to complete the book would get a shilling; which in today's currency would be five pence: that was quite a lot in those days. He had made spinning tops for us, and he demonstrated how best to wind the string in order to get a good spin. He would time us for a while, as we used them, and then move quietly to a corner where he could read the paper. One of the most popular exercises as far as he was concerned, was setting up the ring-board, which was used to help us with our sums. As he often said, there was method in his madness, because it was more than just a game.

There was a blackboard fitted very snugly behind the large kitchen table. When he produced that, and the chalk, I tried to imagine that Mum had some urgent work for me, but he was well aware of my tactics, and Mum was never far away if he wished to check. He would draw a map of Ireland, whilst telling us yet again that it was most important that we knew as much as possible about our native land. Asking him, on one occasion, if it might be possible to draw a straight line from Dublin to Ballinalacken, and fill in the interesting details there simply evoked a sharp retort. He was definitely in a teaching mode and I should have been aware of that. He wished us to learn about the rivers, mountains, lakes and all the main towns in Ireland. He would fill in a river and then ask if anyone could tell him which one it was. My eldest brother Tom was very good at remembering, but the rest of us remained silent, although we all knew where the Shannon was and the three lakes: Lough Allen, Lough Ree and Lough Derg, which formed part of its course. Lough Derg was the easiest one to remember, not only because it bordered Clare, but it was a noted pilgrimage site. Later on he would produce an old colourful map of Ireland, which he spread on the table, and leaving us to it would disappear for a time. This was always guaranteed to be a quiet time, as we looked once more at the Shannon, which had particular interest for us because we lived not too far from it. Tom was very interested in the whole subject: I was usually feeling pangs of guilt at not remembering more: Joe seemed more interested in the fish he could catch in the Shannon if Dad were with him, and Pat, realising that the Shannon was over two hundred miles long remarked on one occasion, after he had learned to swim, that he would swim that river, one day.

They were happy memories, because Granddad was very patient but, as I have already said, he was also very firm. He managed to get the best out of us, whilst reminding us that one day we would be grateful. I heard many years later that he had been a hard task master at school, but dedicated and fair, and I guess with four sons at home, and their like at school, he probably needed to be. I remained intrigued about why he would have chosen this vocation, and why choose this place which was so out in the sticks. As a teacher he would have needed to be master of Gaelic, English, arithmetic, history, geography and singing.

Needlework, which was the other subject taught, was in the domain of the female teacher. Secondary education was not available in the area when he took up his appointment, and the compulsory school ages were seven to fourteen. We know that nowadays children commence on or before their fifth birthday, and many have attended preschool classes. The main reason for delaying the commencement date was the distance some children needed to travel on foot, often coming from far up the mountain. Occasionally younger children could team up with their elders in the next house en route, but the homes were widespread and contact wasn't always easy without phones. Over a period of time I learned that because there was no secondary school available in the area, when the children reached the age of fourteen, Granddad would regularly stay after school to prepare those who needed to take exams for teaching, banking or the civil service. His hobbies, from what I could establish, had been cycling, sport, botany, history and helping people. He certainly helped me to understand how I could best live with myself."

Liam said, "I see, but you haven't said how or why he came to be here and where he came from. You have told me that you were born in Dublin and your coming here was due to the War or the Emergency, as you have often called it."

"You are right," Nan replied. "But that is because I haven't answered the question for myself. I suppose you could say my coming was due to circumstances beyond my control, but that his reason for being here was very different. Of course, in those days, it was considered rude for children to ask adults personal questions, even though I could and did quiz them all the time about unrelated things. Yet this was something which I would dearly love to have known, and I have often thought about it.

Maybe now is the time to focus again on what motivated him and what made his life meaningful."

Having satisfied his need for food, Liam is moving restlessly and looking at the gentle waves lapping the shore. Nan understands and knowing that the water is still likely to be very cold at this time of the year, she nevertheless suggests that they have a paddle. Liam is eager to move, but he is also keen to pursue their conversation as they walk. Bending to retrieve an interesting stone he asks, "What do you mean by meaningful, Nan?" Nan replies thoughtfully, "That is a powerful word Liam; some would say challenge provides meaning, but in essence I believe it is that quality or ingredient which helps us to make sense of life, and yes it does involve a lot of challenge. I believe also that making sense of his life was what motivated Granddad, but what was it that prompted that motivation?"

Liam had begun to laugh as he said, "Could we say that I am motivating you to tell me a story?"

Nan couldn't help but join in his laughter, as she realised that in order to do justice to his request, she would need to imagine Granddad's situation, and try to see the past through his eyes. It would entail looking at the distant past, or what it would have been like long ago, and in his real time. That was the crux of the matter, and looking at Liam she said lightly, "Now, you are putting me in a real predicament, because although I have often wondered why, I have never really chased the subject until now, and to be honest it makes me feel rather uncomfortable."

Liam replied, "Well it seems to be important to both of us, and you know I am very interested in history, so I am going to do what you should have done whilst he was alive – Ask more questions!"

Giving him a wicked grin Nan said, "Oh, I do see your point, but I have explained why: we didn't have the freedom of speech

which you have now. But where do I begin that is my challenge!"
Liam starts to hum a tune but, being deep in thought, it is some
moments before Nan listens and laughs heartily, as she
recognises the melody. She can't resist the temptation to cup a
little seawater in her hand and throw it at him, but he manages to
duck speedily. Being of the same mind, they sang:

Let's start at the very beginning, a very good place to start,
When you read you begin with A B C,
When you sing you begin with Do Re Mi, Do Re Mi
The first three notes just happen to be Do Re Mi, Do Re Mi.

They continued to sing, as they splashed along the water's edge,
until finally Nan said, "I am not sure what Rogers and
Hammerstein would have made of that, but they are not around,
and neither is anyone else. I guess we are *monarchs of all we
survey* at this moment. It's just us, and all that nature has
endowed: the sun in a cloudless blue sky, the sea lapping gently
over our feet, and this lunar, limestone landscape, with its
patches of grass, and all these fissures containing such a variety
of beautiful plants. No wonder it's a botanist's dream. However,
that is today's scene: a glorious one which sadly does change, but
there will be others which are less reassuring. Life and history
can be compared to the weather - never constant - and we must
look at the whole scene in order to do some unravelling."

A silence descends once more as Nan starts to soul-search,
becoming oblivious to all external distractions, until Liam says, "I
know that I tease you Nan, but I wouldn't want to hassle you,
and we don't have to pursue that subject if it is likely to overburden you."

Giving him an understanding smile Nan, tries to reassure him as
she replies, "Once I decide how to give you the best,
uncomplicated picture, I am sure the stress will disappear. But in

order to achieve that, I believe that I will need to cover a whole lot of different topics or subjects, which impact on it such as: the Celts, the Saints, the History of Ireland, the Bible and the Famine. The problem is that I am not a historian, theologian or politician, but surviving here with my family for those years made me aware of the hardships which people must have endured in the past. Because it is experiential, my feelings and emotions are very real, and yet I wish now to give you a compassionate yet detached overview. Although the foundation was laid by my parents, grandparents and others, I have also carried out my own research.

I know that I have told you often that we children were to be seen and not heard. However I was always content to listen when visitors came to call on my grandparents; their conversations gave me a lot of food for thought. Occasionally I could broach a subject after the visitors had left, if the occasion seemed appropriate. Sometimes, to my dismay I was informed that it should wait until I was much older, and very occasionally I was reminded that little children shouldn't have such big ears; it depended on who I asked, and over time I learned to be circumspect about that. Many years later I realised that I had probably complicated issues by asking why people needed to do the things they did, instead of accepting straightforward factual answers. It seemed that Dad and Granddad understood what I was trying to discover, but Dad was always busy and that left Granddad at my mercy. It was not the fact of the matter which seemed to catch my imagination, but the underlying reasoning. The need to know would seem to be part of my character, and although I can also understand how it complicates issues in my life, I would not choose to dismiss it as irrelevant. I am now in a similar situation, because it is not the fact that Granddad chose to sacrifice his physical comforts, in order to help the youth of this place, but how did his early background affect his decision. And why? Perhaps as I recall some of the things, which he and I spoke about, there may be some clues to help us. Let's wait and see."

Having reseated themselves once more, and dried their feet, they sit for a few moments contemplating the timeless scene before them. The changing seasons impact on the foliage, but the sea and surroundings remain unchanged, just as it had done for countless ages. Nan finds herself having to make a determined effort to concentrate on the subject in hand.

"You know we were a family of eight until Grandma passed away," she says, "and mealtimes were very important occasions when we all sat round the table. We four children sat on a bench close together; I sat at one end next to my little brother, who wasn't too keen to be squashed, and he took full advantage of the opportunity to tease his older brothers. There always seemed to be one leg too many under the table, which usually found a target. The older lads wouldn't cry out, and although the weapon wasn't often aimed at me, I tended to keep an eye on my eldest brother's face, which could turn a shade of pink, then red and finally crimson. That was always a danger signal, which made me very uncomfortable. We weren't encouraged to tell tales, but rather than wait for the inevitable explosion, it seemed easier for me to pretend to fall off the end of the bench, so that one of the adults would look in our direction. One look was sufficient, and Granddad would begin, 'Now when I was little...,' going on to remind us about his childhood, and telling us that because he had been one of twelve children, the youngest were obliged to stand at the bottom of the table at mealtimes. We should therefore consider ourselves lucky to have a seat and learn to behave. Although he included all of us, his eyes were fixed on the tormentor's face, and it usually had the desired effect. Those were occasions when I desperately wanted to hear about his family, because it seemed as if they must have been like a clan or a tribe: rather like the stories we were often told, and some of which I had read; but it remained a mystery – a fascinating one for me. During the years that followed I learned that some siblings had died, and some went to Northern Ireland when they were older. I am though at this late stage beginning to discover that I have cousins which I had not been aware of."

"How would you describe a clan or a tribe?" Liam asked.
"Oh! It's not difficult to explain, and we will come back to that later, because right now I want to tell you a story, and you mustn't laugh at me, because it still has the power to make the hairs on my neck quiver!"
Liam noticed the wry smile, which accompanied the statement and retorted, with a grin, "I can only try not to Nan, but should I promise?" Liam replies.
"I get your point," replies Nan. "By the way, have you ever stood outside on a bright moonlit night, and gazed up at the moon?" Liam shook his head. "I didn't think you had, but I often did, and still do. On a really calm winter or summer's night, when there is no wind, if you could stand outside, close your eyes, and listen to the sounds all around you. It would probably be much easier to carry out this experiment when you are not in the middle of a city, but you will find an appropriate moment wherever you are, when it will be possible. Slowly you will begin to feel the stillness and calmness of the night all about you, when everything and everyone is supposed to be at rest. Allow yourself to be drawn into that peace, and then open your eyes and gaze at the moon high in the sky. My brothers and I used to do it, although not always in a peaceful manner; we were very much in awe of the magic of the night, as we gazed at the face in the moon. It didn't stop us playing hide and seek, which was fun but scary too, especially when someone jumped out from behind a bush, and made horrible faces, which reminds me of one very scary incident!

Sometimes, on one of those really beautiful moonlit nights, Mum would decide to visit one of her friends, who lived further up the mountain, taking me with her for company. On one such occasion we had spent a lovely evening seated around an open fire in the kitchen. The mistress of the house declared, on our arrival, that she hadn't got a morsel of cake in the house, and set about making griddle scones, as she and Mum continued their chatting. I was fascinated as I watched the scones being baked on a griddle, set in the open hearth; at home Mum used a range, which seemed much easier to manage; she didn't need a griddle, but used a cast iron pan instead. By the time the scones were cooked, we had been joined by a few other neighbours – it seemed that people knew which house to gather in; there were times when it happened to be ours. I never quite worked out how people knew where the gathering was, except that perhaps with so little traffic movement, and because the houses were so widespread, those who were on the move didn't go unnoticed. Cottages tended to be built quite close to the roadside, and of course all the farmers had dogs, and the cottages had windows, enabling the inhabitants to look out and investigate the cause of the commotion, when the dogs barked loudly, which they invariably did. More importantly, everyone was sociable, when the day's work was done, and I felt good to be a part of it, and so it was on that particular evening.

When everyone had finished eating, drinking and telling stories, a man who had brought his accordion, began to play some of our familiar tunes; before long someone started to hum to the music, and others joined in, and eventually broke into song. By the time we set out for home, everyone was in high spirits. All was well until I remembered one of the songs we had been singing earlier, and couldn't resist the urge to have a go; forgetting one of the rules of the night - *Be Quiet!* I wasn't singing loudly, but I hadn't noticed how close we were to one of the farms, until a dog bounded towards us, barking very loudly. I couldn't suppress the squeal, as I dashed behind Mum for protection. Fortunately it didn't bite, and Mum was able to calm it down, but it continued to bark as it retreated to the farm. It was one of a number of dogs; the others, being shut in the barn, had heard the commotion and joined in. Eventually the barking ceased, apart from one animal which started to howl, and it wasn't long before it found an echo further up the mountain; that sounded very eerie. But it was the sound which accompanied us on the remainder of our journey. The magic of the night had disappeared; Mum wasn't happy and I sensed it was because I had caused the commotion. When I told her I was sorry, there was no reply, and I felt that maybe the eeriness had affected her as well, but I couldn't tell her that I was really scared. The night had become spooky and the hairs on the back of my neck seemed to be twitching. I was so pleased to be back indoors, and because it was quite late, I took myself straight to bed. I prayed that Granddad would be able to give me an explanation for the horrible sensations I had experienced, and perhaps explain why the dogs needed to make such a weird, ghostly noise, which only seemed to happen on moonlit nights."

As Nan came to the end of the story she looked at Liam inquiringly, but far from laughing, he was looking very thoughtful as he said, "A bit spooky that, but I have tried to enter into the spirit of what you were saying. I am sure that had I been there I might have felt uncomfortable too, but I am really keen to know what it has to do with clans!"
"Oh! It has everything to do with clans and tribes, as you will see by and by. I am happy you were able to feel part of the story, and of course you mentioned the one word which I needed to set me on my way. *Spirit!*

One very wet miserable day, shortly after that eventful evening, Granddad happened to be looking out through the kitchen window. The scene would have been uplifting on a bright clear day, but not on that occasion, because it wasn't possible to see much beyond the garden gate. I wasn't surprised that he looked melancholy; he didn't talk about Grandma not being there any more, but I knew she was often on his mind. I decided that it might be a good opportunity to tell him how I had felt during my moonlit excursion with Mum! Although I was sure that he would have heard already, he wouldn't have known how I felt, or so I thought. As I started to speak his face brightened immediately, and I sensed with a sigh of relief that he had been waiting for the opportunity. The creepy feeling returned as I recounted the event, but when I mentioned the magic of the night, he immediately held up his hand and said, 'Now that's a word we should use with caution! I know what you mean by the magic of the night, but it would be better to say the spirit of the night, or even the mystery of the night, because moonlit nights can appear to be very mysterious; they seem to have an other worldly quality about them. That is understandable, because as a rule our normal working activities take place during the day, and night is regarded as a time for sleep, it could seem like another world. But that is not the other world which the Celts believed in. I know how much you love those mythical stories of long ago, but I think it's time for me to try to explain the difference between their beliefs, at the beginning, and our beliefs now. I have noticed how engrossed you have always been whilst listening to the stories told by your Dad, and particularly those told by your Aunt Alice when she has been here. It was good for me to hear them, and to know that they too had listened when I told them all about the Celts, when they themselves were young, just as I hope to tell you now. But first we need to look back to some of those times when we have stood outside, and watched the sun go down out in the west. You have described it in various ways in the past: a ball of fire, a ball of gold, a gentle soft glow fading into the sea. Your favourite seemed to be the blazing light sending its rays upwards through the clouds, changing their appearance, so that they seemed to be endowed with all the colours of the rainbow, which varied in intensity according to the depth of the cloud. I have seen you being enchanted by those scenes, and I have rejoiced with you. It would help if you could keep those images in mind, as we travel back in time. We can look back to when man began, and think about how he developed as an intelligent human being, discovering how he could use bone and stone as his first tools. You won't have forgotten the nasty gash you had in your hand last year, when you were helping your Mum to remove the meat from the chicken carcass. I heard her tell you, as she bandaged it, that you would need to take more care next time, but it made me reflect once again on how bones would have been used as some of the first implements. As you know we give them to the dogs, or we bury them. However, necessity has always been the mother of invention, and for those early folk, it is to their credit that they mastered so many skills in order to survive and progress. Try to think about what it would have been like for them, from the beginning, and through the Ages, The Old, Middle and Late Stone Age, and the Bronze Age, which is supposed to have represented the era from about 2300-700 BC; taking us up to the Iron Age, which is the age associated with the Celts, and the one on which we will concentrate later.

You know the universe would have been the same at the beginning as it is now; the change is in our knowledge and understanding. My reason for asking you to hold on to your images of the sun is that throughout those thousands and thousands of years every sighted human being would have witnessed exactly what you have seen. No matter where they were, they would have seen the sun disappear over the horizon, and out of sight. The difference lies in their interpretation and understanding of what they could see, and of course they would have seen it reappear the following morning. Because they were intelligent, imaginative and creative people, they endeavoured to find a meaning for the ever-changing scenes above and around them. They were affected by the sea, which could be so angry, as it flowed and ebbed, but which so often appeared as calm as a millpond. The sun, which at times could be so intensely hot that it could scorch all in its path, yet at other times could be so mild and gentle: the waxing and waning of the moon, and its various stages, which could appear to be affected by the clouds: the clouds and their immense variety of shapes and depth: the stars, and their many constellations, and of course the wind, which could be ferocious or gentle, according to its mood. They were intrigued by nature also, but it was far too complex for their understanding, except that over time they could see a pattern in what was happening, and they marvelled at what they saw. They were very much in awe of everything because, although they revered it, they didn't understand, and they became disturbed and afraid.

It is that strange inexplicable feeling you had, when you were out with your Mum, that is responsible for this discussion, and I would like you to keep it in your mind for a few moments. When we are out of doors, chatting on moonlit nights or watching beautiful sunsets, we encounter many different emotions as we feel ourselves being drawn into the mystical (mysterious) atmosphere. Your Dad has spoken to you about the wheel, and what the centre represents, but I have talked to you about everybody's dual journey, or the outer and inner journey. The inner journey is the most important because it represents the real person, it is the centre of one's being, and it is called our spirit. You once said, as you watched one of those lovely sunsets, that you wished to be out there in the west. There is one comparison or parallel which should make it easier for you to understand. For instance, when you described the journey with your Mum, you said that the dogs had stopped barking except for one animal, which started to howl, and that the howl seemed to find an echo further up the mountain. It is likely to have been the sound or echo of the first dog bouncing off the mountain and coming back, which can be an eerie sound, but it does happen in these hills, particularly on a night such as the one you described. It could also have been the answering howl of another dog whose spirit was awakened by the first. It wouldn't have felt very pleasant, but you don't need to dwell on that. Concentrate on how you had been feeling beforehand; you had been aware of a sense of mystery, even of excitement in much the same way that you sometimes feel when looking at the sunset. Then you experienced a sensation of beauty, of peace, and of longing. It was that feeling of longing which was responsible for your need or wish to be out there with the sunset. You probably encountered the same emotions whilst you gazed at the moon, longing to know more about it because the feeling seemed to be so deep. It seems as though there is another spirit which echoes your own, and which called to you. There are two words which have very deep and powerful meanings, but which are so closely interlinked that it is difficult to separate them. It's rather like watching your Mum knitting with two colours which are intertwined to become part of a fabric. The words I am thinking of are longing and belonging, because in fact we long to belong. It is part of our nature and you will learn and understand much more about it as you grow older.

On many occasions when we have allowed ourselves to be part of our glorious sunsets, there has been no need to talk or question, because we are fortunate to know and understand what is happening. The longing sensation could inspire us to create all sorts of imaginary stories. No doubt there have been occasions when you may have wished to be a princess, charging through the clouds on a beautiful white horse, which could have been based on stories you have listened to, or you might easily have invented your own. I can see from your smile that I am right, and there is nothing wrong with that. You are simply using the imaginative gift which you were born with, and we are meant to do so, but because we are all individual, we use the gift in different ways. If I am smiling it's because I have heard your

Dad and Mum tell you occasionally that you have allowed your imagination to run away with you. In a way that's what happened with those early people.

Without the knowledge which we have, I am sure that we too would have been inclined to believe that there were entities, which possessed super human powers, enabling them to control the sky, the earth and all its creatures, including ourselves. There would be a need to give everything an identity, and that is what those people did. They invented gods or lords of the sky and they endowed everything that lived and moved with its own spirit. However, they believed that it was the sun and the moon which dominated everything, and as they watched these two objects of power vanishing from their sight, they were convinced that there had to be another world, or underworld. Their confusion arose out of their sense of longing to belong, not merely in this world but in the world hereafter also. That seems to be how it all came about; it would have taken a long time and would have been a long process. In fact it is only the beginning.

Your Grandmother has already told you the story about the beginning of the world, so let's just say we believe that we understand how the world, and ourselves, came to be in existence. However, it is our belief, rather than our knowledge, which enables us to accept all that we have learned about the wonder of creation, but that wonder lies in taking the time to see and feel the beauty which is above and all around us. We have been given the gifts of sight, hearing, scent and imagination. I can share with you all that I know, but I can never convince you. Only you can open your eyes, ears, heart and spirit to what you observe. You are your own person, preparing to live your own life, and that is something no one else can do for you. I can be your mentor but never your master.'

Granddad was smiling as he reminded me of the favourite poem my brothers and I used when we played king of the castle:

I am monarch of all I survey,
My right there is none to dispute.
From the centre all round to the sea,
I am lord of the fowl and the brute.

'I can never be master of all I survey either, but I can try to be a caretaker. For instance, in school I was known as Headmaster, but that was just a title to represent what I did. Master is also a term which is widely used, where people have responsibility for estates, large houses, land or people. The title is only important in that we are all entrusted with the task of caring for someone or something. No man, however powerful, can hope to master the Universe, which is understandable because he didn't create it, and no man has the right to take away another individual's freedom, because it represents his individuality. The real problem for us humans is that, whilst we need and should have our freedom, we also have this longing to belong. In your case, although you may sometimes wish to be part of a beautiful sunset out in the west, you know that you actually belong in this family; you are an important part of it and you are loved for who you are, even when you don't always agree with your parents, and they may find it necessary to chastise you. There is a wonderful word called compassion, which I may have a chance to explain fully later, but for the moment let's just say it's a feeling which is stronger and deeper than love; it is one which your Mum and Dad have to keep in their minds, when you or your brothers are misbehaving, so that any punishment is fair and not guided by anger. You have seen your brothers being angry when they tease one another, and how they can fight when the teasing gets out of hand. Then your parents need to step in, and although they may be angry because of the rumpus, they need to be fair as they try to restore order, using patience and understanding. What you will learn as you grow, and maybe one day have your own family, is that you should become more compassionate and wiser as time goes on.

Your Dad once used the principle of the circle when he spoke to you about the spirit; I think we can follow his example here as we look again at our need to belong. It is possible to draw a small circle and write 'my family' on it, and then draw more circles around it, but keeping them apart, so that you can see how we fit into a higher structure of society. Now the circle your Dad drew had a centre with the spokes radiating outwards to a circular band. That circle represented you as an individual, but our circles go round one another with a space between, and I am wondering if you could tell me what you think might connect them, so that they do not stand alone?'

Oh that was tricky! I had been very comfortable with Dad's description of me as a circle, with the centre representing my spirit, but Granddad was talking about people; lots of people, and that was the answer I gave him. 'That's exactly right, and I need to find a simple means of explaining the complexity of human nature to you, because we must remember that within those circles, which I have mentioned, there are many individual circles which represent human beings just like yourself. Let's say that a peaceful existence means learning to live with or alongside other people, but that means learning how to manage our emotions, since emotions can cause people to react in a variety of different ways. You know what it's like to be happy and sad: to laugh and to cry. You know what's it's like to be afraid; people react in a variety of ways to fear; some become noisy, others become withdrawn and moody, because they don't always know how to cope with fear.' Granddad looked at me gently as he continued, 'At this moment you are a classic case, although you may not be happy to hear it. Just think of the range of emotions you have encountered since your Mum announced that you would be moving.' He could read me very well and I guess my face must have registered some of what I had felt. He analysed my feelings for me: disbelief, shock, anger, tears and reconciliation, with a willingness to prepare for the eventuality. When the move finally took place, I was to realise that the experience itself would be totally different to what I had imagined, but the preparation had helped me to cope with the fear of the unknown. As time goes on you will learn that there are more acceptable ways of coping with those emotions. You could say that there is a code of behavior, which is acceptable in what we call society... and when you have a moment you can look that word up in the dictionary.

'You can see that in order to understand the significance of the bigger community, we need to understand the importance of the family, in the hierarchical arrangement. It is also important to know that when occasionally the argument is between the family elders themselves, they can seek help from someone in the community. That someone can be a friendly neighbour in the parish or town, but if the problem is serious it may be necessary to take it to someone who has been appointed as head of the community. The task of electing a suitable head would take place in the town hall, where the elders would meet to choose a member from amongst themselves to govern or oversee a particular area. The person needs to be seen to be a responsible, caring individual, who is accustomed to listening carefully, able to help people to resolve their disputes, and able to administer justice when the need arises. Now that is the golden rule, but you know that rules are sometimes broken, and not always for the best reasons.

However, I wouldn't have chosen this moment in time to give you all that information, but I hope it will help you to more easily understand the background to the Celtic people. In the past I have limited most of what I have told you to the Irish Celts, and you know quite a bit about them already, but I want to concentrate as far as possible on how they came to be a race of people of whom we can feel justly proud.'

I was happy to be able to tell him finally, that I had wanted to know about tribes for some time, ever since he first mentioned his own large family. He had smiled, but wasn't to be distracted from his story, as he continued, 'It isn't going to be easy to give you a nicely wrapped account of the Celts - Men of Iron as they came to be known - because they were not so called at the beginning, but were members of other named tribes, and we will go into that in detail later. Right now we will look at the Celtic people who are believed to have come to Ireland in approximately 700 B.C.

If you were to imagine drawing more circles you would need, this time, to draw them in sets of two, one for the family and one for the tribe, and place them close together. Continue to draw sets of two, alongside, above and below one another. You could go on drawing for a long time because there are thousands of them, even if you only concentrated on one country. Focus on our own family for a moment. Our smallholding represents a very minute part of the one hundred square miles of carboniferous limestone, which erupted from the seabed over a million years ago. Situated, as we are, half way up the rocky mountain, means that the soil is very shallow and farming it is not easy, but we have enough for our few animals. You will have seen the farmer occasionally taking some of his cattle up to the mountain, because despite the rocks and shallow soil, the grassy patches are full of nutrients which feed the grass instead of disappearing into the soil. However, if we had a very hot dry spell the grass up there would quickly die and the farmer would need to move his animals to new pasture. Valleys, particularly where there are streams, make good grazing areas. If that farmer didn't have alternative pasture he would need to make a choice – lose his animals, or move them and his family, and re-locate them in a more suitable place. Should it be necessary to do that several times in his lifetime, he and his family would be called nomads or wanderers.

The Celts have always been referred to as nomadic tribes, who developed farming communities, as well as practicing their many other skills, but if the land they owned became unproductive through over-grazing, over-cultivation or because of drought, they simply had to move on to pastures new. It is possible that a few of that tribe would decide to stay and make do, until such time as conditions improved; that would depend on the reason for the move. Initially there may not have been too many problems with neighbouring tribes, but as time passed and more territory was occupied and colonized, it wouldn't have been as easy to accomplish. The circles represent those other tribes who wouldn't have taken kindly to being invaded, and it could have resulted in tribal warfare. The migrations, which may have begun as a matter of necessity, would eventually become a way of life. As time went by each tribe became larger, and was better equipped with weapons, which gave them the power to defend their own territory, or to take over a neighbour's territory. At the same time they discovered that there was a growing demand for the commodities, which they were able to produce, and which helped to increase their wealth and power. This progressive pattern continued throughout the different ages, so that by the end of the Bronze Age there emerged a much more powerful group of people. Those people had discovered how to make iron, which was far superior to bronze.

I must say that I have my own special reason for wishing to take you on a particular journey today; there may not be another opportunity like this one. The fog is set to last for at least twenty-four hours, according to the weatherman on the radio, and our armchair journey is a fairly long one. I am going to ask your Mum to make us a picnic lunch, so that we can take it to the dining room where we shouldn't be interrupted. How I wish that your Grandma were still here, and well enough to talk about the Celts. Her interest in them was very deep rooted, and she was usually in her element as she discussed them, which is understandable. Growing up, as she did, in Kilfenora which has its own Cathedral with seven tall Celtic crosses in and around the Cathedral, would inspire most people who had an interest in Celtic art. I have a sneaking suspicion that you would probably much rather hear more about that aspect of the Celts, because you are so interested in painting and drawing.

There was another reason for Grandma's deep interest in the subject, which takes us further afield. I had often heard her talk to your Aunt Alice about the time she spent in France as a governess, but I think I'm right in saying that she didn't tell you about her adventures. What she discovered on her travels will undoubtedly help us on our own journey.'

What I had thought would be a simple answer to my question, had instead become a major episode for Granddad. At first I felt sad that I had caused him to remember Grandma, but I changed my mind because, on that occasion, remembering her as she related some of her escapades, seemed to make him happy. I suppose it helped him to feel close to her as he visualized her in her younger days, rather than as she was before she left us. However, he had said that I would probably have preferred listening to her talking about Celtic design and that didn't bode well for the afternoon; I realized that I was due for a long learning session. Yet I had resolved to learn as much as possible and would need to be patient. Whilst we ate I was able to ask about various points he had made, which weren't too easy to grasp, but mainly about entities, and they sounded really intriguing. Granddad, who was in his seventy-eighth year, seemed rather quiet until we had finished eating, when he said, 'Yes! That's it. I had better start you off with antiquity and archaeology; I don't think you will have come across those two words yet, but they will be good for your spelling book. Antiquity is about ancientness or the quality of being old or ancient, and could refer to ancient times, especially those before the Middle Ages, and it can mean a relic or a monument of ancient times. Archaeology is really the study of antiquities; the art and customs of early people. One additional word, which could link the two above, is artifact and it is the product of human art and workmanship.

I'm sure that it isn't necessary to remind you about your first visit to Kilfenora Cathedral, when you accompanied your Grandma, Uncle Ben and Aunt Alice. Your smile assures me that I am right, but it does give me a thrill as I remember your animated account of the visit, particularly as you spoke about your Aunt Alice lifting you up so that you could look over the wall, in order to see one of the most important Celtic crosses in Ireland, in the field beyond. How fortunate that your great uncle is buried in the Cathedral grounds, or you might have missed a golden opportunity. You were so enthralled by the interior of the Cathedral, and the feeling of aliveness, with regard to those ancient people. Your comment that evening as you bade us all goodnight made us laugh very heartily indeed. I know you had your eyes rested on your Mum when you said, 'You see! I wasn't skiving or doodling when I tried to draw good circles. I must be taking after those Celts, and tomorrow I will practice drawing a cross through the circles, just as they made them.' That was a real beginning for you but it wasn't just you and your Grandma who were interested in them.

Over a period of time more and more people became curious to discover why they were called Celts; where had they come from, and why did it take so long for them to be noticed as a formidable and most interesting people. The Romans are reputed to have described them as barbarous, and you'll have to excuse me if I say that that seemed like the pot calling the kettle black.

You remember the last time I used my maps of Europe, when the visitors were here and we were discussing the Celts; on that occasion we didn't want to confuse you with too much detail, being more concerned about the arrival of the Celts in Ireland. The problem for me this time is that knowing how you feel about beginnings and how everything grows and develops, I hope to give you sufficient information to enable you to feel and understand more fully, so that in the future, if you wish to investigate further, you will have had a good foundation to work from. History is a lifelong subject and learned people love to write about it, adding their own views as they go along. Your Grandma was certain that although there wasn't much written material available, which was easily accessible, the subject of the Celts would, in time, become a dominating influence for many people. The seeds of interest had been sewn long ago, and didn't merely exist on dusty shelves in museums and university libraries, for scholars to access at leisure. The visual evidence existed in so many forms, and the most impressive has to be the Celtic Crosses, with their images and symbols. This was how they told their stories. Signs and symbols are the first and most important proof of the existence of being. If we take time to study the actions and reactions of an infant, we can see that long before it can talk properly it manages to communicate its feelings and needs.

Now, while I go and look for the maps again, will you think about what you feel every human needs in order to live, and we can call that a pre-requisite.'

One of the qualities I loved about Granddad was his ability to approach a complicated issue by relating simple everyday facts, knowing that it would make an otherwise tricky subject more meaningful. However, he had put me on the spot, and I had a moment of real panic. Did it have to be what I thought I knew, or what he thought I should know? I decided that it might be best to think of my own moments of deprivation, such as when I felt cold, hungry, thirsty, tired, and yes there was the occasion when I thought I might have choked, because of a down draught in the bedroom chimney, which caused the smoke to billow into the room. It was difficult to forget because it was during the big freeze – they said it was probably that which had caused it. But being hauled out of bed coughing and spluttering, then marched into the garden, which was in total darkness, in order to get fresh air, didn't fit my image of sweet dreams. In answer to my protestations Mum said, *Well, it's a case of life or death so needs must.*

By the time Granddad returned I had a list of light, air, water, food, warmth, and somewhere to rest in safety, and I could probably think of others. He was smiling as he opened the map and remarked, 'You have given me the basics for survival, and I know that geography is not your favourite subject, but because you like people, I am hoping that the human interest part will help you to travel with me on what was your Grandma's special journey. Of course it was before I met her, and during the years she worked as a governess in Dijon in France. We will have to focus on our map as we cover that route; it isn't complicated but you will just need to keep an eye on the different place names, OK?

She made many acquaintances during that time, and usually travelled with her employers during their vacations. They had been aware of her background and her interests, through an exchange of correspondence which took place before she joined them. Their first holiday with her was to Lake Lucerne, passing Lake Neuchatel en route. Much to her delight the family was able to supply many interesting details about the artifacts, which a wealthy archaeologist had unearthed at a place called La Tène, Switzerland in 1857. It had been a remarkable find, and provided much evidence about the creative nature of early people. The hoard had included horse harnesses and sword hilts, a bronze shield, a helmet, a long sword with an iron blade and lances with iron points. They were all made of bronze or a mixture of bronze and iron, and they had decorations on them. The discovery indicated that there had been a military post situated there, probably to protect a pass between part of the Rhine and the Rhone, and the artifacts were considered to be from the period 450 BC to 15 BC. The soldiers, as warriors, would have been very highly regarded and worthy of the best equipment available. In fact their swords were their prize possessions. However, there had also been a discovery about eleven years earlier in a place called Hallstat, Austria, which had been very exciting and revealing, because it seemed to be the first indication of the progress from bronze to iron. We can look at that later, because even more exciting than the discovery of iron, was the discovery that there had been two different races of people in that area. One group had burned or cremated the bodies of those who had died. The other group, which appeared later, had buried their dead. The period was considered to be around 700 BC. But the finds or discoveries told a different story about the people.

This was Grandma's major discovery whilst she was with the family, and which she shared with me, but it set us thinking about how they came to be in those regions, and why? From that point we journeyed backwards in order to consider where it had all begun. You can use the survival list you have just given me as we consider the first humans, and their successors, trying to survive in caves in the first instance, becoming more adventurous as time went by. For instance, in what regions would they have been most likely to succeed? Can you imagine that happening up here on this mountain? We have only just discovered the first major cave system, and although you can see other evidence of Celtic occupation here in this area, that would not have been consistent with evidence of the presence of the earliest people here in Ireland. However, we know from the primitive art which has been discovered in caves, with some of the first discoveries in France, that man found it to be a means of self-expression from the very beginning. Being confined to caves for long periods, he would have imagined how he would conquer and kill animals. His drawings could have been a means of capturing their spirits, so that he no longer feared them, rather like the effigies you read about in some of those witch stories. It could have been a genuine interest in their form and movement, because he would have had to stalk them before attacking them. It could also have been a means of teaching his sons about animal life, and how to become warriors in their turn. In time that fascination for art form came to include plant life, because don't forget that they had invested all living things with spirits. Although, as I said earlier, man remained fearful of all those things, which he didn't understand, it didn't stop him exploring, because his first need was how to survive, and observation was his most useful talent. His initial task was two-fold: to hunt for food for his family, and to protect his clan or tribe. Hunting became a means of exploring new territory, and he would inevitably have come across large fertile areas, where he found wild animals grazing. He would also have discovered streams and rivers, which were equally essential for his survival. As I have so often said, necessity is the mother of invention, and so it would have been from the very beginning. That phrase applies to me too, particularly at this moment, because I must now consider how to take you into another subject area, which is also important. You could say it is the foundation, which supports the whole structure of society. Before we continue with that topic, I believe it would be good for us to go out of doors for a few moments, and on the way we can ask your Mum if it might be possible to have a drink.'

I could not understand why on earth he would wish to be outside on such a day. He had said that the fog was set for at least twenty-four hours. I followed him through the kitchen, where Mum was baking bread and scones and passing on his request for drinks, we went outside to stand where we always stood when we wanted to think and share our thoughts. I desperately wanted to ask him to explain why we needed to be there, but his stance was such that I knew I must remain silent, until he was ready to speak, and it seemed interminable. Worst of all he didn't want to share his thoughts just then. What was I supposed to be looking for, or at? It didn't feel like day or night; the light would have allowed me to take in the view, which would have helped me to look outward, and so stimulate my thoughts; the darkness would have rendered me motionless, since any movement would have been too hazardous. I was very familiar with those two situations, and although I was completely perplexed, I knew that he would have had a very good reason for taking me there. Still, my discomfort grew as I realized that he would probably ask questions afterwards, and I wouldn't know how to answer them. That thought didn't help, and I had to accept that I really was in a muddle, but hoped that he would help me to see through the mist. He may have sensed that I couldn't cope any longer for he suddenly said. 'OK! That's enough of that, let's go and have our drink, then we can talk, and don't worry because I know how you must have been feeling.'

Well, that was something to hang on to. We stayed in the kitchen with Mum, whilst we had our refreshment, which was a welcome break from the tension, and of course the kitchen was warm, because Mum had the stove on high, whilst she was cooking. Even though it was still summer, the damp air had made us feel cold, and I felt shivery too, but that could have been partly due to my uncomfortable feeling, which hadn't yet been explained away. As we went through to the dining room Granddad resumed, 'I am sure that I have no need to remind you again of your recent visit to the meadow, following your Mum's news about moving, and I only refer to it now by way of example. I took you outside because I wanted you to really experience a feeling of nothingness. Yes we could see a few yards ahead, but that is not enough, because as human beings we feel that we have a need to see much further all the time, and when we can't we can become confused. That I believe is how you felt, but I have learned to cope with those situations, and in this instance I was able to use the time to think very deeply about how I will proceed with the remainder of our story. You could say that the trip outside was constructive for me, but it could have been destructive for you, if you had been on your own and for too long. Hopefully you will be able to understand more easily as we go on.' He had taken care to leave the maps open on the dining room table before leaving the room, and he was able to continue as though we had not even had a break.

'We were talking earlier about the Hallstat and La Tène discoveries, and how people would have lived in caves in the first instance. Now though I want us to really focus on the map, whilst paying attention to those two areas, as we consider what might have happened at Hallstatt and La Tène, to produce enough evidence to convince archaeologists that these regions, and areas in close proximity to them, had to be the starting points for the Iron Age Celts. We could say that those were the areas where the Celts first appeared with the name which has been given to them. We don't know what these tribes were called then, but their emergence has interested scholars and archaeologists ever since. For the moment we need to forget about the Celts, as such, and concentrate on people with beginnings, and of course we need to be thinking about our circles once more. Our most important asset in the study of human behaviour, with its interaction in society, and the discovery of all the commodities which we find so useful today, has been the book called The Bible. Although we can't say for certain when the events recorded actually happened, it nevertheless gives the most wonderful account of how things have come to be. It is all about beginnings, and you are usually at pains to let us know that you are always interested in the beginning of things. I know that you may be sad to hear me say this, but you have declared to your parents and me in the past, that you don't like listening to the readings from the Old Testament in Church on Sundays, because it makes you feel uncomfortable. But I have to tell you that it is the Old and New Testaments together which can take you on a unique journey through history, and be your guide for the future. If I were to ask you to read the Bible as a story from beginning to end, I am sure you would feel the sense of it, despite coming across some difficult names and places. Having got the gist of it you would notice that there are battles and strife occurring throughout the story; tribes at war with themselves, their neighbours and with the Christian God. I say Christian God because at that time the idea of multiple or pagan gods was so prevalent. It tells you about people struggling to survive, sometimes in adverse climatic conditions. There are many people today who feel that, because this book was written so long ago, it is now out of date, and some would say out of time, because life is different now. Yet it is the most widely read book in the world, and although it is old, it will remain forever new. You could say the whole story is supposed to be a bridge, which could take those floundering ancients to a new way of thinking and behaving. Remember what you said about the Cathedral, and being able to sense the presence of those ancient people, the only difference between them and us lies in the fact that we see ourselves as being more cultured and modern, but it doesn't follow that we always behave any better than they did! Over time we know that archaeology will continue to find evidence of the past which will support much that we read about in the Bible.

I do need to share a secret with you, which should make you feel very much better when you hear it; the reason for the smile, which you noticed, is that this is the first time I have had to think so hard in order to find the right level in which to explain what I mean. I know you can't be fobbed off because your questions are very discerning. It was my reason for going outside with you just now; I knew there would be no distractions and I needed to clear the mist inside my head. You see it is all about the process of thinking and feeling, and then doing what feels right for the benefit of others; but I had to work at reaching that level for your benefit, and if you need to ask questions we will sort those afterwards, OK.

We talked about levels of being after your visit to the Cathedral – you spoke about the feeling of aliveness, which you experienced, but you couldn't understand how that could be so because, as you said, you were just surrounded by stone which is inanimate matter. It wasn't the stone which was alive, but the feelings conveyed by the skilled masons as they carved it. Just as you might write a story, which revealed your innermost thoughts and feelings, the mason used his skills to tell the story of his feelings and beliefs. It is indeed very interesting, that although stone has no life, it can be carved in such a way that the carvings speak to us, but that is the creative gift of the stonemason. Stone provided an ideal foundation for the cave painters, and the stonemason can portray his story on stone, but he can never give life to the stone itself; no man can do that.

Now is probably a very good time to complete the picture of man and his many parts, and before your imagination goes into orbit, I don't mean arms, legs and suchlike. You once used an expression, which didn't impress your Grandma very much, but I have to say it could be useful here. At that time we were discussing the Celts and you said you wanted to know what made them tick. In other words you wanted to know about their make-up or nature, which are also the inherent qualities in every person. So let's just say he was created, and in turn becomes creative; learning to use his inventive, and imaginative skills, that's the first part. You have heard people being described as very gifted with their hands, which really means that they are using their learned skills imaginatively, rather like your Mum when she titivates a hat. Then there's his human nature, which means that he has the understanding and kindliness of a man, but also the limitations of a man, that's the second part. We do need to make some effort, but sometimes circumstances or even other people push us to the limit of our endurance, just as your brother tests your patience, and you try not to lose your temper; we need to be constantly aware of our limits, because we can't always undo the things we've done or take back the words we've spoken. The third part is called divine nature, which is something more than our own human nature; you could say it's a guiding force for our lifelong journey.

The reason for my eagerness to share all that with you, is that in many ways, we can make a comparison between the Bible and those ancients; one portrays a message in symbols on stone, and the other a message in words. The stone, if protected against the elements, will continue to convey that same message to future generations, and the Bible will continue to demystify our thoughts, and help to answer many of our questions about our existence. Your Grandma had been very impressed when she visited Rome and examined much of the beautiful art work there; it was so different to the stone work displayed at Kilfenora Cathedral, but in each case the artist was attempting to give meaning to a particular subject. Of course it wasn't art which caused the Celts to be noticed in the first instance; rather their weapons of destruction, which included iron.

Although they had become known as the Men of Iron, who had emerged from the La Tène and Hallstat regions in about 700BC, it didn't follow that it was they who had discovered it, or that they had always lived in that particular area. Your Grandma and I were very excited by the discoveries we made, as we poured over the maps on long winter evenings, before our own children were born, reading once again the old Bible stories, whilst we tried to fathom where those people, who became the Celts, had emerged from.'

Granddad and I spent some time looking at the maps ourselves. He seemed to be staring at one particular area without commenting, whilst I tried to follow his gaze and work out what he might be looking at. Suddenly he sighed wearily, stood up and straightened his back. My heart went out to him and I hoped, once again, that I wasn't the cause of his weariness. When Grandma was ill I had watched her deteriorate, and I felt that he was remembering her, because we had spoken about her, and of course he was feeling his age. He was a tall upright man and he had been bending over the table, which I now realise would have been uncomfortable for him after the first few minutes. I was half lying across the table in order to get a better view, just as my brothers and I did when we played a heated game of snap; a game which was always exciting, relying on sleight of hand and quick reactions. This was the game which the elders dreaded and it usually meant that one of them had to intervene, telling us to be quiet. But it was difficult to say snap quietly, because the first person to get there had to be loud and clear, and so the volume continued to rise, until such time as someone said, Right, that's enough. It's time for bed!

When I returned from my reverie Granddad was saying, 'I'll be back in a moment,' and indeed it was no more than that! When he rejoined me he was holding his pipe, tobacco pouch and matches, and what I called the white caterpillar for cleaning the pipe. I knew then that he wasn't feeling melancholy, but needed time to re-organize his thinking, and plan his way forward. It was a complicated topic, with such a lot of detail. I had been trying earnestly to keep up with him, and create a picture in my mind, because I knew that if I couldn't make sense of the first stage, the remainder would simply confuse me further. I was relieved when, after lighting his pipe, and taking a few puffs he said, 'I have given you such a lot of information, and am concerned now about how to take you forward without losing you in the process. The real frustration for me is limiting the amount of detail, whilst realising that each concept I talk about would fill many books.' With a sigh of relief he smiled suddenly, and looking at me directly said, 'I have a number of books tucked away in boxes. By the way, when you and your parents and brothers came to live here, we needed to pack away many things, and your coming became a life-changing experience for us. We didn't regret it because the Emergency made huge demands on everyone, and we were happy to do our bit for the cause. Of course it was also wonderful to hear young voices about the place, well most of the time anyway. I can now see that I will need to retrieve some of those books, and you will be able to read them for yourself. That is a happy promise for the future, but it doesn't help my present predicament. I need to condense a lot of information in order to take you back to the subject we started to discuss, namely the early people and especially the Celts. It just seems very strange to me that all this has come about because you are preparing to leave this place, and move on to pastures new, a bit like the Celts themselves who were nomadic tribes.'

He may have seen the look of indignation on my face as I decided that I wasn't part of a tribe - that seemed more like the gypsies – and he was only too aware of my feelings about leaving, but he went on, 'Yes, I know I shouldn't have mentioned the move, but be reassured that we will cope, and you know you can share your distress with me. Now, however, in order to prepare ourselves to move forward, let's take a moment to look back at what we have covered so far, and hopefully that will be the bridge to take us to the next stage.' Taking his pen and notebook from the inside pocket of his jacket he started to speak and write at the same time.

'Well, to begin with, I spoke about those spooky feelings which can arise on moonlit nights, and I believe I tried to describe how the ancient people would have come to believe in other worlds, and multitudinous spirits. Following that I touched on the subject of belonging, and everybody's need and longing to belong. Then I explained what being a master meant to me, and hopefully helped you to understand that one man shouldn't be master of another, and neither should anyone be a slave. I asked you to use the principle of circles, so that you could understand the clan or tribal set-up, and the implications of living together in communities. Then there was the story of Grandma's time in France, using maps so that you could identify those places for yourself, particularly Hallstat and La Tene. I reminded you about the need to consider the Old and New Testaments together, and suggested that you try to read both so that you can enjoy the story, and learn the historical facts which they contain. Then I subjected you to that horrible trip outside in the fog, so that you could experience that feeling of nothingness. I didn't like doing that, but I think you now understand why I did it. I spoke about the early people and their cave paintings, which provided them with a means of self-expression and communication. That seemed to take us back to Kilfenora and Celtic art, when I described the difference between the type of art which Grandma had examined in Rome, and the Celtic art which is so abundant in Kilfenora. Finally I mentioned man and his levels of being - creative nature, human nature and divine nature.'

When he came to the end of the list, he presented me with the book saying, This should help you later as you think about what I have said, and you can use your copy book to write up your own account." I guess I knew that there would be some work for me, but I didn't mind, and I realised that he had a good reason for doing what he did: his summary notes would make all the difference. Writing my own account would encourage me to remember what he'd said, and it would help to reinforce it in my mind. One of his many favourite expressions was, 'Tell me and I may forget: show me and I might remember: involve me and I will understand.' With so much information coming my way, I knew that I would need to do it sooner rather than later. In fact there would be a lot of writing to do, as I was about to discover.

As he collected the Bible which usually sat on the little side table, he smiled broadly remarking, 'If you write your story soon, there is a good chance that you will remember much of what I've said, and I will be around if you come unstuck. Of course it won't be exactly what I've told you, because we all interpret things differently, but that's fine. Now though we need to go back into the past again in order to look at other people's records. There are many accounts of ancient times, which were often written well after the events took place; relying on the good memory of the writer, and being based on information which had been passed from one person to another, but they were written by and about the people and circumstances of that particular time. We could say that there are two stories to be told; the first could examine where people as civilized human beings seemed to have emerged from and the second could be the Bible which is an historical as well as a spiritual record of man's earthly journey. Mind you the world was intended as a home for all people, and many were and still are nomads or wanderers even today.

Trying to establish a formal, factual pattern of when time began, and what has happened since, has never ceased to perplex mankind. I believe that in the years ahead, man will make confident strides forward, using his scientific knowledge, as well as the hordes of archaeological evidence yet to be discovered, but it is not within man's capability to determine exactly when time began. If you want to have fun with your brothers ask them to count how many times you use the word time every day, lots of times I think! Now though we are journeying back to the period before recorded time and events began. There is just one thing which I feel can help us to bridge that tricky gap, and that is a reference in the Book of Psalms, which you will have heard occasionally on Sundays, when you've been to Church. The Psalms actually form part of the Bible; they were written around 1,000 BC, and are attributed to King David's era, because they are poems which are thought to have been written by David himself and others, when David was King. They are religious poems and prayers, some worship and praise God, whilst others are pleas for help or forgiveness. They are personal and national prayers, which represent the needs and feelings of all the people of God. I mention this only as a means of explaining how difficult it is for us to understand time as it was then. For instance, Psalm 90 tells us that in God's time a thousand years are like one day; they are like yesterday, already gone. Even though we know that the ancients couldn't measure time as we can today, they could at least measure the length of a day, and it seems that they were able to discern the seasons with such structures as the great stone henges. They had formed themselves into clans or tribes, and eventually social groups, which became more civilized as time passed.

Looking back through the family history and census forms, has highlighted the problems which can arise when people are registered under a particular Christian name, but thereafter referred to in a more familiar way. For instance a census could list names such as Margaret or Cornelius in a particular family, and the next census would refer to Madge or Maggie, Nelius or Neil in the same family. To complicate matters further I have discovered that occasionally when parents lost an infant they would register the next one of the same sex under the same name as the deceased baby as a memorial. I know in Granddad's situation, that although he had many siblings, the mortality rate was high at that time. Even so, they would still have seemed like a tribe or a clan, and Granddad had often used those terms when he spoke about the Celts, who had a tribal family set-up, which is not so usual today."

CHAPTER V

THE DREAMER

Hic, hic, hic... Eventually the repetitiveness of the sound interrupts Nan's thoughts, and opening her eyes she surveys her listener who, judging by the half empty Coca Cola bottle, has been quietly sipping throughout. Of course she knows how it has come about, but he must have swallowed a lot of air too. Needing to have a drink herself, she suggests to him that having some water could help to get rid of the problem. As she prepares to drink from her own bottle, she is catapulted back to that other occasion, when she had been listening to Granddad's story. She can no longer suppress the laughter, which began to erupt when she heard the first hic, but which now overtakes her. Slowly the tears roll down her cheeks, but they are mixed tears because the memory is so vivid. She finds herself back in Rockville, listening to Granddad's laughter as he exclaimed, 'You have done it! You've given me the clue I needed, with your hic, hic, hic!' The two situations were so similar, and she had been in the same predicament all those years ago, although it wasn't Coca Cola, but fizzy orangeade, which had caused the problem. Fortunately Liam doesn't realize that her tears of laughter are mingled with tears of sadness, nor can he taste the extra salt, which they seem to contain. She is happy for him to remain in ignorance, as she explains the cause of her mirth, but she really wishes that Granddad was here to share it.

"They have gone now," Liam exclaims. "The combination of the water and listening to you laughing seems to have stopped it, but what caused Granddad to laugh, and did he do it as loudly as you?"

"Oh yes he did," Nan replies. "Mum heard the laughter and

rushed through from the kitchen to reassure herself, and then she asked us whether we would like a scone. Granddad was quick to remark that everything was fine, but added that sipping and listening intently had probably caused the hiccups. He said that a scone and a drink would tide us over until dinnertime! Mum and I would have liked an explanation for his laughter, but it seemed that we would have to wait until he was ready. We hadn't heard him laugh so heartily for such a long time; at least not since Grandma had become seriously ill, and I was able to console myself with that thought. Mum had already laid the table, and as we prepared to enjoy our break, Granddad dropped his clanger! He had said that before we went back to our task, he was going to ask me what I knew about the story of Joseph and his colourful coat. Mum looked at me, then at Granddad, and as she looked at me again I could see that she was unhappy, even slightly angry. Granddad interpreted the look and said reassuringly, 'You mustn't worry Annie, I am not going to overstretch her. By the time she looks tired I will have had enough too, and there is always tomorrow.' Seeing that this reassured her, and whilst addressing both of us, he went on to explain, 'It probably does seem a very strange request, but I have good reasons which you will hear bye and bye. I often looked in on you three – meaning Grandma, Mum and me – when you were having your quiet time in the afternoon. I know you two were busy with your hands, and Grandma was happy to reminisce. Of course, as you know, she liked to tell stories too. I have to admit that I eavesdropped on one occasion, because she happened to be telling you the story of Joseph and his multi-coloured coat.'

Mum laughed when she heard that and said, 'I do remember because I was making a patchwork bedspread with all the odd bits of fabric I seem to collect, it was that which reminded Grandma about Joseph's coat, but I really enjoyed putting all the interesting pieces together,' and looking at me continued, 'and you loved having it on your bed. You were lucky that your brothers weren't fussy or they could have been jealous.' I loved that quilt, and maybe it helped the story to remain with me. I didn't have to write it down however: that being an exercise which only applied to the Christmas story, with the other Joseph, and to other New Testament stories, which were no problem because I could imagine the people as I wrote. Granddad said, very mischievously, 'Just tell us your version, and afterwards I will read the whole story to you. It's in the Old Testament, and we know how you feel about that!' I was still very flummoxed and shy, because I had to talk about something I wasn't sure of. I knew that I didn't need to impress them, but the scone remained untouched as I started…

A long time ago there was a man whose name was Jacob, and he had twelve sons. His eleventh son was called Joseph, and even though he was not the baby of the family, he was still the apple of his father's eye. Because Jacob loved him so much, he made him a special coat with sleeves, which was very beautiful. When they saw the coat the brothers became very jealous. Then one night Joseph had a dream, and next day he told his brothers about it. He said that in the dream they were binding sheaves of corn out in the field, when suddenly his sheaf rose and stood up straight, and that their sheaves gathered round it and bowed to it. After that he had another dream, and he told them about that one too. In the dream the sun, moon and eleven stars were bowing down to him. The brothers hated him after the first dream, and they hated him even more after the second, because they thought he was making himself more important than them.

One day when his brothers were far from home, looking after the sheep, Jacob asked Joseph to go and search for them, and make sure they were alright, then report back to him. The brothers saw Joseph coming and said, "Here comes the Dreamer, let's kill him and get him out of the way," but his brother Reuben told them that it wasn't right to kill anyone, but that they could put him in a pit instead. Now Reuben had hoped to come by later, remove Joseph from the pit, and take him back to their father. However, Reuben was missing when the others saw a merchants' caravan approaching, as they were sitting having their lunch. The caravan was on its way to Egypt, and the camels were loaded with spices, balm and myrrh. As they watched it approach, the brothers decided to sell Joseph to the Merchants and keep the money for themselves; that way they would be rid of him for good. When the Merchants had gone, they began to scheme again about what they would tell their father. They decided to tear Joseph's coat, then find a goat and kill it, so that they could put its blood on the coat; then they could say that a wild animal had got him. When Reuben came back and saw that the pit was empty, he tore his own clothes in distress, and when they returned and showed the coat to their father he was broken hearted. They were horrible brothers letting the father think that his son was dead when all the while he was safe in Egypt. That was the end of the beautiful coat.

I finished my account very quickly, because I didn't like the story and then I waited, and waited, and waited, until finally Granddad asked if there was any more. When I said that Grandma hadn't told me any more, and that we had only been discussing coats and things, Granddad said, 'I see! Well, that was very good: of course I didn't wait to hear the end of Grandma's story, and you were much younger then. Now I think you are ready for the full story, which is more interesting and it has a much happier ending. Let's return to the dining room and I will read it to you.' Casting an eye on my snack he said, 'You might like to take those with you; you might enjoy them now.' As we prepared to leave the kitchen, he looked at Mum and remarked that it would be good to feel young again, and that he and I were about to embark on an exciting imaginary journey. Was it the journey, or the reason for it all, which was making him so excited? He knew that I was a little exasperated, because I wanted to share the reason as well as the journey, but it looked as though the journey was to be a means to an end, and I would need to be patient. Despite my frustration, I couldn't help feeling excited for him, and it was wonderful to see his exuberance. I decided it was better to eat, drink, and just listen, as he chatted to himself, whilst searching for the appropriate page in the Bible. But it was unthinkable - for me - not to be caught up in the moment, and I couldn't help adding my own silent commentary as he started, 'It's early on in Genesis; there's Adam and Eve.' Oh, I knew about them! 'Then there's Noah with his ark, and the Flood.' Yes I knew that one too. 'There's Sodom and Gomarrah, with Lot and his wife.' I knew that Lot's wife had been changed into a pillar of salt, but I couldn't remember why. 'Then there's the birth of Jacob and Esau.' I thought that Jacob could be the one in my Joseph's story; I hoped so, because I suddenly had an urge to giggle, as he continued to rustle through the pages. 'Yes there's a lot about Jacob, his family, and their descendants. Ah! Finally here we are: **Joseph is sold by his brothers.'** Turning to me he said, 'Now my little friend, I want you to listen very carefully, because this is not just another fairytale; it is full of hidden meaning, and it has played a very important part in the history of that particular time and place. It has also had many consequences for all of us who live in the western world. I won't be asking you to write your account this time, but I will ask you to read it yourself afterwards, even a few times, so that you can feel the sense of it, and get used to the different sounding names. Then we can talk about it so that I know you understand its meaning. Only after all that can I share with you my reason for laughing earlier!' Of course he laughed again which was infuriating, but I could feel the excitement as he began to read. He almost seemed like a very young person, who had become part of the story, and hoisting me onto his back, we took off to those biblical places.

We went to Egypt, where Joseph was sold to a man called Potipher, who was one of Pharaoh's officials and captain of the guard. We saw Potipher's wife, who was a very selfish and unpleasant lady, who made false accusations about Joseph, so that her husband became very angry, and had him put in prison. We heard Joseph interpreting the dreams of two of the inmates, who had been working for Pharaoh, before they were imprisoned for wrongdoing. Joseph told the first man that his dream meant that he would be hanged within a few days, and he told the second man, who was a cup bearer, that his dream meant that he would return to the court of Pharaoh within three days, and asked that when he did so, would he please tell the Pharaoh that he himself had been imprisoned unlawfully. The second man forgot Joseph's request until the Pharaoh had dreams himself, and when he failed to find anyone to interpret them, the cupbearer remembered the promise he had made to Joseph, and told of someone he knew who could interpret dreams. When Joseph was released from prison, he explained that the seven fat cows in the Pharaoh's dream foretold of seven very prosperous years, and the seven lean cows foretold of seven years of famine and drought. He also advised the Pharaoh to find someone who could prepare for the bad times, and how he thought it could be done. Not only was Joseph appointed to do the job, but Pharaoh also gave him complete authority over his palace, and his people, telling him that he had displayed much wisdom. Once again Joseph was dressed in a beautiful robe, but this time it was made of the finest linen. Pharaoh then put a gold chain round his neck, gave him horses and chariots, and told him that he was putting him in charge of all Egypt. During the years of plenty Joseph travelled about the land making preparations for the years of famine to come. He arranged for mountains of corn to be collected into storehouses, wherever he went. When the famine became severe he opened the stores and sold the corn. People came from all over to buy from him. So too did his brothers who travelled from Canaan. It had been twenty years since they had sold Joseph into slavery, and they didn't recognise him, but he knew them, and he tested them severely, because of what they had done to him. After playing many tricks in order to teach them a lesson, Joseph revealed his true identity. They were full of shame, but overjoyed to find that he was still alive and so successful. Joseph told them to go back and bring their father, their wives, families and all their animals, but not to worry about their other possessions, because all of Egypt would be theirs. For themselves he provided new clothes, and for their Father he gave them ten male donkeys loaded with the best things of Egypt, and ten female donkeys loaded with grain and bread for the return journey. Then sending them on their way he admonished them not to quarrel on the journey. When Jacob heard what they had to say, he exclaimed that he now knew that his son was alive, and that he would see him before he died.

I had been completely immersed as Granddad was reading: almost sensing Jacob's happiness, as he realised that he would see his son again. So much so, I forgot the rule about interrupting and shouted, 'Oh Granddad, that's a much better ending than Grandma's story.' I had jolted Granddad back to earth too, but he said, 'Oh! That's not the end of the story!' Then looking at me closely he continued, 'But I think your Mum might have been right after all, and we could leave it there, until tomorrow. I do feel as though I have been on a long journey too, and I'm not as young as I used to be, but it has been exciting. Maybe you will feel like reading up to that point this evening, or in the morning, and tomorrow we can concentrate on the impact of the famine.' There was no argument from me, as I desperately needed some time to catch up with all the new revelations."

"Wish I had been there to share it with you, and I hope there's a lot more to come," Liam rejoined eagerly. "Oh yes there's more, but we will have to wait and see how interesting you find it." Nan replied. "Although Granddad was tired he was quite jubilant over dinner, and Dad and Mum were really happy to notice the change for the better. Meanwhile I excused myself as soon as we had eaten, and collecting the Bible and a cushion, retreated to the front porch, where I hoped to find peace and quiet. Normally I would have taken myself off to the meadow, where peace was guaranteed, but the fog was still dense and going outside was unthinkable. The porch wasn't really intended as a place for sitting in, being quite small, but it had a deep window sill, which was decorated with potted geraniums. The plants were covered with red and white flowers, which looked really colourful, but it was the aroma from the leaves which captivated me, transporting me to warmer climes. Despite the chilliness out-of-doors, it was warm in the porch, and depositing the cushion on the quarry tiled floor, I settled down to capture again the excitement I had experienced earlier. Granddad had left a marker in the Bible, and I began to read, but my progress was very slow, and I quickly realised that it wasn't going to be as before. Granddad had read quickly and positively, emphasising the names and places so that they almost came alive, whereas I was stumbling over the names and forgetting the gist of what I was reading. I began to feel very disheartened; how could I have believed that, by the time we resumed next day, I would be able to prove that I was equal to the challenge, even a bit clever, some hope!

The light was fading as I finished, and I could hear Mum calling my name. Having checked the bedroom where she thought I should be, and knowing that I wouldn't have gone outside, she was sounding slightly exasperated, until I opened the inner door of the porch, 'Oh! There you are. Well no one would have thought of looking in the porch!' Despite feeling miserable because of my lack of progress, I had to laugh with her, as she told the others where I had been. Granddad patted my shoulder as he retired, telling me not to lose any sleep, and we would be ready to make an early start next day. I knew I would have to wake up promptly, so that I could have another go before we resumed. As I drifted into sleep I had to admit, rather shamefully, that I really wasn't clever after all. I tried to think about the hardship of the seven-year famine, but it was impossible to imagine, since I was only three years older than that particular time span. The thought was still uppermost in my mind, when I awoke early next morning, and I hoped that my second attempt would be easier and more fruitful than the first. I tried to think about the journey, the distance and how people travelled; those would be some of the questions I would need to ask. Thankfully it seemed to be slightly easier the second time around. My confidence returned slowly, and by the time I reached the end, my inquisitiveness had got the better of me, as I noticed the next chapter heading, *Jacob goes to Egypt.*

There were none of the usual early morning bustling noises emerging from the kitchen area, and feeling sure that Granddad wouldn't mind if I continued, I read on,

> *Then Jacob set out from Beer-sheba; and the sons of Israel carried Jacob their father, their little ones, and their wives, in the wagons which, Pharaoh had sent to carry him. They also took their cattle and their goods, which they had gained in the land of Canaan, and came into Egypt, Jacob and all his offspring with him, his sons and grandsons, and his daughters and granddaughters - all his offspring he brought with him into Egypt.*

It then listed all of Jacob's sons and their families, which so addled my brain that I was about to give up, until I noticed the numbers,

> *All those who went to Egypt with Jacob, those who were his direct descendants, not counting his sons' wives, numbered sixty-six persons. With the two sons who had been born to Joseph in Egypt, the members of Jacob's family, which went to Egypt, were seventy in all.*

By then I knew that Mum had arrived in the kitchen, and I had begun to feel guilty, because I didn't know what Granddad's reaction would be. The question was should I tell him what I had been up to! I guessed I would have to, because what I had just read reminded me of the circles, clans and tribes he had spoken of the previous day; I desperately wanted to know how far they would have travelled. It seemed to be quite a move, and what a tribe! It would be interesting to discover how many miles they would have covered from Beersheba to Goshen, which was the land the Pharoah had promised them.

Mum was making porridge, but she hadn't begun to prepare Granddad's tray. I knew that it would be some time before he made an appearance. Having finished my breakfast, I asked her if it was possible for me to go to the dining room to check some maps. Giving me a wry look she said, 'I hope he is not filling your head with too many high-faluting ideas, and I suppose your other chores will need to wait, and mind what you are doing.'

Fortunately the maps lay undisturbed; some of them were fairly dog-eared, and others had additional names written on. There was the map of the Holy Land, which when I opened it looked similar to one already open, but so many of the names were different. Remembering Mum's words of warning, I refolded it quickly and hoped that there would be an opportunity to look at it again later. On the opened map I was able to see the Mesopotamian area, with the cluster of names surrounding it. As a fertile valley, with desert on one side, and mountains on the other, it was easy to follow – as maps go. What I really wanted was to track where Joseph had lived before going to Egypt, and where his Father, and his tribes had settled when they arrived there. I had read that they had left Beersheba and travelled to Egypt, eventually settling in Goshen, and it was easy to locate those places. I could see the rivers and the mountains, but with no roads to follow, I had no way of knowing which route they might have taken. Waiting for Granddad wasn't easy and I began to think about the story I had read. Why did I still have the same feeling, which I sometimes experienced in Church, when we listened to the readings from the Old Testament. God seemed to be angry with, and punish so many people; would I ever understand why? Well that was to be a huge question for Granddad. As I abandoned the dining room, I couldn't help thinking that I was so glad I knew about the Son, because I really couldn't understand the Father, yet. Mum sensed my impatience, but she was a strong believer in finding work for idle hands, claiming that doing so helped one to think creatively. I had no means of proving her wrong, particularly when she said that we should prepare the apple pie early; she would prepare the pastry and I could practice peeling, coring and slicing apples as thinly as possible. A sharp knife demanded full concentration. When Granddad appeared, she told him he looked very spruce and cheerful. As he smiled he looked through the window, and remarked that they weren't wrong, and the wretched fog looked set for most of the day, and looking at me he added, 'But we have some unfinished work, and a little bird has told me that you have already been to look at the maps.' I supposed she had done that when she had taken him his breakfast tray: Mum, I mean. It seemed that nothing escaped their notice! I couldn't help giggling because that was only half the story; I hadn't told Mum that I had been reading the Bible earlier, because she insisted that we had proper rest. I would wait and tell him when he and I were safely ensconced in the dining room.

Summoning all my courage, I told him about the additional reading, but added that apart from all the questions I had stored up, I really was unhappy with the Old Testament. Looking at me very thoughtfully he said, 'I know that we pull your leg about that, and perhaps the time has come for me to explain, because I certainly wouldn't wish you to go on feeling that way. Let's see if we can't do some unravelling today, and maybe you will begin to have a better view of it. Mind you I can't ever tell you what to think; I can only tell you what I think and believe. Will that be alright?' I explained how I had felt during both reading sessions, and the extended reading I had done. I pointed out the various places on the maps, and then listed the questions which were bugging me. Why was Jacob sometimes called Israel? How far was it from Beersheba to Goshen? How long might it have taken? How far could they travel each day with their animals? Where would they get water if everywhere was as parched as a desert? Why are the tribes always fighting and why is God always angry? Granddad held up his hand saying, 'Enough, enough for now, at least. The question about Jacob and Israel you can answer yourself, by reading the beginning of Genesis – before the Joseph story. We will concentrate on the last question first, that is: Why are the tribes always fighting and why is God always angry? Now though, can you recite for me the first two questions and answers of the catechism, which tell us who made us and why? Good Heavens, I thought, that was like being back in school, and I wasn't sure if I should stand erect and look straight ahead, because that was what we had to do in school. Maybe it proved to be my first step towards adulthood, because I realised that this was my Granddad and me, not teacher and pupil, and anyway he was smiling at me, so I related the first two items.

'1. Who made you? God made me. 2. Why did God make you? God made me to know him, love him, and serve him in this world, and to be happy with him forever in the next.' 'OK. That's fine and it also applies to all mankind, including all those people we are discussing in the Old Testament. You have also learned the Ten Commandments, and I think we should go over those together now. You already know the story of Moses in the bull rushes. Unless I am very mistaken, you will be eager to know more about him, because God chose him to lead Jacob, and his whole family, who had increased in vast numbers over about four hundred years, out of Egypt. The Commandments, which are really just a list of rules, were God's law for mankind, which enable all men to live together in peace and harmony. Do you remember our discussion about the circles and what was most important if people were to live together? God's law is no different to the laws of our land, which have been instituted for the wellbeing and safety of all. In both cases there is punishment, which is meted out for wrongdoing, and today we have prisons for people who become a real threat to society. I suppose you could say that the first is a set of spiritual rules, which means that we are guided by the spirit, which is part of our conscience, and we are supposed to listen to it. You know that's why children need to wait until they are seven years old before they are allowed to make their first communion; they are supposed to know the difference between right and wrong, and put it into practice.

The civil laws needed to be introduced because of man's failure to listen to his conscience or his spirit, which is our guiding force; they are a practical answer to a major problem. Just imagine for a moment an occasion when you had evil thoughts about anyone or anything. Oh! I can see from your smile that I am on the right track.' I had to admit that the last occasion had been when I captured the hen for Mum, but I had been full of remorse when I thought about her fate. However, Granddad knew of a more serious incident, which had happened a few years earlier. I had a beautiful doll, which was my prize possession. Mum had bought it when I was born, and before the emergency had taken its toll on our resources. She gave it to me on my fourth birthday, but told me to take good care of it because the head, arms and legs, which were moveable, could be damaged if it were dropped. The body was made of linen fabric, and stuffed tightly so that it had a lovely rounded feel to it. The face was so beautiful with its long moveable eyelashes over deep blue eyes, and cherub shaped bright red lips. Her hair was a flaxen colour, and was soft and curly. Mum had made extra clothes so that there was a selection of little knitted hats and cardigans; there were lots of pretty cotton dresses, and a variety of white pantaloons with frills. Dad had made a cradle and Mum made the bedding. Apparently I became the quietest person in the house when it was time to play with my doll, but as I said it was my prize possession.

Unfortunately my younger brother was aware of that, and probably very angry, because I preferred to play with the doll, called Marie, rather than with him. When he wished to be a torment he snatched it from me and teased me unmercifully. One day he was in a very vexatious mood and, taking Marie and one of Mum's large needles, he attempted to make large holes in the body where he felt they ought to be. Yes, there were screams and tears when I happened upon him, but I also knew that I wanted to snatch the needle and attack him with it. I remember it vividly, and Mum didn't forget either because some time later, when the subject came up, she reminded me that although I was one of her children, he was her child also. She added that although the doll was my favourite toy, I should not consider harming my brother because of what he had done. Granddad was privy to all that had happened because, as head of the house, he made it his business to know about all those things which could affect its smooth running, and he was eager to use that episode as we continued our discussion.

'There are a number of things I want us to think about as we move on, such as those early people; their worship of multitudinous gods; the family unit as a circle; all those other circles, which represent related tribes; where they lived, and how they behaved. The first commandment states that, *Thou shalt not have strange Gods before me*. It also tells us that we should not carve, sculpt, engrave or make any graven thing for the purpose of adoring or serving it. It is not what we make that is in question, because people are capable of producing works of art, which are truly beautiful and often very useful too. The problem lies in how we treat what we have made or own: how possessive we become. Your experience with your doll is an excellent example, because nothing else mattered to you at the time, and you became too angry, with a tendency to lose control of your emotions. Remember the fifth commandment, *Thou shalt not kill*. You are now older, and can understand the implications of not listening to your conscience. However, there was another reason for that first commandment which, in a sense, you encountered with the doll. Patrick had been jealous because you had something which he knew you prized, and which he wanted. Added to which he wanted your time, so that you could play with him. He was too young to understand, and you are only twelve months older than him, but it was a dangerous situation, if understandable. Of course some people grow without learning how to cope with those situations, and unfortunately behave in a very immature manner when they are tested. I know how upset you were when you saw the dogs fighting, but they don't know about compassion and compromise, as we are supposed to. Those early people were no different to us: they would have had the same feelings and emotions, but because they served so many gods, they became confused, which resulted in fear, suspicion, superstition, and an unwillingness to trust neighbours. Their thoughts were often evil, and for those who practiced black magic, the doll-like images, which they created – many were likenesses of people they knew, and wished to hurt – became a means to an end. The images were called effigies, and people put curses on them. Their actions were full of evil intent.'

Although I realised that he had simply used my bad behaviour as a mild example, my eyes had remained downcast, and I was deeply saddened, as I realised that he was describing real people and events, whereas until that moment, I had believed that the stories I had heard, and read were the stuff of imaginary fiction. I remembered the meadow, and the desolate feeling I had experienced there; it seemed like a repetition of that, and once again my dreams were being shot to smithereens. I do not know how long the silence lasted, but as Granddad gently cleared his throat, I couldn't avoid looking at him, and he couldn't help noticing the tears, which hadn't overflowed. Neither could I fail to see his eyes well up, but there was also a gentle smile, which implied that he knew exactly how I was feeling. As I continued to look, the smile spread and spread, until his face was beaming, and he said, 'You know that, for every sad story you hear, there will be one which is uplifting, and that's what you need right now. I believe it's time to tell you about my merriment yesterday, when I heard you hiccupping. You see there was a name, which I couldn't recall, because it isn't in the Bible, but when I heard your hic, hic, hic it jogged my memory. You'll have to excuse my lapse, but I needed to go back to those days about forty-five years ago, when Grandma and I poured over our books and maps in the evenings. Grandma would probably have it on the tip of her tongue, because she believed that the Celts and the Hyksos – there I've said it – were of the same group, if not the same. As far as we knew, no one had ever made that claim, so why did she feel so strongly? I haven't really thought about it since those days, but I have sensed for some time that the excitement she felt about Celtic art, which is distinctive from any other type of art, is borne out in you. More importantly, Celtic art had stood the test of time, and she had no doubt that it would make a solid impression on future generations. Again, like you, she wished to know as much as possible about the beginning of things, so that when it came to the subject of the Celts, she wasn't content with the knowledge that they had emerged from the Alpine region about 700 B.C. She said that although they emerged from there, she was convinced that they had their beginnings elsewhere, but where? That became her quest, and it was during our research that we discovered the Hyksos, who were also a formidable people, like the Celts. Now, let's see!' Well that sounded much more promising, even exciting but, oh dear, was I in for another eye-opener!"

.

CHAPTER VI

MEN OF IRON

"The twinkle remained in Granddad's eyes as he continued, 'Well I think this is the story you have been waiting for, although I haven't yet ironed out all the finer points. Let's just see where it takes us. I may need to have another rummage in my box of books, although I hope that won't be necessary, because it could mean calling on your Dad for assistance. Mind you I think he would find it fascinating, because it's one aspect, which I never covered with him or your uncles. Now! I am not as young as I was when your Grandma and I ventured down this road, and my eyesight is definitely not as sharp as it used to be, but that is where you can be really useful.'

I immediately felt at least two inches taller – to be useful to Granddad was something very new, and grand! Feeling certain that he was about to use one of his old sayings, I took the liberty of saying it for him: *concentration is the name of the game.*

'Yes indeed, and our journey doesn't begin with where those men of iron emerged from, but rather where they began. Grandma and I had recourse to three main sources of reference, which we considered to be reliable: the first source was the maps: the second was the Bible, and the third was a book entitled, *The Works of Flavius Josephus.* I am going to read a few lines from an extract, which appears at the beginning of Josephus's book. It says, *This history is spoken of in the highest terms by men of the greatest learning and the soundest judgement, from its first publication to the present time. The fidelity, the veracity, and the probity of Josephus, are universally allowed; and Scalinger in particular declares that, not only in the affairs of the Jews, but even of foreign nations, he deserves more credit than all the Greek and Roman writers put together.*

Now that was an extract taken from lectures given by a Bishop Porteus, but I am not going to worry you with his details, nor with the meaning of some of the words, which I have just read, not at the moment anyway. It was in the book by Josephus,that we first read about the Hyksos.' I was glad he had said not to worry, because if I'd had to tell him the truth, I would have had to say that apart from the word Hyksos, the remainder had gone right over my head, and that I realised what Mum had actually meant by the expression high falutin. Next moment I felt guilty because he was saying, 'I know that's of no particular interest to you now, but it could be useful sometime in the future. However, since our search for iron starts at the beginning of the Bible, I think we should have a look at the chart which appears at the back, and which gives us an outline of Biblical History.'

At this point Granddad opened our family Bible, and referred to some sections of explanation about its contents.

'The Books of the Law cover three different, and distinct periods of Jewish history. The First section tells us that God creates a good world, but man is affected by evil.

The next section here deals with the Ancestors of the Israelites at the start of the second Millennium BC. Here we are told about Abraham and God's promise to him, that he will be the father of a great nation, in a land which God will provide for him, his son Isaac, his son Jacob and his descendants who become the twelve tribes of Israel. One of Jacob's sons was Joseph, who became adviser to the King of Egypt, and you know a little about that.

The third section includes the Books of Exodus, Leviticus, Numbers, Deuteronomy, and is the story of Moses and the flight of the Israelites from Egypt; and the wanderings in the wilderness, when God gave Moses the Covenant, the agreement which was about the special relationship which existed between

God and the his people.

There are many more Old Testament Books, which continue this story, right up to the coming of the Messiah in the New Testament, but we are going to focus mainly on just the first two books, since they outline what I hope to tell you about the background to the whole story of iron. There are a few long excerpts, which I wish to give you, because they have a very significant bearing on the beginning of iron, and I know that beginnings are all-important to you. However, you may not understand until we reach our conclusion; in the meantime I must ask you to trust me.' I always trusted him, because he had never let me down, but it all sounded a bit grand, and I really only wanted to know about the Celts! Still, I trusted Granddad. 'So let's kick off with you reading the passage about Cain, in Genesis – just give me the names as you see them, and I will make a list for later.'

I read that Cain's descendants were Enoch, Irad, Mehujeal, Methushael and Lamech. Lamech had four children. First there was Jabal, who was the father of all those who dwell in tents and have cattle. Then there was Jubal, who was the father of all those who play the lyre and the pipe. The third son was called Tubal-Cain, who was known as the forger of bronze and iron. Finally there was a girl called Naamah. Noticing that I had become rather flummoxed each time I attempted to say the name Methusheal, Granddad stopped me at that point. He wasn't sure why I hesitated, and I needed to tell him that that wasn't how we spelt the name, and why. It was his turn to look bewildered and he asked me to explain. Of course he hadn't been present when it had become an issue, during one of Uncle and Aunt's visits from Dublin. I told him that I had been there when they had been having tea with Grandma. Grandma was talking about an old acquaintance, but when they inquired about the person's age, she had laughed and said that the lady was as old as Methuselah. On over-hearing the name I couldn't resist laughing with her and tried unsuccessfully to repeat it. Grandma wasn't over pleased with my interruption and sensing the tension, Aunt Alice quickly found a piece of paper and a pen in her handbag, and printed the name for me, whilst whispering to Grandma that it would be good for my spelling. Aunt Alice had a very happy light-hearted nature, and she loved children, which was probably why she chose to teach infants, whilst Grandma had been ailing most of the time, and not really at her best. As the tension eased I began to feel that Methuselah was a name I was never likely to forget.

Granddad breathed a sigh of relief and said, 'Now I see your problem, but of course I hadn't got to that stage of the story yet. There are indeed two very similar sounding names: the one you have been trying to read, and another Methuselah. Perhaps I should do a family tree like the one I have done for this family. As I am thinking about that, I wonder if you could pop along to the kitchen and tell your Mum that we would love a drink, just to aid our concentration! Mum agreed to make the tea but asked me to feed the fowl in the meantime. Outside the fog remained dense, even misty, with droplets of water clinging to everything. It was a very gloomy picture, and the hens looked really woebegone, but although I longed for the sunshine to re-appear, I was also eager to hear about the origin of iron. Well I couldn't have it all!

Returning to the dining room with tea and biscuits, I found that Granddad had finished the family tree, and was in the process of lighting his pipe, which was always a leisurely procedure. I was grateful for his preoccupation, as it allowed me time to study what he had done.

ADAM – EVE

SONS

| CAIN | ABEL | SETH |

I was also very grateful for the chart and he commented, 'Some of the descendent's names are highlighted, (See Genealogy List), because I want to tell you briefly about them.

Methusael and Methuselah - We can discuss those in a moment. Cain's descendent Lamech had two wives who were called Adah and Zillah.
Adah had two children named Jabal and Jubal.
Zillah had two children named Tubal-Cain and Naamah.

Seth's descendant Noah had three sons who were called Shem, Ham and Japheth.

I have also done a smaller chart for Lamech and his descendants because they are some of the main characters in our story.'

LAMECH (Cain's descendent)

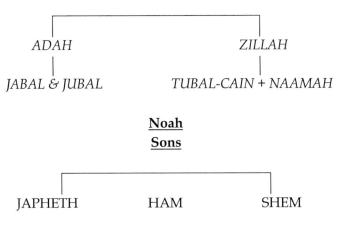

ADAH   *ZILLAH*

JABAL & JUBAL   *TUBAL-CAIN + NAAMAH*

Noah
Sons

| JAPHETH | HAM | SHEM |

They were very clear charts, starting with Adam and Eve and descending from them to Cain, Abel and Seth. I was aware that each name also represented a new generation. There was Methusael in Cain's column and Methuselah in Seth's column. It was interesting to see that they each had a son called Lamech. Cain's descendent Lamech was the father of four children, including the son called Tubal-cain. Seth's descendent Lamech had a son called Noah. Granddad confirmed that it was the same Noah who had built the ark, and that it was believed that he had married Naamah, Tubal-cain's sister, but he wasn't quite sure where that information came from. However, the marriage would have meant communication between the two tribes, and a sharing of knowledge and ideas, which no doubt included the smelting and forging of metal.

Having puffed his pipe and sipped contentedly for some minutes, he suddenly laughed and said, 'Oh! That's much better, and how do you feel now?' I sensed that he was pleased with his efforts, and I told him that I had a much clearer picture, except for Abel! His smile disappeared as he continued, 'You remember our earlier conversation about people who allow their emotions to get out of hand? I know you do and that is what happened here. You see Cain was jealous of, and killed his brother Abel, but you already know that story, and we won't talk about it now. You can have a look at the Book of Genesis, when you have time, but don't be down-hearted; you will understand in due course, and I think you will also understand my need to prepare you for your own journey.' I needed to trust his wisdom if I were to remain strong and determined. I was really looking forward to some quiet time, when I could sneak away to the meadow with the Bible and the charts. However, Granddad had other ideas, and had started talking, 'The next stage is going to be fairly long and tricky, because although you have a framework for your picture, the main focus must be the Celts and iron. Therefore it is most important that you ask questions as I proceed, that is if you need to. You know sometimes questions, even from someone as young as you, are good for us old fogeys, because they can demonstrate a different way of thinking and saying things. So this time you mustn't hesitate. As I said earlier, you will be able to answer your first question about Jacob being renamed Israel, when you read Genesis, and we have already dealt with your last question, about tribal fighting and God's indignation. Hopefully we will be able to cover the other questions, such as the distance from Beersheba to Goshen, the time it might have taken, how far they would be likely to travel each day with their animals, and where they could get water in the desert.

I must emphasise, however, that it isn't possible for me to physically transport us to that time period, or to create the right atmosphere, but you can try to imagine the hottest day we have had here, and it would be necessary to double that temperature. Then imagine a vast expanse of sand, whichever way you looked, with the heat beating down on it. That is a desert!

In the past, and recently, we have talked about how people progressed through the ages. With the aid of our circles, we discussed the growth of tribes and their behaviour, but that was all on a small scale. Now we have to imagine all those clans and tribes, as their numbers reached colossal proportions over a period of four to five hundred years. For instance you will be able to read about the census at the beginning of the Book of Numbers. I know the period is after the Flood, and during the time of Moses, and that it covers the twelve tribes of Israel, but you will notice that it doesn't cover all the people, merely those men who were twenty years and over, and who were able to serve in the army. You will also notice that the descendants of just one man called Simeon, and his tribe, reached 59,300. Another man called Gad, and his tribe, numbered 45,650. It is not a concern for the moment, but it helps to give us a perspective on numbers.'

The list he had made was a real boon, especially being able to identify Methuselah in Seth's column. It also helped to give me a good visual foundation for the creation, but the chart, particularly the time span, was difficult to understand at that moment. Hearing a mention of the twelve tribes, and their journey sounded really interesting. Even so it all seemed like an uphill struggle for me, and I needed to remind myself again that Granddad wouldn't have started if he had thought it too complicated; I would trust his judgement. Before setting his pipe aside, he picked up his own list and said, 'I know this helps to give you an idea of who's who in those families, but there was that other reason for preparing it. Do you think you might be able to tell me what it might be?' He had said that I was to ask the questions, but I guessed that I also needed to prove that I had been listening, even if I got some of it wrong! He held out the list for me to look at, and I remembered his earlier comment about being focused on iron and the Celts. I asked him if it could have something to do with the Celts, but I really wanted to know more about the numbers which appeared in Seth's column, and why there wasn't anything similar in Cain's column. He said the numbers represented the age of each person when he died, and once again there was cause for laughter, when he mentioned Methuselah, who was reputed to be 969 years old. Well, it had to be the best story of all, and it explained why Grandma used the expression. Even so, in my wildest imaginings I couldn't see how anyone could live to be so old, after all I had seen Grandma growing old and leaving us at the age of 70. Granddad was pleased to see that I was happy, but then declared, "When you eventually read on, you will see that God decided to reduce the age limit, and it became more like our own life expectancy, which as you know is three score years and ten. We must remember too that it is only the first son of each generation who is mentioned, until we reach Noah, and his three sons. In fact they all had many sons and daughters, and Grandma and I worked out the total years from Adam to Noah as being about two thousand years. During that time all those tribes would have continued to grow in size, and don't forget although we haven't mentioned Cain, and his family, they would also have continued to multiply. So we are looking at millions of people. That is a lot for you to take on board, since the largest group you've known to date will have been at Mass, where the numbers are in the hundreds, and then people disperse fairly quickly afterwards. You will need to multiply those numbers again and again in order to reach the right proportion. The tribes were spread over a wide area, but still existed in massive groups. The Bible tells us where they settled, and we will come back to that later. At the beginning of this journey, we talked about the early people, who had many gods and corrupt ways. I know that you have been familiar with aspects of the Noah story for a long time, since you loved to recite, *The animals went in two, by two and it rained for forty days and forty nights.* This time I will read those parts which are relevant to our story, and you can read the whole chapter bye the bye.

God said to Noah, *I have decided that the end has come for all living things, for the earth is full of lawlessness because of human beings. So I am now about to destroy them and the earth. Make yourself an ark out of gopher wood. Make it of reeds and caulk it with pitch inside and out. This is how to make it: the length of the ark is to be three hundred cubits, its breadth fifty cubits, and its height thirty cubits. Make a roof to the ark, building it up to a cubit higher. Put the entrance in the side of the ark, which is to be made with lower, second and third decks. For my part I am going to send the flood, the waters, on earth, to destroy all living things having the breath of life under heaven; everything on earth is to perish. But with you I shall establish my covenant and you will go aboard the ark, yourself, your sons, your wife, and your sons' wives along with you. From all living creatures, from all living things, you must take two of each kind aboard the ark, to save their lives with yours; they must be a male and a female. Of every species of bird, of every kind of animal and of every kind of creature that creeps along the ground, two must go with you so that their lives may be saved. For your part, provide yourself with eatables of all kinds, and lay in a store of them, to serve as food for yourself and them.* Noah did this, exactly as God commanded him.

God said to Noah, *Go aboard the ark, you and all your household, for you alone of your contemporaries do I see before me as an upright man. For in seven days' time I shall make it rain on earth for forty days and forty nights, and I shall wipe every creature I have made off the face of the earth.* Noah did exactly as God commanded him. Noah was six hundred years old when the floodwaters came over the earth. Noah with his sons, his wife, and his sons' wives boarded the ark to escape the waters of the flood. Seven days later the waters of the flood appeared on earth. And heavy rain fell on earth for forty days and forty nights. The waters swelled, lifting the ark until it floated off the ground. The waters maintained their level on earth for a hundred and fifty days. But God had Noah, and all the wild animals, and all the cattle that were with him in the ark in mind. God sent a wind across the earth and the waters began to subside. Little by little, the waters ebbed from the earth. After a hundred and fifty days the waters fell, and in the seventh month, on the seventeenth day of the month, the ark came to rest on the mountains of Ararat. The waters gradually fell until the tenth month and, on the first day of the tenth month, the mountain-tops appeared. At the end of forty days Noah opened the window he had made in the ark and released a raven, which flew back and forth as it waited for the waters to dry up on earth. Then he released a dove, to see whether the waters were really receding. But the dove couldn't find anywhere to land and returned to the ark, for there was water over the whole surface of the earth. Noah waited another seven days and released the dove once more. In the evening, the dove came back to him carrying a fresh olive leaf in its beak and Noah realised that the waters were finally receding. Having waited another seven days, he released the dove again, and it didn't return. When Noah opened the hatch of the ark he could see that the surface of the ground was dry! Then God said to Noah, *Come out of the ark, you, your wife, your sons, and your sons' wives with you. Bring out all the animals with you, all living things, so they can multiply on the earth and be fruitful and increase upon it.* So Noah came out with his sons, his wife, and his sons' wives.

God spoke as follows to Noah and his sons, *I am now establishing my covenant with you and with your descendants to come, and with every living creature that was with you: birds, cattle and every wild animal with you; everything that came out of the ark, every living thing on earth. And I shall maintain my covenant with you: that never again shall all living things be destroyed by the waters of a flood, nor shall there ever again be a flood to devastate the earth. And this,* God said, *is the sign of the covenant, which I now make between myself and you and every living creature with you for all ages to come: I now set my bow in the clouds and it will be the sign of the covenant between me and the earth. When the bow is in the clouds I shall see it and call to mind the eternal covenant between God and every living creature on earth, that is, all living things. That,* God told Noah, *is the sign of the covenant I have established between myself and all living things on earth.*

The sons of Noah who came out of the ark were Shem, Ham and Japheth. Ham was to become the father of *Canaan.* These three were Noah's sons, and from these the whole earth was peopled. Noah, a tiller of the soil, was the first to plant the vine. He drank some of the wine, and while he was drunk, he lay uncovered in his tent. Ham saw his father naked and told his two brothers outside. Shem and Japheth took a cloak and they both put it over their shoulders, and walking backwards, covered their father's nakedness; they kept their faces turned away, and they did not look at their father naked. When Noah awoke from his stupor he learned what his youngest son had done to him, and said: Accursed be *Canaan,* he shall be his brothers' meanest slave. He added: Blessed be the Lord, God of Shem, let Canaan be his slave! May God make space for Japheth, may he live in the tents of Shem, and let Canaan be his slave! After the flood Noah lived three hundred and fifty years.'

Well that had been much more to my liking, with a beginning and an end, although it wasn't quite as I had read in my own books. I must have had my eyes closed until Granddad said, 'I think you enjoyed that one, and yes it's an interesting, if sad story, especially when we consider the reason for it, but the message is a hopeful one, with the rainbow being an ongoing sign of hope; it was intended to be a new beginning, but with a difference. Do you have any idea what the difference was?' I told him that I had thought about that when everyone went into the ark, they would have lost all their belongings, and their livelihood, but they couldn't lose what they already knew, or the skills they had learned. They had cultivated the land as we did, and kept animals and fowl as we did. They had discovered metal, and invented tools, which made tilling the soil much quicker and easier. So the discovery of metal and forging skills had to be one of their major achievements. Because I often accompanied Dad to the Smithy when the horse needed new shoes, I was aware of some of the skills, which the forger needed. Our smithy was a very kind person who chatted to Dad as he worked. When he noticed my presence, he occasionally asked me if I would like to work the hand bellows, which pumped the air into the fire. Unfortunately my help was more of a hindrance, because I hadn't got the strength to pump fast enough. The red coals began to look like dying embers, although the heat remained so fierce that I wanted to stand back, when my face began to burn, and I was usually thankful when the smithy said, 'Oh! Macushla, let me take over now.' I knew that the coals needed to be intensely hot so that the colour of the iron bar, which he inserted, would change from a dull grey to a yellowish white; only then could he remove it with long tongs, and place it on the anvil, to beat it furiously with a heavy hammer. Still holding the iron bar with the tongs, in one hand and the hammer in the other, he proceeded to mould and shape the shoe, until it was the right size for our horse's hoof. He also needed to make a number of nail holes in the shoe, so that it could be attached to the hoof. If the iron bar lost its heat too quickly, it needed to be replaced in the coals, and the fire blasted again. When he had completed the operation, he quickly immersed the shoe in a bucket of water, to cool it down. It was fascinating, time consuming, but oh so hot, and that was just working the iron, but what about those people who first discovered how to smelt it. How courageous, hardworking and inventive must they have been!

I shared my thoughts with Granddad, who was sitting back in his chair, puffing contentedly, as he gazed at the ceiling. Surveying his pose, I hoped that he had been listening to what I'd said. There followed what seemed to be a long silence, until he commented, "Yes! How lucky you are to have a Mum who is creative and skilful, because I think some of it has rubbed off on you.'

I gathered that he had approved, and agreed that I wanted to be like Mum, and make beautiful things, although I wasn't sure that it would be hats, even though that had been Mum's occupation before she got married. We all knew that she had had her own milliner's shop in Dublin, but she made other lovely things too, and was happy when she was being inventive. However, we were about to discover that she could be less than happy with herself, and those around her at times. Her voice reached us from the end of the hall, 'If you two want any lunch it is ready and waiting.'

'Oh dear, I think we might be in a spot of trouble here, and we will need to tread very carefully, because I want us to come back to this once we have eaten.' He sounded like a real conspirator, and took care to compliment Mum on her cooking: promising to dig more potatoes when the sun came out, and asking her whether there was anything else she needed. We were to have salad for tea, and she needed lettuce, radishes and scallions. But I knew that what she needed most was for me to be available to help with the chores, and I had always done it willingly. The guilt began to overwhelm me as I tried to eat, yet I knew that the time I was spending with Granddad was intended to help me to prepare for moving, and who told me that we were moving, Mum! Nevertheless when she went to the porch to collect the custard, I whispered to Granddad that I would like to help with the washing up before we returned to our task. He sensed my need as well as Mum's, and was happy to agree, saying that it would give him time to listen to the forecast on the radio.

Back in the dining room, he declared that the widespread fog had actually cleared, and it must be a sea mist, which was still with us, but hopefully it would disperse soon. Rubbing his hands together, he said, "Meanwhile this is our golden opportunity and it needs this concentrated effort, even though your Mum would wish it otherwise. Don't fret because I will talk it over with her later, and tell her that the work we are doing will set you up for the future, regardless of what you decide to do with your life. Now, where were we? Oh yes! I know you were listening carefully when I read about the flood, and you were right about the knowledge and skills, which Noah and his family took on board the ark. It was good to hear your description of the smithy, and so interesting too when we consider that some of Noah's family could have been responsible for what you witnessed at the forge. It's a long way from the Middle East to Ballinalacken, wouldn't you say? It might sound more exciting if I said that it is a long way from the Fertile Crescent, in Mesopotamia to the Fertile Rock, in the Burren." I couldn't say, because I didn't know, but he did and that was good enough for me, and I definitely wanted to know more.

'My conundrum right now is how to take you from where we were, at the end of the flood, to where we need to be in order to pick up the story, since there is a wealth of information, and facts, which we could spend time on, but I don't want to overburden you or have you lose interest.' As he was speaking he was leafing through the Bible, in a distracted fashion. I thought he was looking for inspiration, but was soon enlightened when his efforts were rewarded, as he held aloft some sheets of paper and continued, 'Goodness, I thought we had lost these, and that would have been a pity, because your Grandma took great care in preparing them.' There was a look of sadness on his face, as he examined the familiar writing, but it was only a moment, until he said, 'Thankfully it will make things a lot easier. The first list concerns Japheth, Ham, Shem, and their children, the second is an extended list of the children with additional notes from Josephus, and the third is a map, which shows where those people lived. The first, as you can see is a chart for Noah's three sons, and their children." Clearing a space at the end of the table he said, "I am going to place this alongside the family tree so that you can keep your eye on our progress.'

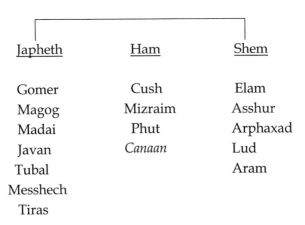

Noah
Sons and Grandsons

Japheth	Ham	Shem
Gomer	Cush	Elam
Magog	Mizraim	Asshur
Madai	Phut	Arphaxad
Javan	*Canaan*	Lud
Tubal		Aram
Messhech		
Tiras		

It was a flimsy piece of paper; no wonder it had disappeared among the pages of the Bible. I attempted to pronounce the name Arphaxad, and Granddad looked at me as he laughed and said,

"Now I am glad you did that, because there are other spellings for the name; that's the problem, which we must address before we look at the next list, because it's one which could flummox you. People are apt to change names, other people's names and place names. You have already come across the situation of Jacob being renamed Israel.'

Without warning he laughed aloud, whacked his knee and said, 'Here am I trying to find an example for you, when there is a perfect example right in front of me.' I wasn't sure how I could be a case in point, but I was all ears as he continued, "You see I am not sure if your Dad and Mum have told you, but in any case, yours is a very good example of what I mean. Did you know that you were christened Anne Jane?' I told him that I did, and I was referred to by the name of Nancy; that was a fact, but I didn't know why it should be so, because we had never discussed it. Granddad was saying, 'I guess it is the fact of the matter that could be a problem in the future, because your birth certificate is a formal declaration of who you are, and you will probably be required to produce it at some time. You became Nancy for the sake of convenience, because Anne sounded too similar to your Mum's name, which is Annie, and it was causing confusion for some people, but you can always revert to Anne when you are older, if you wish to. However, what is even more confusing, is the fact, that you sometimes use your English name, whereas at other times you use your Gaelic name. Then Anne becomes Áine and Nancy becomes Neáns, and of course you are accustomed to hearing both, and now can you see the problem? Don't forget that none of that changes your identity.'

I couldn't resist the temptation to ask him if life would always be that complicated, but he reassured me that it wouldn't be so, and that he was only making me aware of those complications, so that I could make more sense of what we were preparing to do. I was grateful when he said light-heartedly, 'Remember we are looking back over thousands of years of history, and no one seemed to have worried about any complications we might face, whilst trying to resolve our own particular problems.

Now this next list mustn't confuse you either. Simply study it for a moment and you will recognise all those names from the previous list, under the Bible names. The first name you will notice is Gomer, which is one we will pursue, but all those names are located in the map I have just found, which was prepared by your Grandma. As you can see Josephus and the Greeks also implemented changes. If you look at the Table of Nations in the Book of Genesis, you will notice that the tribes of Japheth, Ham and Shem become known as Japhethites, Hamites and Semites. You will also notice that your Grandma and I have circled the name *Canaan*, because *Canaan* in Ham's column was the father of Heth, whose tribe became known as the Hittites; and they are also very relevant to our story. So, have a quiet look whilst I browse this map, it's a long time since I last looked at it.'

Bible Names of Noah's sons and Grandsons, and description by Josephus

Japheth's Family

Gomer **'those whom the Greeks now call Galatians, [Galls], but were then called Gomerites.'**

Magog 'Magogites, but who are by the Greeks called Scythians.'

Madai 'from Madai came the Madeans, who are called Medes by the Greeks.'

Javan from Javan Iona and all the Grecians are derived.'

Tubal 'Thobel founded the Thobelites, who are now called Iberes.'

Meshech 'the Mosocheni were founded by Mosoch; now they
are Cappadocians.'

Tiras 'Thiras also called those whom he ruled over Thirasians,
but the Greeks changed the name to Thracians.'

Ham's Family

Cush 'Chus; for the Ethopians over whom he reigned, are even
at this day, both by themselves and by all men in Asia
called Chusites.'

Egypt 'The memory also of the Mesraites is preserved in their
name; for all we who inhabit this country [of Judea] call
Egypt Mestre, and the Egyptians Mestreans.'

Put 'Phut also was the founder of Libya, and called the
inhabitants Phutites.'
Canaan *'inhabited the country of Judea, and called it from his own
name Canaan.'*

Shem's Family

'Shem, the third son of Noah, had five sons, who inhabited the
land that began at Euphrates, and reached to the Indian Ocean.'

Elam 'Elam left behind him the Elamites, the ancestors of the
Persians.'

Asshur 'Ashur lived at the city Nineve; and named his subjects
assyrians, who became the most fortunate nation,
beyond others.'

Arphaxed Arphaxed named the Arphaxadites, who are now
Called Chaldeans.'

Aram   'Aram had the Aramites, which the Greeks call Syrians.'

Lud   'Laud founded the Laudites, which are now called Lydians.'

I sincerely hoped that Mum wouldn't need the dining room table for quite a while, because I could see that my free time would need to be divided between the dining room and the meadow, until I became familiar with the maize of maps, papers and information. Was that what a wilderness felt like? I could feel myself beginning to go round in circles. I didn't wish to harass Granddad, and I certainly didn't want him to feel that he had failed in his attempt to take me to our destination. After all, he had reassured me every step of the way, and I consoled myself with the knowledge that he would be available to help me fill in any gaps during the following days.

He had opened Josephus's book and was reading quietly to himself, and occasionally studying the map. The English he was speaking sounded so different to the English we spoke, and I became completely mesmerised as he continued, *Now the sons of Noah were three, - Shem, Japheth and Ham, born one hundred years before the Deluge. These first of all descended from the mountains into the plains, and fixed their habitation there; and persuaded others who were greatly afraid of the lower grounds on account of the flood, and so were very loath to come down from the higher places, to venture to follow their examples. Now the plain in which they first dwelt was called Shinar.'*

Granddad muttered, 'Well I know that Shinar is another name for Mesopotamia,' and he continued reading, *God also commanded them to send colonies abroad, for the thorough peopling of the earth.*

We also know that they didn't want to do as they had been commanded, and we have the story of Babylon, which tells us what happened next.   Only then did they become dispersed abroad.

Each colony took possession of that land, which they lighted upon, and unto which God led them; so that the whole continent was filled with them, both the inland and maritime countries.   There were some also who passed over the sea in ships, and inhabited the islands: and some of those nations do still retain the denominations which were given them by their first founders; but some have lost them also; and some have only admitted certain changes in them, that they might be the more intelligible to the inhabitants; and they were the Greeks who became the authors of such mutations; for when, in after-ages, they grew potent, they claimed to themselves the glory of antiquity, giving names to the nations that sounded well (in Greek) that they might be better understood among themselves; and setting agreeable forms of government over them, as if they were a people derived from themselves'

As I said I didn't think that he had been reading to me, but Josephus had drawn me into his account, and very slowly the light began to dawn.   In all the confusion of names, places and identities, I sensed that there was a worthwhile story unfolding; I wasn't merely learning about the Old Testament or the Celts, I was also hearing a lot about humankind and their idiosyncrasies. Even so, I wasn't very impressed, and without warning the words just slipped out, 'Oh, Giminy Cricket, Granddad!'

Before I had a chance to apologise for the slip, Granddad said, 'Oh, I'm not really surprised at your reaction and it is time for a breather.' 'Oh! But Granddad from what you have been reading it seems to me that the Greeks were telling lies? You once said that potent meant mighty or powerful, and it sounded as though they were claiming the praise for all the hard work which had been done by the first settlers.' He smiled and, without explaining that point, he took me back to a previous discussion, when he had spoken about what the term master meant.   He added that men are given power by others to carry out certain tasks, and honesty is considered to be one of the necessary qualifications, but people weren't always as honest as they should be.

He had been looking at me very earnestly, and realising that I had been listening-in as he investigated Josephus, he remarked, 'Good, that saves me a lot of work, and of course it is what the Bible is all about: man's journey through life, and the wilderness. I am pleased that you were listening, and now we can proceed with our map and the charts we already have.

Those people wouldn't have arrived at their destinations immediately, but would have been wilderness wanderers or nomads for a long time beforehand. We are fortunate in that your Grandma was very thorough in all that she undertook to do; she was very fortunate in having many friends, and an uncle who was a Priest, who all shared her enthusiasm. I see that she has added additional notes or references at the bottom, which are very relevant. You can see that she has completed a name list for Japheth's descendents. She also included some place names such as Assyria, Babylonia, Ararat, Ur and Chaldea...and I would wish that she had been here to share this journey with us.

Now, without losing sight of our maps and where we are going, I want to spend a few moments discussing God's plan, because I hope it will help you to come to terms with those Bible stories, which disturb and upset you. You will need to tell me what you think so that I can fill in any gaps for you.'
Well that did upset me! There I was trying to take all he said on board; trying not to be depressed by the never-ending destruction and power struggle, yet trying not to lose touch with my deeper self, where I knew I could always find peace. Unfortunately the tears overflowed and Granddad, sensing that I was overwhelmed, put his arm round my shoulders and squeezed tightly, adding, 'I do know how you feel, because I have been

there too, so try not to fret. You and I know that you have already found your deeper level, and that peace which is so important to everyone. Let's just gloss over all those disturbing issues, which came about because of man's refusal to obey God. We know that war and peace can never go hand in hand, and when man tries to play at being God, things go badly wrong. You know that the reason for the flood was to bring about a new beginning, and what happened?' The arm about my shoulders, along with his soothing voice restored my optimism, and I was able to consider his question, which had been to do with God's plan. I could only think of the first Commandment, which stated very clearly that God created us to know, love and serve Him. I repeated it to Granddad but realised, as I did so, that there were no Commandments before the Flood. Granddad interrupted me to say that even though the Commandments hadn't been written, God had used the patriarchs, who tried to pass on His message, but that men didn't always wish to listen to other men without apparent good reason. Going on he said, 'Now that is the crux of the problem, so keep it in mind as you find your way through the Bible, OK!'

A quick look through the window confirmed that the sea mist was beginning to lift, and he said rather quickly, 'Right then, there should be enough time for a little geography. We need to find Shinar, which is also known as the region of Mesopotamia, because that's where the inhabitants of the Ark first settled. You can, for instance, see Ararat, the Tigris and Euphrates rivers, and further down the entrance to the Persian Gulf, near where Sumer is situated. The people who were called Sumerians were known to be skilled metal workers. Sumer was made of many states, but the people didn't band together. It is the same old tribal problem.' I asked him why so many people settled in that one area, to which he replied, 'Because it's the nearest point to the Persian Gulf, which was an ancient sea; the river at the confluence there would have been a large flood plain, and water was essential for the growth of crops.

I know that you sometimes accompanied your Dad to the vegetable plot, when he needed to water the crops there. Because it is not close to a river, it was necessary to either save the rain water in butts, or transport it from our nearest river. Those river valley civilisations became very adept at saving the water, and knew how and when to sow, and reap the harvest; that's why they grew in numbers, because they were able to feed their tribes. Grandma's map shows some of the names and places, but the main map shows the main rivers and tributaries, and the mountains and desert areas. It's good to have that mental picture, and you could also imagine where the term Fertile Crescent comes from. You can see that to the north of this Fertile Crescent, there is a vast range of mountains, which extends right into Europe. However, those we are immediately concerned with are called the Zagros range, which includes Mount Ararat, and Grandma has added that to her map. We believe that the mountains are chiefly limestone, which is interesting because, as you already know, the Burren region where we are, covers one hundred square miles of carboniferous limestone, and we have discussed that at length. You will have seen the water cascading down the mountain after very heavy rain, creating deep fissures in the rocks, and some of those fissures penetrate right through to underground caves. The reason for telling you this is that the water flow carries with it various nutrients, which help to enrich the soil. It is a known fact that most rivers sometimes overflow after a deluge, unless their banks are raised, so that digging ditches and making banks would have been one of the first tasks, which faced all the settling tribes, both in the Mesopotamian region, and in Egypt where the Nile flows. We also know from our general history, that the need to control seasonal floods became the main incentive for all people living in low lying areas to overcome their animosity, and work together for their general good. So too with the Tigris and Euphrates: the valley became lush and nutritious, making it ideal for farmers and shepherds, but that also gave rise to warfare, because farmers and shepherds needed their own space. Unfortunately it was necessary for the shepherds to move to new pastures on a regular basis, which would have meant that they probably encroached on the farmers, and that was not acceptable. Remember the story of Cain and Abel: Cain was a farmer and Abel was a shepherd. If there was so much enmity between brothers in that situation, imagine the problems where large tribes existed. Added to which they all worshipped their different gods. How on earth could they ever see eye to eye? Their gifts of intelligence and imagination helped them to thrive, but not to be happy and peaceful. Looking at Grandma's map, you can see where she has placed Babel: where all those tribes were, and the story of the Tower of Babel in Genesis, tells us exactly what happened. If you could read that to me it will give you a little more background.' Of course I did as I was told!

Now the whole world had one language and a common speech. As people moved eastward they found a plain in Shinar and settled there. They said to each other, 'Come let's make bricks and bake them thoroughly.' They used brick instead of stone, and tar instead of mortar. Then they said, 'Come, let us build ourselves a city, with a tower that reaches to the heavens, so that we may make a name for ourselves; otherwise we will be scattered over the face of the whole earth.' But the LORD came down to see the city and the tower the people were building. The LORD said, 'If as one people speaking the same language they have begun to do this, then nothing they plan to do will be impossible for them. Come, let us go down and confuse their language so they will not understand each other.' So the LORD scattered them from there over all the earth, and they stopped building the city. That is why it was called Babel – because there the LORD confused the language of the whole world. From there the LORD scattered them over the face of the whole earth.

'Oh! There are so many stories, and they aren't all full of anger and destruction. God's message is so simple really: love me, and love your neighbour as yourself.' For the first time in our discourse, I sensed real frustration in Granddad's voice. 'But let's see where they put down their new roots.' Old Testament! New Beginnings! New roots! Had I been dreaming that Granddad merely wished to educate me on the history of the Celts, or was he trying to prepare me for my new beginning, all in one go. My sense of humour got the better of me, and I couldn't suppress the giggle. That warranted an apology and an explanation, but fortunately he saw my point and shared the laughter as he said, 'Well you could call that a happy accident; because you were listening, you found an analogy or parallel reason, which applied to your own impending move, but it wasn't all part of the original plan. Now without more ado let's set out with those people.

They came down from Mount Ararat to settle in the lush valley in lower Mesopotamia, the region which eventually became known as Babylonia. You can see from the colour coding on Grandma's map that Japheth's family is written in black, Shem's family is written in blue and Ham's in green. When you study the map later you will notice that one of Shem's sons named Lud appears with Japheth's family, and one of Japheth's sons named Maddai appears with Shem's family. That is a very interesting fact, but we won't digress now. In general terms we can say that Japheth (Japhetites) located northwest of Israel, and close to the Black Sea; the area is designated Europe. Shem (Semites) and his family travelled east and southeast to the area known as Asia, and Ham (Hamites) ventured to the southwest to the area known as Africa.

When we set out on this journey of discovery, I was only interested in Noah's son Japheth and his family; particularly his son Gomer, because if you look at Josephus's chart, you will see that Gomer is described as *those whom the Greeks now call Galatians, [Galls], but were then called Gomerites*. Now, however, there is a big *but* because I am reminded of your hic, hic, hic…'

I was so grateful to hear those words, and I jumped off my chair and headed for the dining room door. Granddad said, 'And where might you be off to now?' I was laughing as I told him that I suddenly realised what Mum meant when she sometimes said, 'Oh! I'm at the end of my tether.' But he and I knew that he was totally absorbed in his story, and had temporarily forgotten what he had said earlier about overloading me. Looking through the window he exclaimed that the sea mist had indeed lifted and the sun was shining. Taking his watch from his waistcoat pocket he exclaimed, 'Where does the time go? No wonder you need a break and a drink.'

"Oh! How right he was, but it was my brain which needed the break, and yes I was thirsty too. However, what I needed most of all was to run about barefoot in the meadow, knowing that after the prolonged mist, the grass would have the right amount of moisture and feel absolutely wonderful under my feet. Mum was busy sewing in the kitchen when we appeared, and with a hint of frustration commented --it was usually the quiet time which we shared – 'I wondered when you two were going to appear, and I hope that's it for today.' Granddad looked at me, and agreed that it may be best, since there was a lot for me to digest, but there was a note of regret as he said, that we could come back to it again soon. I needed to be reassured that the dining room wasn't going to be disturbed for a few days, and having had my drink I headed for my favourite place.

It was the most glorious and desperately needed moment: as my bare feet came into contact with the soft, wet grass. Never before had I experienced such a moment, wanting to throw myself face down, and become immersed in the grass and the soil. The grass was too wet, and Mum would never forgive me if I were to add to her burdens. That was to be a different journey: not for sitting and musing, but one of movement and observation, with no attempt at analysis, just seeing and feeling, and so I wandered slowly around the outer edge of the meadow, noting the wet blades of grass as they appeared between my toes, which after a time looked rather pale and wrinkled in stark contrast to the new bright green blades of grass, which felt so smooth and refreshing. I had resolved not to think, but couldn't help noticing the textural contrast, and I let it be so. In those moments, time was not important, and I had no means of knowing how long I spent walking, but I became aware that each time I completed a circuit of the meadow, I moved inwards because I didn't wish to retrace my steps. Having resolved not to think; in fact not wishing to consider my head in the slightest, but rather to detach myself from it, I continued my journey.

Before escaping from the dining room, I believed that I would have run and jumped, as I watched the butterflies or the birds - after all it had so often happened before: that electric feeling as soon as my feet touched the smooth grassy surface. This was a new and different journey. Fortunately, it wasn't a very large meadow, and eventually I found myself in the centre. Inevitably thoughts flashed through my mind, and I noticed the bees, and heard the birds singing, but it was all the more noticeable, because they seemed to have a sense of exhilaration after the prolonged foggy spell. There was, as always, that feeling of space and timelessness. With the sky above, and the earth beneath my feet, I felt connected with both. Once again I was merely a being learning to be, learning to be part of creation and its energy. Granddad had so often told me, I knew and I felt centred.

There had to be a moment of reawakening; I had unconsciously created a continuous circle and taken myself to the centre. I surveyed where I had been: it was easy to see, because the grass which I had walked on, seemed to have lost its lustre, probably because I had knocked the moisture off, and it wasn't glistening as before. Standing stock still I was about to the experience the full impact of what I had done. Words always seem so inadequate when trying to explain a feeling, because our senses are something quite different. The sensation was that of tingling in my feet, and then the laughter which seemed to start there, and work its way upwards. Oh my! What a truly joyous moment. I didn't think. I merely jumped up and down, and did handstands: inevitably getting my dress wet, when I collapsed on the grass. With the laughter came the feeling that my head felt much better. The pressure had gone, and I was able to think freely once more, and think I must. First of all, I needed to decide how I was to find my way back to the beginning of that journey. I could retrace my steps, and if I ran it wouldn't take too long, but I didn't wish to do either. What I needed was a stone to sit on, and there were lots of those at the edge, since the meadow had to be cleared of stones, which could blunt the scythe when the grass was cut. I carved a straight line outwards, and finding a suitable flat topped stone perched myself on it, as the questions began to surface. Why! Oh why had I unconsciously created a continuous circle? I could have walked back and forth; my feet would have felt just as good, or would they? My feet were carrying the whole me, and they had guided me to the centre. The decision to create a line was a conscious one, and as the picture emerged, I could see that I had also created the first spoke. Was that what Dad had meant when he had spoken about the circle and the centre of our being. Well, that didn't seem to matter too much then: what intoxicated me was the fact that I had created something for which the Celts were renowned, the circle, and they were also grounded in creation and the earth. That realisation was very comforting, and I was able to understand how it would help me to make sense of the previous few days. Being remote from the house, and particularly the dining room, enabled me to make a detached assessment of what I had been doing and hearing.

There was another question to answer! How would I have felt had I been one of those people of whom Granddad had been speaking: people who spent so much time walking in the desert? Yes, I could have created a big circle and made many patterns, just as I did when we went to Fanore beach, but in all other respects it didn't bear thinking about.

I loved Granddad deeply, and knew there was a sense of urgency in what he was trying to do for me, but I sensed that even he wasn't altogether prepared for how his story was enfolding, and the length of time it was taking. I knew he found it exciting and emotional at times, because of Grandma. But I think he had temporarily forgotten his advancing years, and my young brain. I was able to think about what lay waiting for me on the dining room table, but not too deeply, since there would be some time to absorb it, and Granddad would be on hand. I would need to understand so much before we moved on.

As I journeyed home I realised that the sun had dried my dress, except for the patch I had been sitting on, and hopefully Mum wouldn't notice that. Nearing the house I noticed the spiral of smoke rising from the field across the road from the house, and knew it was Granddad who would be sitting there on his favourite stone. I guessed he too was just being, and I joined him there. We could just be together for a while, and there was no need for words.

His voice was quiet when he spoke," 'Your Mum was annoyed with me after you disappeared, and I needed to explain to her about the other you, who is part of this place. We parted good friends, and she has agreed that she will leave the table undisturbed for two weeks, provided you are available to help her when she needs you.' "That was music to my ears, and he had added that at the end of that period, we would be ready to move on. He was laughing as he said," 'You see I was being young again, but it was quite wonderful: still I am a little tired now.' "I gave him a hug, before hurrying back indoors to help Mum: how I would miss those times I shared with him. Best to make the most of the time I had left and be thankful. As I said before, harmony was important too; Mum was busy and, as I appeared, she said," 'There are a lot of mouths to feed.'

My resolution not to think about the input I'd had lasted until I began to say my bedtime prayers, and the thoughts came crowding in. However would I make sense of it all? Mum would have said, 'Sleep on it and everything will feel better in the morning,' but Dad would have recited the poem, 'Little by Little'. Perhaps I could do both! After prayers I thought about my own plan. I would need to skip my playtime with the lads, and hope they would understand. Two weeks seemed a long time but it would soon vanish."

CHAPTER VII

LITTLE BY LITTLE

'Little by Little,' an acorn said,
As it slowly sank in its mossy bed,
'I am improving every day,
Hidden deep in the earth away.'

Little by little each day it grew,
Little by little it sipped the dew;
Downward it sent a thread-like root,
Up in the air sprang a tiny shoot.

Day after day, and year after year,
Little by little the leaves appear;
And the slender branches spread far and wide,
Till the mighty oak is the forest's pride.

'Little by little,' said a thoughtful boy,
'Each precious moment I will employ,
And always this rule in my mind shall dwell:
Whatever I do, I'll do it well.

'Little by little, I'll learn to know
The treasured wisdom of long ago;
And sometime, perhaps, the world will be
Happier and better because of me.'

Anonymous

"The sun was shining brightly when I awoke next morning.

Feeling full of courage and determination I marched quietly towards the dining room, but a quick look at the mess on the table immediately deflated my bubble of enthusiasm. I all but forgot my resolutions of the previous evening: little by little an acorn said, as it slowly sank in its mossy bed. The new exercise book and pencil were placed where I couldn't fail to see them, and there was no need to ask who had anticipated my next move. I picked them up, and walked round the table, glancing at each map, book and piece of paper. I wasn't really sure whether to laugh or cry as I stood there thinking, all this because I like those men of iron, and what a long journey. However, the account of their journey had started in the Bible, at the very beginning, and that's what Granddad and I had been about, beginnings.

All I needed was an outline, yet I should acknowledge that although my first interest was in the Celts, they were only part of the wider scheme, and I couldn't ignore that fact, even in order to suit my own convenience. The Celts were fearless people, and Granddad had helped me to see the Old Testament in a different way. As the light and heat from the early morning sun began to move across the table, I felt more at ease with all that lay before me. I made a few more circuits of the table, looking again at the maps, whilst seeming to hear the voice of Granddad, as he talked me through each stage. Later I would take some of the papers across to the meadow and think about them, but not until I had already written something in my brand new copybook, and the first word was always the most difficult. I knew I was hedging, because I didn't wish to spoil the book; the invention had been someone's special idea at some time – a very useful creation. But what of the first creation!

That was it! Creation would need to be my first word, and so it was. In the beginning God created the heavens and the earth, but he had created the earth as a home for all people. His hope had been that man would live in harmony with his fellow men as they cared for his provision. It didn't happen as he had planned, and the problem started with Adam and Eve in the Garden of Eden. God had told them not to eat from a particular tree, which was in the centre of the garden, because it represented good and evil. Eve couldn't resist the beautiful fruit, which grew on the tree, and persuaded Adam to eat from it. However, as soon as they had eaten the fruit, they knew that they had done wrong. They were ashamed of themselves, and later God told them what would happen because of their disobedience. So they became as we are to this day, a mixture of good and evil, like the Tree of Knowledge. They had children called Cain and Abel, and much later, Seth. Next came Noah and the flood, but by that time the population had grown to very large proportions, from small units to tribes, and in time to nations. But it was not as God had intended: the mixture of good and evil caused many to kill, live corrupt lives and have false gods. God chose Noah, who he saw to be a good man, and told him to build an ark, because he was going to send a flood to wipe out all people except for Noah, his family, and a collection of all the animals and living creatures which he had created. For with Noah there would be a new beginning.

After the flood, the population grew again, but even though Noah was a good man, his descendants were really the same mixture as before the flood. To begin with they didn't obey God's instructions to them when they left the ark: to go forth and people the earth, and learn how to live in harmony. Instead they built the tower of Babel saying, *Come, let us build ourselves a city and a tower with its top reaching heaven; so that we may become a great people, and not be scattered over the face of the earth*! God was not happy and confused their language, so that they didn't understand one another, and they had to do what he had asked them to; go people the earth. Over the next few hundred years, God could see that there was little change, and finally he chose Abraham, with his wife Sarah, to start all over again. He had promised, after the flood, that he would never destroy the world again, and he needed a new and different plan, or beginning.

I had stopped to read what I had written. Good or bad it was my first picture. I had two weeks to go over all the details again, and I would be reading the whole of Genesis, and not just my favourite sections, since it was the most amazing story about the beginning of beginnings. The sun, which had warmed the room as I worked, was moving on, and once more the shadows appeared. I had become aware that Mum was moving in the kitchen, and the thought of porridge was really welcome. As I shivered, I realised that I hadn't stopped to wash or dress before making my way to the dining room, and I couldn't appear in the kitchen until I had done so.

Although I was my bright and breezy self when I arrived, Mum cast a searching glance at my face, as she served my porridge, whilst saying, 'I don't want those shadows under your eyes to deepen, my girl. You must be fit and well before returning to school.' I smiled at her and said that all would be well, really! Feeling much more comfortable with the porridge inside me, my first task was to feed my friends outside. I couldn't restrain the laughter as I tossed the food into their midst; so much clucking, squawking and pecking of one another, as they chased what always seemed to them to be a bigger and better morsel. I didn't think that humans would do that, because they had intelligence. Well that would need to be something which Granddad might explain. My task was to find out what else I needed to do for Mum, as it seemed that harmony was something which we needed to work at.

The days passed with lightning speed. I didn't neglect my duties but I didn't take time to dream as I carried out the mundane tasks, but hurried through them. Early morning and after supper were the best and quietest times for being in the dining room. I didn't need to take the books or papers to the meadow, but I took a piece of paper and pencil stub in my dress pocket, because on my first outing I had come up with questions which I needed to check as soon as possible. When I couldn't find answers I copied the questions to the back of my copybook, so that I could ask Granddad later.

Indeed as time passed the questions grew, but I didn't let it worry me. When Granddad asked if all was well, I told him it would be, and that I was saving the questions for him. I knew he was eager to finish what he had started, and that we were due to have visitors sometime soon, but I needed to listen to my arguments, and find some solutions so that I was happy to journey on. Towards the end of the second week, the opportunity did arise because the clouds, which had been gathering over the previous days, gave way under their own pressure. Even I, who didn't mind soft rain, had no urge to be out of doors. It was inevitable that Granddad and I would find our way to the dining room. Once there I related my story, as he listened thoughtfully; afterwards I showed him my list of questions, which had grown considerably. Having read them, he exclaimed that there was nothing major there, and it wouldn't take us long, and it didn't. He seemed quite pleased as he announced, 'Well! That's that, and I believe we are both happy. Now! Do you remember where we had got to before you escaped?' How could I forget, and I hoped it wasn't going to happen again, but I needn't have worried because he carried on, 'Yes, well it was that hic, hic, hic, and that's exactly where I want to start now. When you went shopping with your Mum recently, I had a few quiet hours to think about the completion of our journey with the men of iron. Of course I also wanted to tell you very briefly about the Hittites and the Hyksos, because it is all intertwined. In order to do that, we must quickly recall some of our earlier facts, and check again the dispersal map, which shows Noah's descendants. The map you've seen already tells you where Noah's sons Japheth, Ham and Shem were dispersed. However, I came across another flimsy map, which your Grandma must have completed on one of her excursions to Kilfenora, before your Uncle Ben was born. This map is more extensive, but it made it easier for me to build my own account for you. You don't need it at the moment, but I think you will certainly find it very interesting another time. Not only does it show you where the main characters settled, but also their children and grandchildren, and how widespread they were in Asia and Africa. When tribes moved on to unconquered land, the new territory was named according to the head of the tribe.

We know that the two great nations in Biblical times were Egypt and Mesopotamia, and include an area which is often referred to as the Fertile Crescent. We have talked at length about the river valley civilizations, and how they multiplied. From the map you can see that Ham's first son Cush named his region Cush, now known as Ethiopia, his second son Misraim gravitated towards what we know as Egypt. His third son Phut moved further west to what is now called Libya, and his fourth son *Canaan* inhabited the country called after his name, also called Palestine, but what we now call Israel. However Japheth's descendants remained in the North: apart from one of Noah's grandsons, who settled in Tarshis in Western Italy, and we are told that it was Gomer, Japheth's son, and his descendants, who eventually penetrated Europe.

Well that's just a geographical picture, and we can now keep an eye on the map, as we set out with those people on their turbulent journey. So let's think about the Hyksos, who are not mentioned by that name in the Bible, but are referred to as wandering shepherds, or Shepherd Kings, instead. We all know that eventually, when tribes grew to very large proportions their leaders – and there had to be a leader – became King, or ruler overall.

I believe that you are comfortable with the story of Joseph and his abduction, and with his progress in Egypt; also with the journey of his father Jacob, who travelled from Canaan to Egypt, and settled with all his tribes and animals, where they grew to be very powerful. Now, can you imagine how Joseph's family might have been feeling, as they established themselves; there they were, living in what was the best land, given to them by no less than the Pharaoh himself, and with a brother who was considered to be almost as powerful as the Pharaoh; a brother who managed the whole of Egypt, even allocating the distribution of the grain which was keeping everyone alive. Goodness me, I don't know why I would try to explain because the Book of Genesis does this part much better, so I will read from it, but I want you to listen especially carefully, whilst considering all that we have been discussing since we set out on this journey.

Joseph settled his father and his brothers, and granted them a holding in the land of Egypt, in the best part of the land, in the land of Rameses, as Pharaoh had instructed. And Joseph provided his father, his brothers, and his entire father's household with food, according to the number of their dependents. Now there was no food in all the land, for the famine was very severe. The land of Egypt and the land of Canaan languished because of the famine. Joseph collected all the money to be found in the land of Egypt and in the land of Canaan, in exchange for the grain that they bought; and Joseph brought the money into Pharaoh's house. When the money from the land of Egypt and from the land of Canaan was spent, all the Egyptians came to Joseph, and said, "Give us food! Why should we die before your eyes? For our money is gone." And Joseph answered, "Give me your livestock, and I will give you food in exchange for your livestock, if your money is gone." So they brought their livestock to Joseph; and Joseph gave them food in exchange for the horses, the flocks, the herds, and the donkeys. That year he supplied them with food in exchange for all their livestock. When that year was ended, they came to him the following year, and said to him, "We cannot hide from my lord that our money is all spent; and the herds of cattle are my lord's. There is nothing left in the sight of my lord but our bodies and our lands. Shall we die before your eyes, both we and our land? Buy us and our land in exchange for food. We with our land will become slaves to Pharaoh; just give us seed, so that we may live and not die, and that the land may not become desolate." So Joseph bought all the land of Egypt for Pharaoh. All the Egyptians sold their fields, because the famine was severe upon them; and the land became Pharaoh's.

As for the people, he made slaves of them from one end of Egypt to the other. Only the land of the priests he did not buy; for the priests had a fixed allowance from Pharaoh, and lived on the allowance that Pharaoh gave them; therefore they did not sell their land. Then Joseph said to the people, "Now that I have this day bought you and your land for Pharaoh, here is seed for you; sow the land. And at the harvests you shall give one-fifth to Pharaoh, and four-fifths shall be your own, as seed for the field and as food for yourselves and your households, and as food for your little ones." They said, "You have saved our lives; may it please my lord, we will be slaves to Pharaoh." So Joseph made it a statute concerning the land of Egypt, and it stands to this day, that Pharaoh should have the fifth. The land of the priests alone did not become Pharaoh's. Thus Israel settled in the land of Egypt, in the region of Goshen; and they gained possessions in it, and were fruitful and multiplied exceedingly. Jacob lived in the land of Egypt seventeen years; so the days of Jacob, the years of his life, were one hundred forty-seven years.'

When he finished reading there was silence for a few minutes until he said, 'Well!' I had listened very carefully, and it seemed to be a picture which became bigger and bigger, a powerful picture. I didn't like it, but I understood, and I had read in the Book of Genesis, that the Egyptians hated the Shepherds; I had also noticed that they had addressed Joseph as Lord. I shared my thoughts with Granddad, and he added, 'That's right and the reference to it appears just before the piece I have read to you, when Joseph rides out to meet his family, who have almost arrived at their destination. In Genesis it says,
When Pharaoh calls you, and says, 'What is your occupation?' you

shall say, 'Your servants have been keepers of livestock from our youth even until now, both we and our ancestors'- in order that you may settle in the land of Goshen, because all shepherds are abhorrent to the Egyptians.

There is another snippet which we could add to our argument. Although the Egyptians may have hated the shepherds, the Pharaoh was well disposed towards them, because he believed Joseph to be a man of God. Here, I'll read that section to you in order to round off this part of our story,

So Joseph went and told Pharaoh, "My father and my brothers, with their flocks and herds, and all that they possess, have come from the land of Canaan; they are now in the land of Goshen." From among his brothers he took five men and presented them to Pharaoh. Pharaoh said to his brothers, "What is your occupation?" And they said to Pharaoh, "Your servants are shepherds, as our ancestors were." They said to Pharaoh, "We have come to reside as aliens in the land; for there is no pasture for your servants' flocks because the famine is severe in the land of Canaan. Now, we ask you, let your servants settle in the land of Goshen." Then Pharaoh said to Joseph, "Your father and your brothers have come to you. The land of Egypt is before you; settle your father and your brothers in the best part of the land; let them live in the land of Goshen; and if you know that there are capable men among them, put them in charge of my livestock." Then Joseph brought in his father Jacob, and presented him before Pharaoh, and Jacob blessed Pharaoh. Pharaoh said to Jacob, "How many are the years of your life?" Jacob said to Pharaoh, "The years of my earthly sojourn are one hundred and thirty; few and hard have been the years of my life. They do not compare with the years of the life of my ancestors during their long sojourn." Then Jacob blessed Pharaoh, and went out from the presence of Pharaoh. Joseph settled his father and his brothers, and granted them a holding in the land of Egypt.

Well, all that is from the Genesis story, and as I said it was to round off this part of my own account. You see Grandma and I agreed with Josephus, that the Hyksos and Joseph were in Egypt at the same time, and that the reigning Pharaoh happened to be a Hyksos King. I will try to come back to that another time, and many years from now, when I am no longer with you, you might wish to consider this argument again.'

Yes, it all made good sense, but I so wished he hadn't said, 'When I am no longer with you.' How could he even think about it? It was the last thing I wanted to hear. In a desperate attempt to stop the sad thoughts flowing into my mind, and because he had been describing Joseph's family, I focused on my own family instead; after all I had a brother Joseph too, and an Uncle Joseph in America... I couldn't help thinking of my aunts and uncles, who had emigrated to America due to shortage of work, and the cousins that I had never met, but wondered if I ever would. I thought of my two sisters, Bríd (Bridget) – named after one of the patron Saints of Ireland – and Mary, who would have grown up with me, had they not died in infancy. If I were to meet any of those surviving relatives at a later date, how would I react? Would we behave like strangers or even enemies? When I shared my thoughts with him I saw the flash of pain move across his face, but he was gentle as he said, 'Well, those are questions for another time!'

"Nan!"
"Yes Liam."
"You haven't spoken for some time."
Although the sound of his voice had startled her, she didn't look at him as she replied. "I am sorry Liam but you see, in trying to describe all that happened during that summer period, I have also unavoidably reconnected with many of the emotions which I experienced: just as Granddad did when he referred back to his journey of discovery with Grandma. I guess if the journey is real, it isn't always easy to separate fact and feeling. I have to admit that I am finding it disconcerting, but in a way I suppose that in

- 181 -

telling you the full story, which is a first, I am tending to evaluate all that happened. I have mentioned some of my outbursts, when everything seemed to be above and beyond my comprehension, and there were many occasions when I stood alone looking down to the sea, or out to the west as the sun went down, wondering how I could make sense of all the information I was being given. I loved, admired and respected Granddad, as did many others, but I couldn't help wondering once or twice, whether I had become a target for a long forgotten story. Fortunately, those thoughts only crept in occasionally…when I really longed to be outside playing with my brothers. Had I shared the thought with Mum, she would certainly have put an end to it all…I didn't want that either, so I focused instead on one of her favourite expressions, *Good things often have a high price tag.*

Although Granddad was determined, he wasn't an ogre, and he wouldn't chastise me. However, there was a contrary thread running through the whole of that period…As I said there were those occasions, as the sun was setting, when I felt weighted down.

You know Liam up there on the hill it is so easy to feel lost in time and space. If I can feel that now, just imagine how it was for a nine and a half year-old: feeling so small and insignificant…until one particularly beautiful evening, just before bedtime, when I slipped outside. It had been raining very heavily for most of the afternoon, but when the rain stopped, the clouds dispersed, revealing a beautiful sunset, and a magnificent rainbow. My head had seemed jam-packed with information, yet it was impossible to stand in that glorious environment and actually worry about anything. I know there is no order or pattern in the scene itself, comprised of fields surrounded by randomly built walls, scrub land, trees, overgrown bushes and hedges, rocks strewn all about… and that is just one part of the bigger picture; looking to the right or left revealed completely different scenes. Yet it all looked right and natural. That thought seemed to put everything else into perspective. Once again I recalled Granddad's comments, *one needs to be here.* There was also his episode with the box camera, when he said, *you cannot capture the whole scene at once, but merely take a number of pictures and piece them together later. You can still focus on each picture individually. Even then it isn't possible to capture the atmosphere, but the pictures jog the emotions as well as the memory.*

On that particular occasion, the scene and the memory of what he had told me, proved to be a revelation, which has continued through my life: it opened the door to a new way of thinking and coping, and I decided that I would simply divide the story into sections, and create a mental picture for each. It would be a little by little approach, which I could add to as the need arose, allowing me the space to focus on the most important issues. Mum had opened the window to announce very loudly that it was way past my bedtime. Following one last look at that memorable scene I skipped indoors, stopping briefly by Mum who, although agitated by my dithering, was nonetheless reluctant to spoil my happy moment. Yes, I may have felt little but I was no longer dwarfed."

Unfortunately, I am now in the same predicament, which Granddad had been in, as he recalled his story, and I also realise that, in some respects, it could be more difficult for you, since Granddad and I had maps and lists to work with. Of course I know that you are older than I was, and you have a sound geographical knowledge, which will help you. I realise that we all have access to the Internet these days and it will be possible for you to verify much of what I say. I have also visited the multitudinous sites which explore my subject... the amount of information available has been increasing over the years: in books and articles initially, and later on the computer. This has now reached staggering proportions, but unfortunately for me it becomes increasingly confusing, because so much information seems to be hypothetical and contradictory, despite all the archaeological discoveries. However, with the exception of the maps, I prefer to rely on the sources which Granddad used, and which took us to the conclusion which he desired.

Needless to say, as his story progressed, I continued to have rebellious moments, but following that encouraging experience, as I watched the sunset, I had resolved before going to sleep, that I would practice reciting the names and places, which had occurred in our story so far. After all that's what we had to do in school, and at home when we were revising our school assignments."

"Nan!" As she turned to look at him he continued, "Did you really go about practicing all those names out loud?" She was unable to control the giggles as she remembered, "Oh yes, but not to the family or even myself. You see, my first task before breakfast, was to slip into the dining room and look at the lists and maps; my next task after breakfast was to feed the fowl, including a number of ducks, which suddenly became very important. We had two cockerels; they looked very superior with their bright red combs sticking up: their eyes always looking very bright and aggressive, as though they were ready for a fight. There were many hens with various demeanours, which seemed to depend on whether they thought they were to be the prize catch, or simply had a clutch of chickens. I didn't take too much notice of the ducks; they just seemed to waddle about going quack, quack, and I didn't like duck-eggs. As I said they became useful, for a time... they all became my audience, acquiring new names in the process, and the high garden became a sort of geographical scene, over which they spread. Observing a territorial cockfight had a new significance, and when I fed them the whole scene became a noisy battleground, as each one chased what he or she thought was the best target. Mind you, it did help me to focus, and it became fun to do." Still laughing, she continued, "Of course I didn't share that information with anyone... just in case. The fowl may have considered my behaviour to be very different, when I took their food next morning, because I talked at them rather than to them. I spoke over their heads, whilst indicating with my finger, as I visualised Noah's list and the dispersal map. The area to my left would be Egypt, and it included Libya and Ethiopia; in front of me there was the red sea leading up to Canaan, near the Mediterranean Sea. Just above that there was Syria, and further north still was Black Sea. To my right there was the vast expanse of the Arabian Desert, Mesopotamia and Assyria, with the Persian Gulf at the bottom, and the Caspian Sea at the top. That seemed to be the geography; then it was time to connect with Noah, his sons Japheth, Ham and Shem, and their descendants. I know that Granddad had mentioned them a number of times, and I had been doing my revision, but I needed to make them part of my own outline story. It was a sad fact, that for some time after we began our mega exercise, I would seem to have a bright clear picture one moment, but adding one extra detail, would jumble the whole scene, and I would have to go back to the beginning and start again. That was the problem and the frustration; I hoped that the new strategy would help me to overcome that difficulty.

Fortunately the fowl had settled down to eat, which meant that they stayed still long enough for me to whizz through Japheth who had Gomer, Magog, Madai, Javan, Tubal, Messhech and Tiras... I indicated the Black Sea and put them there: I wasn't going to worry about them yet. Then it was Shem's turn, and his sons who were Elam, Asshur, Arphaxad, Lud and Aram; they were slightly more complicated, with the majority to my right, but with Lud up near the Black Sea with Japheth's family. Josephus had said that Asshur gave his name to the Assyrians. However, my main interest was in the third son Arphaxad, since he was the ancestor of Abraham, who was born six generations later. I could look at them another time. There remained Noah's other son Ham, and his sons who were Cush, Mizraim, Phut, and Canaan. With exception of Canaan, who was already in place in front of me, the remaining three all went to my left: westward, where Cush became Ethiopia, Mizraim became Egypt and Phut became Libya. I couldn't help thinking that my task would have been so much easier if they had all remained close to their paternal groups, but I had to smile when I remembered that God had said to Noah, *Go out of the boat with your wife, your sons, and their wives. Take all the birds and animals with you, so that they may reproduce and spread all over the earth.* He hadn't actually said where... Anyway I had a bigger problem because I knew that, as soon as Granddad had breakfasted, he would be eager to take up where we had had left off. His last comment had been that we would need to look at Abraham and the Hittites, and maybe another look at the Hyksos, leading on to the Celts. It was time to leave the garden and the fowl, and head indoors, hoping to sneak past Mum, who was in the kitchen, so that I could have another look at the Table of Nations and Genesis; also my outline notes concerning the beginnings in the Bible.

'So that's where you are'. The sound of Granddad's voice startled me. 'Mum thought you were still feeding the hens, but I thought otherwise. I am delighted that you are so eager, because we will need to keep our wits about us.' He was smiling as I told him that I needed to keep going over what he had already said, and I had wanted to check the maps again. 'Now, that's what I like to hear, and I am not forgetting your Celtic friends, and how they eventually arrived in Ireland. After all they are the main reason for setting out on this journey. If you can think of the journey as the background to their arrival, it will make all that I am passing on to you so much easier, I hope! I have been thinking of the next most important step before we talk about the Hittites and the Hyksos, but feel that it might be easier for you if you read the last paragraph of your outline story again, and read aloud the last two sentences.' He had found my notes as he was speaking and handed them to me. I nodded as I prepared to read,

After the flood, the population grew again, but even though Noah was a good man, his descendants were really the same mixture as before the flood. To begin with they didn't obey God's instructions to them when they left the ark: to go forth and people the earth, and learn how to live in harmony. Instead they built the tower of Babel saying, Come, let us build ourselves a city and a tower with its top reaching heaven; so that we may become a great people, and not be scattered over the face of the earth! God was not happy and confused their language, so that they didn't understand one another, and they had to do what he had asked them to; go people the earth. Over the next few hundred years, God could see that there was little change, and finally he chose Abraham, with his wife Sarah, to start all over again. He had promised, after the flood, that he would never destroy the world again, and he needed a new and different plan, or beginning.

'Thank you, and now you can sit back and listen whilst I tell you about the man who was to be the new beginning. I know you have the story of Abraham in your storybook, and it is a wonderful story, but I have written a very short summary story, which provides extra details, and it should help us to reach our own conclusion. You can keep the map near you because it was a long journey, and remember that Abraham's faith in God is being sorely tested: not once, but twice.

Abraham had grown up and married in the Mesopotamian region, in a city called Ur, known as Ur of the Chaldees. Terah his father, decided to move his family, which included Abraham, his grandson Lot, and his daughter-in-law Sarai, and journey from Ur to Canaan. Terah liked Haran and they remained in that area until he died at the age of two hundred and five years. Then it was that God called Abraham with these words, *Leave your country, your kindred and your father's house for a country which I shall show you; and I shall make you a great nation, I shall bless you and make your name famous; you are to be a blessing!*

Abraham did as God asked and he took Lot with him; he was seventy-five years old when he left Haran. He passed through the country as far as the holy place at Shechem, where he built an altar in order to worship. The Hittites were in the land of Canaan at that time. From there he moved on to the mountainous district east of Bethel, where he pitched his tent and erected a second altar. Then he made his way stage by stage to the Negeb. There was a famine in the country, not the Famine of Joseph's time, and Abraham went down to Egypt to stay there for a while, since the famine in the country was severe. There is a very moving story about that visit to Egypt, but you must read it for yourself. On leaving Egypt he went back to the Negeb - he and his wife - with all he possessed, and Lot went with him. By this time he was very rich in livestock, silver and gold. By stages, he journeyed on from the Negeb to Bethel, to the place where he first pitched his tent and built an altar. Lot also had flocks and cattle of his own and tents too. The land was not sufficient to accommodate them both at once, for they had too many herds and possessions to be able to live together.

Disputes broke out between the herdsmen of Abraham's livestock, and those of Lot. Abraham said to Lot, *We do not want discord between us or between my herdsmen and yours, for we are kinsmen. So they parted company but Abraham had been very gracious and said to Lot, Is not the whole land open before you? Go in the opposite direction to me: if you take the left, I shall go right; if you take the right, I shall go left.* So Lot chose all the Jordan plain for himself, moving eastwards; living among the towns of the plain, and pitching his tent as far as Sodom. I know you have the story of Sodom in your story book, but it will good for you to read the Bible version also.

Abraham settled in the land of Canaan, and it was there that God spoke to him again saying, Look all round from where you are, to north and south, to east and west, for all the land within sight I shall give to you and your descendants for ever. I shall make your descendants like the dust on the ground; when people succeed in counting the specks of dust on the ground, then they will be able to count your descendants too! On your feet! Travel the length and breadth of the country, for I mean to give it to you. So Abraham moved his tent and went to settle at the Oak of Mamre, at Hebron, and there he built an altar to God. God spoke to him in a vision, asking him not to be afraid, but Abraham replied, *My Lord God, where are your promises? I am still childless and the heir will have to be a member of my household.* God replied, *Such a one will not be your heir; no, your heir will be your own flesh and blood.* Then taking him outside, he said, *Look up at the sky and count the stars if you can. Just so will your descendants be,* he told him. Abraham put his faith in God, and this was reckoned to him as uprightness. God then said to him, *I am the Lord who brought you out of Ur of the Chaldaeans to give you this country as your possession.* Abraham was still unable to understand, and asked how he could know that his children's children would possess it, but God said to him, *Bring me a three-year-old heifer, a three-year-old she-goat, a three-year-old ram, a turtledove and a young pigeon.* He brought him all these, split the animals down the middle and placed each half opposite the other; but the birds he did not divide. And whenever birds of prey swooped down on the carcases, Abraham drove them off. Now, as the sun was on the point of setting, a trance fell on Abraham, and a deep dark dread descended on him. Then God said to Abraham, *Know this for certain, that your descendants will be exiles in a land not their own, and be enslaved and oppressed for four hundred years. But I shall bring judgement on the nation that enslaves them, and after this they will leave, with many possessions. For your part, you will join your ancestors in peace and you will be buried at a happy old age.* That was the Covenant God made with Abraham, and the dream referred to Abraham's grandson Jacob's family in Egypt, after he joined his son Joseph there.

Sarai could not have any children of her own, and she arranged for her Egyptian maid Hagar to have a child instead. They had been in Canaan for twelve years when Hagar had a son, and they christened him Ishmael; Abram was eighty-six years old at that time. *When Abraham was ninety-nine years old God spoke to him again saying, I am God Almighty; walk before me and be blameless. And I will make my covenant between me and you, and will multiply you exceedingly. Then Abraham fell on his face; and God said to him; Behold, my covenant is with you, and you shall be the father of a multitude of nations. No longer shall your name be Abram, but your name shall be Abraham; for I have made you the father of a multitude of nations. And God made a new covenant with Abraham, and then said, As regards Sarai your wife, you shall not call her name Sarai, but Sarah shall be her name. I will bless her, and moreover I will give you a son by her; I will bless her and she shall be a mother of nations; kings of peoples shall come from her. Abraham laughed and said to himself, Shall a child be born to a man who is a hundred years old? Shall Sarah, who is ninety years old, bear a child? And Abraham said to God, Oh that Ishmael might live in thy sight! God said, No, but Sarah your wife will bear you a son, and you shall call his name Isaac. I will establish my covenant with him as an everlasting covenant for his descendants after him. As for Ishmael, I have heard you; behold, I will bless him and make him fruitful and multiply him exceedingly; he shall be the father of twelve princes, and I will make him a great nation. But I will establish my covenant with Isaac, whom Sarah shall bear to you at this season next year.*

So it came to pass, in the region of Beersheba, that Abraham and Sarah became the proud parents of Isaac. It was whilst they were in this place, that God would test Abraham once more, but this time it concerned his son Isaac. God said to him, *Take your son, your only son Isaac, whom you love, and go to the land of Moriah and offer him there as a burnt offering on one of the mountains I shall point out to you. Abraham rose early next morning, saddled his donkey, and took with him two of his young men, and his son Isaac. He chopped wood for the burnt offering, and set out for the place to which God had directed him. On the third day, Abraham looked up and saw the place in the distance, and he said to the young men, Stay here with the donkey. The boy and I will go over there to worship, and then we will come back to you. Abraham took the wood for the burnt offering, and laid it on Isaac his son. He carried in his hand the fire and the knife. As the two of them went on together, Isaac spoke to Abraham, his father, Father! And Abraham replied, Yes my son? Isaac said, the fire and the wood are here, but where is the lamb for the sacrifice? Abraham replied, God himself will provide the lamb for the sacrifice.*

They went on, the two of them together, until they came to the place to which God had directed them. When Abraham had built the altar, and set the wood on it, he bound his son Isaac, and laid him on the wood. He then stretched out his hand to seize the knife and slay his son. But the angel of God called to him from heaven, Abraham! Abraham! And he said, Here I am. Do not lay your hand on the boy; do not harm him, for now I know that you fear God, and you have not held back from me your only son. Abraham looked around, and saw behind him a ram caught by its horns in a bush. He offered it as a burnt offering in place of his son. Abraham named the place 'The Lord will provide.' And the saying has lasted to this day. God was happy with these events and promised, I will surely bless you and make your descendants as numerous as the stars in the sky, and the sand on the seashore. Your descendants will take possession of the lands of their enemies. All the nations of the earth will be blessed through your descendants, because you have obeyed me. Then Abraham returned to his servants, and they set off together for Beersheba, and it was there that he stayed. Sarah lived until she was a hundred and twenty-seven years old. She died near Hebron in the land of Canaan. Abraham didn't own any of the land, being a sojourner, and he didn't have a plot in which to bury Sarah. He approached the Hittite community, and said to them, I am only a stranger among you; give me a burial place among you, so that I may bury my dead. The Hittites replied, Hear us, my lord. You are God's prince among us; bury your dead in the best of our tombs; none of us would refuse you a tomb to bury your dead.

There followed a lot of bartering, which resulted in Abraham purchasing the tomb and the field in Machpelah, to the east of Mamre, for which he paid four hundred silver coins. Then

Abraham buried his wife Sarah in the cave of Machpelah. The unused field, and the cave that is in it, were given to Abraham as a possession for the burying place, by the Hittites. When Abraham died at the age of a hundred and seventy-five, he too was buried in the cave with his wife Sarah. It became the final resting place of Isaac, Rebekah and Leah. In the story of Joseph we heard that, when his father Jacob died in Goshen, Joseph had his physician embalm him, before they journeyed from Egypt, in order to bury him in the cave in the field of Machpelah; the cave which was to become known as the Cave of the Patriarchs: in the heart of the Hittite country.'

Granddad took a long deep breath, and whilst looking at me, and rubbing his hands together said, 'Now you can see that although they dispersed over hundreds of years, they remained intermingled and intermarried, so there we go!' I couldn't really go anywhere, because I had two queries regarding Abraham which I put to him. The first concerned God's covenant, in which he appeared to be telling Abraham that he was to be a sojourner on earth, having all he needed to survive, with power and riches, but with responsibility for a nation; and he would need to exercise his power for the greater good, and not merely for himself. He would not own any land in his lifetime, since God had told him that it would be his descendants who would inherit the land, but that he would have a long life on earth, and a permanent and happier one in heaven, if he only remembered the Covenant they had made. If his descendants listened to his teaching, they too would have an eternal reward. Granddad listened carefully, and then said ruefully, 'Well! That seems to sum it; you see when we leave this world we can't take anything with us: only the knowledge that we have done our best to help others, and we can be happy knowing that it was the right thing to have done. For my part, I hope to pass on as much wisdom as possible, before I join your Grandma.' I could see that he immediately regretted having made that statement, as he continued very quickly, 'Still! We have another journey to complete which promises to be a lot of fun.'

Although I agreed that it would be wonderful for us to launch into the last stage of, what had seemed to be an epic journey, there was one other question which I needed to ask beforehand. He always seemed to know when there was a question pending, or when there was something bothering me. He had stopped talking and was waiting, until I blurted out that I wasn't sure about the story of Abraham and his son Isaac; because God had asked Abraham to sacrifice his only son, but at the very last moment stopped him from doing so; yet, he had sent his own son to be a sacrifice for all of us. Why? Granddad had taken my hand, and looking at me very steadily said, 'The answer to that question, my little friend, is love. Abraham was tested to his limit, but was prepared to make the necessary sacrifice, in order to prove that his love for God was greater than his love for his own son. Later God chose to send his own son to be sacrificed in order to prove how much he loved mankind, hoping that we in turn would begin to understand. That love however is a very deep love, which over time and, maybe because of suffering, becomes a compassionate love. To know that type of love, you may need to wait until you are older, but I am very glad you asked the question.

OK! Right then, we have put Abraham to rest in the heart of the Hittite country, and we hope now to form a connection between the Hittites, the Hyksos, and our friends the Celts, or men of iron. There is, of course, the ongoing problem... where to start, and how much information you need to keep your picture concise.' He had begun to run his hand over his bald head, which he often seemed to do when he was trying to find answers. Noticing his discomfort, I almost blurted out what I had been doing in the garden, and had put my hand up, forgetting that I was not in school. We were both laughing, as I decided that I didn't have to say exactly where; instead I said that I had been checking, and checking, and re-checking all the lists, as well as looking at the maps and reading the story again, and again in the books of Genesis and Exodus, because I wanted to extend my outline story.

The elders had often laughed at my serious look when I needed to concentrate on what I was telling them; even Granddad had commented on the line between my eyebrows, saying that it would be a deep furrow before I was grown up. I always tried to do as I was told, but in that situation, I found that, if I focused on keeping my eyebrows straight, I forgot the essence of my story; until I decided that it was going to be me, with my furrows, and that was that. Granddad, who was looking at me quizzically, seemed to make a snap decision. 'Now that's wonderful, and it might be good for me to hear your version, before you add it to your own outline.' Oops! I thought, how can I make it real, and fun, since I am not in the garden? Yes, Granddad could be Japheth, up near the Black Sea, and that would provide the perspective for the remainder. He was laughing as I explained, but then it was time to be serious. Having related my experience, I told him that I was really interested in Ham, and his son Canaan. Granddad took my hand and said, 'You have been working very hard, and I think you have a good understanding, but now it is time for a break, for two reasons: we need some refreshments and you need some space and time to think about what I've told you. When we return, we are going to concentrate on the Hittites: meanwhile don't forget what I said about Abraham, who set out with his father to live in Canaan, although his father didn't complete the journey having died on the way. Also, after his sojourn in Egypt he returned to Canaan, where he settled amongst the Hittites... more about that later.'

Granddad was right about my need for space, and nobody seemed to worry when I took myself out-of-doors, which I needed to do on that occasion, whilst Mum prepared a drink. It was to be a brief escape: to the top garden, and my new-found friends, since I needed to re-connect with my earlier visit and bring myself up-to-date. I also wished to get back to the dining room and read, for myself, what Granddad had read to me. I knew from the Table of Nations, that Canaan's second son was called Heth, and his tribe became known as the Hittites. So far I was happy with all the main characters which we had covered; I heard many of them mentioned in the readings, which we had at Church; some had appeared in my children's story books, and Granddad had been at pains to enlighten me further. However, I had not heard the name Hittites until Granddad began his story, although I had seen references to them as I had read the Bible, yet they suddenly appeared to be a big deal, in the offing. A quick look at the index list in the Reference Bible revealed numerous entries for those people. Realising that there wouldn't be time to check the entries because my drink was waiting I joined Granddad and Mum in the kitchen. I had just one question, and it couldn't wait... Why were the Hittites so important? I repeated the question to Granddad as soon as I arrived, adding that I had looked at the number of times they appeared in the index. Sensing my frustration, Granddad looked at Mum, saying, 'It seems that this question won't wait... perhaps we could take our drinks with us.'

On our way to the dining room, I continued with other questions, which had bugged me each time I looked at the dispersal map. I had difficulty understanding why Ham's other three sons took off to Egypt. As their father, wouldn't Ham have journeyed to each district, to reassure himself; I thought that that's what parents did? If Abraham could travel from Ur to Canaan, then on to Egypt, and back to Canaan, wasn't it possible that others travelled those routes: there and back again? The map had shown clearly where the sons of Japheth, Ham and Shem had settled. In time they would become parents, grandparents, uncles, and so on, so that they would be the heads of their tribes.

I told him that even though I enjoyed the Abraham story, I had become lost when I thought about it afterwards. I had re-checked the table of nations, and also read what Josephus had said about them; in particular Ham's son Misraim, where he wrote: *Egypt, The memory also of the Mesraites is preserved in their name; for all we who inhabit this country [of Judea], call Egypt Mestre, and the Egyptians Mestreans.* But none of that explained why they went there; nor why Heth, whose tribe became known as the Hittites, should be any more important than his brothers? 'Oh my goodness, I can begin to see why you are upset. Now, you enjoy your drink, whilst I worry about how to unravel those questions.'

CHAPTER VIII

THE HITTITES IN CANAAN

Granddad appeared to be busy loading his pipe, as he surveyed the papers and maps which lay on the table. Preparing to light it, he turned to me saying: 'you know you don't need to worry about this next stage, because we have done all we needed to do, and I think you understand it so far. I simply want you to relax and enjoy what we are about to discover regarding the Hittites, but a quick re-cap will help to focus our minds, then we will be looking at two distinct areas which we need to examine, namely: the Bible story, and the archaeological discoveries. We believe that the Bible is a spiritual story which describes people, their lives and their journeys, and I will tell you how the Old Testament has been brought to life by archaeologists who discovered the first clay tablets, which helped to enforce the validity of the Hittites.

Don't forget that we have been looking back over the last 10,000 years, when people began to form tribes of very large numbers, who lived in the fertile plains, namely the Mesopotamian region, and that area of the Nile, which we call Egypt. Their inhabitants were divided into two groups, those who became nomads and lived in tents, and those who built villages, which they would later defend. We believe that about 3,500 years BC there were two main empires centred on the plains of Egypt and Chaldea, which is near the confluence of the Tigris and Euphrates rivers. Chaldeans were the more progressive of the two, having constructed walls of baked clay and invented writing, whilst in other parts of the world at that time people were still living in caves. More importantly they had formed a properly organised system of government. The two empires maintained contact with each other, for reasons of trade. The trade routes they used took them through the small country called Canaan, later known as Palestine or the Holy Land. In fact, it was the same route, which if you remember was used by Abraham. They became empires because they knew how to grow and develop. Unfortunately their growth sometimes relied on power and greed, which gave rise to conflict and loss of life. That was the situation, which existed before the flood.

You have already told me that Noah and his sons would have taken all their skills on board the Ark, including those handed down by Tubal-Cain, who was known as the forger of bronze and iron; remember the beginning of Genesis. Don't forget though, that they would also have taken their memory of how they had developed, and where. We can assume that their first concern, after the flood, would have been to restore what had existed before, and then move on from there. We believe that approximately 420 years elapsed between Noah and Abraham, with eight generations between them. I have referred to the two great empires, which existed before the flood, namely Egypt and Chaldea, but after the flood three major empires ruled for a time; they were Egypt, Babylonia and Assyria. Their main overland route would have been the same as before, although they carved another route further inland, and by that time, they had built ships, which enabled them to travel further by sea. We can see from our map where Canaan settled, and where Heth, who was his second son, was established. Canaan's tribe had become known as Canaanites, and Heth's descendants became known as Hittites. One of the confusing aspects of reading about the Hittites is that they are also sometimes referred to as Canaanites. By the way, when you checked the entries for the Hittities in the Concordance Bible, did you count how many there were?' I admitted that I had done so, but confessed that as I counted up to fifty three entries, I had become upset, because I couldn't imagine having to read that many stories. Granddad had begun to laugh, 'Now I can see why you were a bit distraught...I also understand why you have sometimes become frustrated with the extent and complication of this story.' He was smiling at my discomfort as he continued, 'Yes, I know how you are feeling, but introducing you to the Bible wasn't merely a means of opening up your spiritual horizon. In fact the real reason has been to allow you to see for yourself, how and where the smelting of iron began, and re-emerged. As you know, Kilfenora – the town of the Celtic Crosses – where Grandma grew up, was her inspiration to uncover the real story of the Celts.

However, I haven't yet told you about the archaeological discoveries which occurred in 1906. Were it not for those dedicated enthusiasts, our own story would have remained simply our point of view. The archaeological finds confirmed that the Hittites were responsible for producing iron, and as a consequence became a powerful Nation: a war-like people who established themselves in Anatolia, now Turkey. That is the historical story, which is developing as man continues to uncover further proof. It is a fascinating study for scholars whose debates will sometimes be conflicting...but I don't need to burden you with that right now, later maybe.

The real story, as we know it, started with Tubal-Cain, before the Flood, and re-emerged with Noah and his sons after the Flood. Since I would like to feel that you have a full understanding of the background to the Hittites, I want us to read the end of Noah's story, where we are told of Noah's reaction, when Shem and Japheth told him that Ham had discovered him naked and drunk in his tent. They had walked backwards into the tent and covered their father, whilst keeping their heads turned away. When Noah was sober and learnt what his youngest son had done to him, he said: *A curse on Canaan! He will be a **slave** to his brothers...Canaan will be the slave of Shem. May God cause Japheth to increase! May his descendants live with the people of Shem! Canaan will be the slave of Japheth.* There lies the foundation of what follows.

Your question regarding Heth's identity, and importance, is woven into the story because of Canaan. Remember that, before the Hittites came into being, Heth was a Canaanite, because he was of the tribe of Canaan. The two names are intertwined like a hand in a glove. Grandma and I believed that over time people referred to Canaanites, when they meant Hittites. You have said that you found fifty-three entries for Hittites in the Concordance Bible, but with the exception of a few, the entries refer to them merely in connection with other named tribes. However, it is still worth mentioning the few.

The first reference is to Esau, Jacob's twin brother, who disgraced his family by marrying a Hittite woman, as well as a Hivite woman, resulting in their tribe, who became known as Edomites, being half Hittite and half Semite. You can see on your map that Edom is adjacent to Canaan. The second reference is to the burial place of Abraham, and you will begin to see the importance of his story, since it tells you that initially he set out with his father to travel from Ur to Canaan. After his father's death he set out again, arriving in Shechem; here we are told that the Hittites were in the land of Canaan at that time. Abraham travelled to Egypt, later returning to Canaan, where he settled. When his wife Sarah died, he negotiated with the Hittites to buy the field with the tomb, where she and other members of his family are buried. Remember particularly the interchange between Abraham and Ephron the Hittite: *I am only a stranger among you; give me a burial place among you, so that I may bury my dead.* The Hittites replied, *hear us, my lord. You are God's prince among us; bury your dead in the best of our tombs; none of us would refuse you a tomb to bury your dead.* You can see that they were already worthy of note. One other reference to them occurs in the Second Book of Samuel, since King David chose Uriah the Hittite to be part of his mighty army, because he was also known to be an upright man.

Well that was a brief summary of the Hittites as far as the Bible is concerned. Now, can you tell me what a nomad is?' I replied that I thought it meant wanderer! 'Yes it is that and more.' Granddad was smiling as he decided to find a simple analogy for me. 'We have our own nomads in this country, as you already know. They are known as travellers, but we call them tinkers, because repairing tin buckets and other items is one of their main skills. You will have seen them mending pots, and trying to sell jewellery and other items to your Mum: some of which they will have acquired on their travels, but other articles they will have made themselves; I might add that they are no mean crafts people. Sadly they are not literate, because they have no formal teaching, and they are of no fixed abode. They were not originally nomads by choice, but represented many who had their lands taken from them by the English landlords.

Over a period of time, travelling became a way of life for them. Although the groups vary in size, they remain small in number, and they can be seen travelling the road in their horse drawn carriages, with a few goats tied to the back; the goats are needed to provide milk, but they often ask a farmer for milk, as part payment for work which they have carried out. As a rule they use what we call common land as a temporary place to reside, but occasionally they park themselves on a farmer's land; most farmers are very tolerant for a short period, but need to keep an eye on their fowl. I know there is very little comparison between their numbers, and that of the people who started in the Fertile Crescent, except that they all had small beginnings, and would at times have felt dispossessed.

Now civilisation and cultural refinement could have been a major problem for those people. It would take too much time to describe in detail, how they endeavoured to serve their gods, but you know what happened in the story of Babel. When God confused their language they were compelled to move to new territories, with a new identity. However, they continued to progress in agriculture, mining, trading and seafaring, the arts and later in science. In addition, they became very proficient crafts people, where the men focused on metalwork and all types of heavy material, and the women concentrated on textile craft, where they excelled. So when you see Mum doing her creative work, you will know that it had its roots in those very early times. However, in order to make real progress, they needed to adopt a civilised approach, particularly when they travelled, and wished to sell their wares. For instance, they couldn't barge into another city, and expect to be treated in a civil manner, unless they observed a decent code of behaviour. Occasionally it seemed to be the case that a leader became too powerful and domineering, wanting even more, and deciding to attack and overthrow his neighbouring kingdom or city. Further complications arose when the nomadic tribes wished to establish a firm base, by invading someone else's territory.

The tinker's story relates to the small families, but our eastern friends grew from clans to tribes, until they became as many as the specks on the ground, fulfilling the promise made to Abraham: *I shall make your descendants like the dust on the ground; when people succeed in counting the specks of dust on the ground, then they will be able to count your descendants too!* Their reason for moving would have been overcrowding and the need to search for fertile pasture, as with Abraham and Lot, who agreed to go in separate directions, or because they fled rather than be crushed or overcome. Whatever the reason, we know that some of the Hittite tribes moved northward into Japheth's territory, now called Turkey. It is safe to say they left their patronymic name Canaanite behind, and firmly established themselves as Hittites. We know that they built a fortified city there called Hattusa, and that it was from there that the power of the Hittite empire emerged. The question is did they discover that the area near the Black Sea was a rich source of minerals – including iron – before or after their move? It doesn't really matter, what is important is the fact that they amalgamated with the descendants of Japheth, who were already established in Anatolia. In Canaan they had become integrated with the descendants of Shem, which included the Edomite tribe. Tribal migration was an ongoing event, and it involved massive colonisation, warfare and power seeking. Later on I will refer back to this point when I talk about the Celts, but now I want to focus on the archaeological discoveries, without which, the Hittites would still be seen as a minority group living in the hills of Canaan with a few other tribes.

History is a fascinating subject, because it tells us about past events which often impact on the present; what happened before events were recorded is described as a myth or legend, and often ascribed to imagery, and the gods. Indeed, that is the manner in which the Bible came to be viewed by many until historical proof became available. The evidence came to light with the discovery of the first 10,000 clay tablets in 1906, and with the further discovery of ruins in the Hittite capital of Hattusa in Anatolia. That was just the beginning, since thousands of additional tablets, documents and artefacts were unearthed as the ruins were explored. Those tablets changed the face of history where the Hittites were concerned. Until then they were known as the dark, fearsome descendants of Heth who lived near Canaan. However, the discoveries revealed that they had become a major empire, ruling from Hattusa in Anatolia, and extending as far as Mesopotamia and Syria. The Egyptians had also kept records but their recording system was not exactly the same as the Hittites.

We won't go into detail about how the discoveries came about, but I know you will want more information later. The Hittites used cuneiform script and the Egyptians used hieroglyphs. You will feel much happier about those writing systems if you read for yourself, which you can do from the dictionary, whilst I light my pipe... just read it to me.' Finding the words became quite a procedure since Granddad needed to spell them, letter by letter, but having done so, it was fascinating to note the small pictures containing symbols alongside:

Cuneiform: wedge-shaped: applied especially to the characters anciently used in writing in Persia, Assyria, etc. or to the writing itself. When I finished reading Granddad said, 'There is some additional information which I would add, simply to make it more interesting. First of all the wedge-shaped marks were made on wet clay, using a reed stylus, similar to a pen...you use your nib pen, a development from the quill, but the ancients used reeds, which were shaped as needed. Secondly, the first clay tablets were discovered in Sumeria. One of the chief towns was Ur and you remember that Abraham lived there.'

Hieroglyphs: figure of an object standing for a word, syllable or sound, as used in ancient Egyptian and other writing. Once again Granddad commented, 'Good! Now it is believed that it was the Hittites from Anatolia, who took their knowledge of writing, and other skills, to Egypt, but how would that have come about?

Fine, now I have also been looking for an opportunity to round off the story of the Hyksos, and this would seem to be the ideal time. Although there was no reference to them in the Bible, Grandma and I read and re-read the Biblical passages on Noah, Abraham and Joseph; partly as background, and so that we could achieve a deeper understanding of that time, and those events. That exercise, and our reliance on the writings of Josephus, enabled us to reach a conclusion. For instance, we realised that, in Noah's case we could appreciate not merely why he was asked to build the ark, but also how technically accomplished he was, in order to build it according to specific instructions. We were able to conclude that ships were already being built at that time.

With regard to Abraham's time with the Egyptians, Josephus writes that: *For whereas the Egyptians were formerly addicted to different customs, and despised one another's sacred and accustomed rites, and were very angry one with another on that account, Abram conferred with each of them, and, confuting the reasonings they made use of, every one for their own practices, demonstrated that such reasonings were vain and void of truth: whereupon he was admired by them in those conferences as a very wise man, and one of great sagacity, when he discoursed on any subject he undertook; and this not only in understanding it, but in persuading other men also to assent to him. He communicated to them arithmetic, and delivered to them the science of astronomy; for before Abram came into Egypt they were unacquainted with those parts of learning; for that science came from the Chaldeans into Egypt, and from thence to the Greeks also.* I can add that he wasn't averse to fighting, as we read, when he needed to rescue his nephew from the Kings who had abducted him.

Then we come to Joseph... now there's a story which has entertained many children, and intrigued many scholars. Joseph's story has withstood the test of time, mainly because his father Jacob had given him a specially embroidered robe with long sleeves. This immediately set him apart from his brothers and brought their wrath upon him; well that's what many remember, including you before we started on this journey. Of course the deeper meaning tells us that Joseph didn't choose to be abducted; he would appear to have been destined to be in Egypt, and he is a descendant of Abraham, Isaac, and Jacob. Joseph's descendants formed two of the tribes of Israel, namely Manasseh and Ephraim.

How could Joseph be connected with the Hyksos and Hittites? We started with the Celts, hoping to reveal where they began, although not with that name. We have spoken about the Hittites who were sometimes called Canaanites, before they became a powerful nation in Anatolia; and we have the Hyksos, who were as powerful in Egypt as the Hittites were in Anatolia, but we believe, once again, that the problem is not when they went to Egypt, but how they became the formidable tribe, with the name Hyksos.

We know that an ancient civilisation developed in the river valley region of the Tigris and Euphrates, and similarly in the Nile Valley. The Canaanites were aware that Egypt was a flourishing state, as indicated by Abraham's journey when famine threatened. Although Abraham returned to Canaan, we consider that immigration was an ongoing occurrence, with some migrants returning. Those tribes would have been an amalgam of the Canaanite tribes, which no doubt would have included some of Heth's descendants. Their integration would have included sharing their skills and their possessions, which included the horses and chariots. Josephus gives a very enlightening account of the Hyksos during that period... *and there came, after a surprising manner, men of ignoble birth out of the eastern parts, and had boldness enough to make an expedition into our country, and with ease subdued it by force, yet without our hazarding a battle with them. So when they had gotten those that governed us under their power, they afterwards burnt down our cities, and demolished the temples of the gods, and used all the inhabitants after a most barbarous manner; nay, some they slew, and led their children and their wives into slavery. At length they made one of themselves king, whose name was Salatis.*

We like to think that Salatis was the ruling Pharaoh who had the dreams, which Joseph interpreted. We read in the Bible story that Joseph used his bargaining power to extort money and possessions from those who travelled to collect corn. Meanwhile, some of those powerful Hittites were pushing their way back down from the North, using the iron chariots which they had developed, and which enabled them to overpower all before them; they too would have become victims of the famine, and made their way to Egypt. Just imagine Joseph's delight when he found an opportunity to trade corn for the secret of that most powerful asset, iron.

Oh! I so wish we had lots of time, because there is so much I would like to share… still, on this occasion I must be circumspect and say that there will be a wealth of reading for you to do in the future, if you wish to pursue the subject. I realise that for you one of the distressing aspects of reading the Old Testament has been the constant warfare and bloodshed. Despite men's accomplishments, power and riches, they never seemed to be at peace. In fact the stories which unfolded as the cuneiform tablets were translated, portray a similar picture, even though they were acclaimed as highly accomplished civilisations; many of the buildings and artefacts are testimony to their intelligence and imagination. You are aware that the Bible includes a long list of Kings: so too with the Hittites, and indeed, the Egyptians. Sadly, with so many different titles for people and rulers, as well as uncertainty about dates, it has been difficult to find common ground, although there are similarities in the details.

However, we do know that trade is the most important requisite, if growth is to be maintained, and using the most efficient trade routes is essential. You already know about the tinkers peddling their wares: there is no point in producing merchandise if it can't be marketed. Take for instance two of the main powers, Egypt and Assyria: Egypt had been determined to open up the best trade route, and proceeded to conquer all those territories and people in its path. The Hittites, who had become a force to be reckoned with, became a major impediment. The battles for supremacy had gone on for a few hundred years, before culminating in the battle of Kadesh, which took place on the Orontes River, in modern day Lebanon, in 1275BC. It is supposed to be the first major battle in which disposition of troops was recorded.

In Egypt, at that time, the ruling Pharaoh was Ramases II, and the ruling Hittite King was named Muwatalli II. Both sides had developed a battle strategy in anticipation. I think you would enjoy hearing the full story surrounding that battle, because it involved spies, but this is not the right time to distract you. An account was given by the Egyptians using hieroglyphs, which appeared on the walls of temples. In Hattusa the Hittite account was recorded on clay tablets, but it is probably most renowned for the number of chariots involved, particularly because it was established that the Egyptians had taken delivery of a few thousand chariots some time beforehand.

When the battle reached a deadlock, with heavy losses on both sides, and neither side prepared to cede, but not wishing to retreat either, it was agreed that there should be a cessation of hostilities. However, the treaty, which is referred to as the Treaty of Kadesh, didn't take place for another fifteen years. Meanwhile there were many skirmishes between the opposing sides, but the Hittites retained control of Kadesh, and the Egyptians had to bow to pressure for the sake of commerce. The Treaty, which was created in c.1259BC, was drawn up by the Hittites, and inscribed on a silver tablet, which was delivered to Ramases II. The Egyptians produced their own version, but included some of the content of the silver tablet, so we are told. Although the outcome of the Treaty was to be peace, it remained an uneasy peace, because the Egyptians had failed to conquer Kadesh. Now, alas we must leave it there.' I couldn't suppress the sigh, which escaped when he finished, since the detail would have been exciting, and it had a peaceful ending... as Granddad had said, time, or lack of it, could be very frustrating!

CHAPTER IX

A DAWNING

Nan casts a brief furtive look in Liam's direction, hoping that he hasn't become despondent by the fact that she hasn't given him a direct answer to his question, regarding Granddad's reason for remaining in what seemed to be an out-of-way place. If possible, she doesn't wish to enter into a dialogue with him at this stage. Thankfully there is no reason for concern, as he is lying sprawled on a grassy patch, in the process of using a small sharp stone, and carving his initials on the smooth rock nearby. The scratching stops momentarily, and she realises that he is waiting for her to continue. Hurriedly she transports herself back to the dining room, where Granddad is waiting to continue his journey.

"Somehow Liam, it all seems so real now; as though it is the recent past and not all those years ago: even the aroma of the bread and scones, which Mum had been baking had filtered through to the dining room. The aroma reminded me that I should really have been in the kitchen helping, but I also needed to know what was coming next. Granddad began to laugh, as he too had inhaled the delicious smell of home baking, and sensing my feelings declared, 'I could keep you locked up here for ever and a day, but I think your Mum would never forgive me. Even then it would be impossible for me to share all that I would wish; still there will be more time later.

We have really immersed ourselves in these past weeks, and I am glad to see that you have been able to keep up with me. I don't for one moment feel that you will regret it, even though I know it's just an overview. As I've already said, the most difficult part for me has been condensing a wealth of information, whilst hoping to open many doors for you.

It grieves me to say that I will need to continue in the same vein, but so be it. Before I move on though, there are certain issues, which I would like to look at, and the first one is to establish what the word Celt means. We are told that the Latin name for Celt or Kelt is *Celtae*, and the Greek name is *Kelto* or *Keltoi*. A Celt is known as *a race of central and western Europe, described by the Romans as tall, blond, and large bodied*, or, *An individual of any of various Celtic-speaking peoples, including the ancient Gauls, the Britons and the modern Bretons, Welsh, Irish and Gaelic Scots.* We know that those are the people believed to have come to Ireland about 700 BC. The second issue and a real teaser for me is that, whilst we accepted the facts which we were given, Grandma and I needed to develop the theory. For instance, we needed to examine Greek and Irish mythology, both of which complemented all our other sources of information.

When you are an adult, you may wish to have a look at Greek mythology, and in particular, read about a man named Homer, who was an epic poet. He produced two great poems, the Iliad and the Odyssey. The Iliad describes what happened in the Trojan War, which took place between Greece and Troy. The Odyssey tells us how Odysseus secured victory for Greece in the Trojan War. We believe that Homer described the beginnings of Greek history. I know that you have heard the story of the Trojan horse, and I have a particular reason for mentioning Homer now, but we will come to that. Otherwise, we needn't concern ourselves too much with Greek mythology, at this stage. Irish mythology is another matter altogether, but apart from the mythological stories you have read and heard, it hasn't been a suitable subject for you.

So far, we have read about many places and discussed many people, all of which should merge as we take on our final hurdle. So, in order to simplify our task, we are going to tidy the table and lay out all the relevant lists and maps we have compiled, or discussed. Then, in your best writing, I want you to identify each document and make your own master list.' Well that got to me, and I couldn't suppress the giggles, but to avoid seeming rude I needed to explain. Fortunately he seemed to be light hearted; that could have been because we were on our homeward journey. I told him that I felt as though I was already back at school, even though we weren't due to restart for a few weeks. In which case, could I tell my friends that I had been doing a summer school. He had laughed loudly, and replied, 'I like that, and yes you have been working diligently, but don't forget life is about learning, as well as living. It is really a lifelong journey, and even at my grand old age I realise that there is so much I don't know, so I too will go on learning. Our own journey over these past weeks has been a huge exercise for me, because I have needed to develop the best means of inspiring you to do the same. But I don't want your Mum's wrath descending on me again, and so we must make haste; we both know that when the cooking is finished, there will be a need for a spare pair of hands in the kitchen. Yet, I need you now to put those hands to good use to produce the list.' Having found a name for our exercise made me feel good; summer school described it well.

It didn't take long, and I proceeded with my list, as Granddad read the descriptions to me.

Adam and Eve, with their descendants (Two main characters Lamech and Noah).
Lamech (Cain's son), and sons; refers to the beginning of metal forging.
Noah and sons.
Noah's sons and grandsons.
Bible Names of Noah's sons and grandsons, with dispersal description by Josephus
Map indicating dispersal of Noah's sons and grandsons.
Map indicating the dispersal of the descendants of Heth

(Hittites) the great grandson of
Noah through Ham and Canaan.

When the list was ready Granddad said, 'Can you now look at
the outline you wrote, in conjunction with your new list: it should
give you a solid foundation.' Having gone back to my early
account, I read about God's provision, and man's refusal to listen;
all the way through to Abraham, when the hope was for a new
beginning. I read the outline account to Granddad, and having
discussed it, and reassured himself that I was comfortable with it
he went on, 'Here now, let me borrow your copybook, and I will
write in the names: Shem, Terah, Abraham, Isaac, Jacob, Twelve
Tribes of Israel and Moses. Our friend Josephus tells us that it
was Moses, who was seven generations removed from Abraham,
who led the Israelites out of Egypt. The Book of Exodus tells us
that the Israelites had been in Egypt for 430 years.

Finally, The Book of Genesis tells us that Jacob's sons were
named: Reuben, Simeon, Levi, Judah, Issachar, Zebulun, Joseph,
Benjamin, Dan, Naphtali, Gad and Asher. The descendants of
these sons were the tribes who were to be led out of Egypt by
Moses. In the Book of Genesis Joseph had assigned his sons
Manasseh and Ephraim to be heads of their own tribes."

Whilst he was writing and speaking, I listened and studied the
papers before me: being constantly aware of the tantalising aroma
coming through from the kitchen. Granddad must have been
similarly tempted, because he placed the pen and book on the
table, picked up the Bible, and proceeded to find the maps at the
back. Then pointing to one, which said The Twelve Tribes of
Canaan, also called Israel, he gave me such a wicked grin as he
said, 'I am going to take my courage in both hands, and venture
to the kitchen; there's got to be something nice to eat, with a cup
of tea, but I will need to be very circumspect and ask your Mum
to release you until we have completed our present task. While I

am away you can use the quiet moments to build a mental picture: look at the lists, maps, tribes, and this map in the Bible which confused you earlier. Now, what do you think of that?' Still tickled by his grin I quipped, 'I think my stomach might be happier, but I don't understand what circumspect means; are you going to tease Mum too?' 'I will explain when I return if it works, but I mustn't use any pressure, because that could be my undoing where your Mum is concerned.'

Well then, I wouldn't feel any pressure either: he would forgive me and help me out of the quagmire if I got stuck, and I knew he would be away for some time. What of course I didn't realise, until I was much older, was how well he timed his breaks. The quietness in the room was intended to help me to home in on the scene before me, and I appeared to have all the material I needed. Except that the scale of the Bible map was different to that of the ones I had used earlier and that foxed me. When I tried to compare them, I became thoroughly confused then miserable, as I thought, 'Oh dear, you are not on a sound footing yet.' At which point I gave up the ghost, and decided to wait for the Master: but not before I had noticed that Dan's tribe appeared to have settled in two areas some considerable distance apart. Meanwhile, I tried to think about all we had discussed, as I surveyed the table. I could take time to acknowledge and be grateful for all he had taught me, and to marvel at his patience; but I so wished that I knew for sure, why such an accomplished man had chosen to live in that out-of-the-way place; I had begun to suspect, but would I ever get him to confirm my suspicions, only time would tell.

The dining room door was ajar, and I didn't hear him approach until he whispered, 'Success. Look what I've got, and some extra time as well, but we must make a space for the tray.' What a conspirator I thought, as we moved the papers, but I realised that we were to continue our quest as we enjoyed our refreshments. I had no quibble with that, since I was eager to ask the first question: why had Dan appeared twice in the map, in such small areas, and how big was the land area which all those people occupied? Granddad said, 'Ah! I see you have overtaken me, but that is good. Now, if I said that the whole area of Canaan was approximately 10,000 square miles, and Ireland measures 32,524 square miles, we may be able to see that the area occupied by those tribes is slightly less than one third the size of Ireland. Does that help you?' I had to admit that it didn't just then, I couldn't stretch my imagination that far, but would be able to think about it later. He answered the question about Dan by saying, 'Well he was only allocated one portion of land but that's a story for another time. The important thing is, you have an idea of roughly where they all went, and you remember that they had been in Egypt for 430 years, plus another 40 years wandering in the desert, whilst they became a great nation.

I would like to take you to that area in the north of Canaan, which was occupied by Dan's tribe, and hopefully that should lead us to our homeland. I have not forgotten the Celts in Ireland, you know! For now, Dan's our man! But I won't attempt to talk through the Biblical story, which is an exciting, frustrating and often tragic account of man's struggle to survive, and in some cases, to achieve power over others. The Book of Joshua is actually the story of the Israelites incursion into Canaan. You will remember that this was the place described by God as *a land of milk and honey,* which he had chosen for them. He had passed to them the rules or Commandments necessary, if they were to live in peace. However, there were many people, including branches of the Hittites, who had not migrated into Egypt during the famine, all those years before. Just as the Israelites had increased massively in Egypt, so too had those Canaanite tribes who had remained behind. However, the Israelites had experienced a conversion during their years in the wilderness, accepting one God, and mending their ways; whilst those who had remained behind had continued to prosper materially and practice their old beliefs. It was never going to be what one would call a happy marriage; sadly over time the Danite tribes became integrated with the established tribes, eventually adopting their pagan beliefs and customs.

In your quiet moments you can read about them in the Book of Judges. In fact in the Book of Amos, you could read that the people swore by the idols of Samaria, or *by the God of Dan*. Finally, in the Book of Revelation, at the very end of The New Testament, you could also read about the Tribes of Israel, who had been marked with a special seal, it does not include the Tribe of Dan, we will discuss this later. You must thank your Grandma for the time she spent exploring those people, and for her interest in ancient cultures.'

I had nodded vigorously, but I was feeling a little impatient, because I wanted to know where it was taking me, especially as he had spoken about Irish Mythology earlier. I couldn't resist the temptation to ask him about Homer, who seemed to be an outsider in our story: what had he to do with Irish Mythology, and why was Dan the Man so important? He had sensed my impatience and replied, 'Well you have heard the story of the Trojan horse, which begins... *A long time ago...* and that's because the writers had no dates. It is mainly about war between the Greeks and Trojans, who at one time had worked well together until they fell out. Why might it be important? Because the Greeks and the Trojans were simply a mixture of all those peoples we have been talking about, and the Hittites occupied the same Anatolian lands, which were later part of Troy. But then, there would have been Hittite descendants amongst the Greeks as well. It is likely that both sides may have included many of Dan's tribe. It is sufficient to say that they became opposing groups, and this led to a ten year war, which came to a head at Troy, an ancient city state on the Turkish coast. Now, in the book entitled the Iliad, Homer describes the last twelve months of that war, which culminated in the battle for Troy.

Indeed it is Homer who gave us our first insight into the connection between Greek Mythology and Irish Mythology, because we discovered that the Greeks referred to the Danites as Danaan, and this is the term which Homer used in his writing. You know we have discussed name changing and borrowing, so just for a moment, think about all the people and their names. There would have been so many variations of Dan, which could be used for identification applied to places and people, both men and women. A small sample would be Danes, Danites, Danu, Danaan, Danube, and there would be others. However, Danaan seems to be generally accepted as part of Greek Mythology, and it interacts with Irish Mythology, providing a necessary link in our story. Even more relevant, is the knowledge that all those people who lived near the Mediterranean Sea had built ships, which were seaworthy; there is ample proof of that in the Bible. One instance in the Book of Judges tells us that *Gilead stayed beyond the Jordan and Dan, why did he abide with the ships,* and of course, there are other references. Nemed and Dan are names which appear in the early history of Ireland: we'll be discussing that shortly, and I hope you feel that it's been worth the journey.

'Oh! But Granddad I'm not really happy, and you did say that I should let you know if I didn't understand.' Granddad merely said, 'Out with it then.' 'Well I asked you earlier why Dan appeared twice on the map, and you said that he was only allocated one portion, but that you would tell me another time… and you've said just now that he wasn't given a special seal with the other tribes. I just don't know what to think; were they like black sheep?' Although my last question had made him smile, he was stroking his head in agitation as he replied, 'Goodness me, but you won't be fobbed off, and I'm not sure where you heard that last expression. However, the reason I didn't enlighten you with regard to Dan's two parcels of land, is that it is a complicated story, and although I know you like rumbustious stories with happy endings, this is not one of them. Still, let's see what we can do! I have already given you some background information regarding Dan, and I don't wish to complicate that. In the Book of Joshua, it is recounted that Moses appointed Joshua as his successor, to lead the Israelites into the Promised Land. It was he who apportioned the land, which each tribe was to inherit. Somehow it seems that the amount of land allocated to Dan's tribe was not large enough, and the neighbouring states, which included the Philistines were hostile, so that most of Dan's tribe took to the hills. The Danites were not happy or settled, and it was decided to send five warrior scouts to explore the country to the north of them. Eventually the warriors arrived at a place called Laish, near the river Jordan, where they found the inhabitants to be very peaceful and the land fertile. The inhabitants were remote from their nearest neighbours, the Sidonians, and content to keep themselves to themselves: not fearing any intrusion, they were unprotected. The warriors surveyed the whole scene and decided that this was the place for them... and this is what they reported back to the head of the tribe. Now the Book of Judges and Josephus provide much information about what followed, but I must summarise.

So Dan's tribe, who had been involved in guerrilla warfare with the neighbours, the Philistines, but without success, marshalled an army of 600 warriors and headed for Laish. However, on their scouting trip, the five warriors had stayed with a man named Micah. This man was an idolater who had his own personal priest. The priest, on being questioned as to why he was there, replied, *I have an arrangement with Micah, who pays me to serve as his priest.* Now when the army was making its way northwards, the scouts said that they should revisit Micah's house, where they removed *a wooden idol covered with silver, other idols and the ephod –* a priest's vestment – *while the priest stayed at the gate with the 600 armed men.* When the priest asked what they were doing, they told him to be quiet and said, *wouldn't you rather be a priest for a whole Israelite tribe than for the family of one man? This made the priest very happy, so he took the sacred objects and went with them.*

The reason I didn't want you to hear this story is that those warriors wiped out all the peace-loving people of Laish and renamed the city Dan after themselves. Indeed we are told that Dan's tribe was the first tribe to abandon the laws passed on by Moses, and plunge into idolatery. They retained a foothold in the south near the Philistines and in the north near the Phoenicians. Of course Phoenicia was a collective name for those two areas known as Tyre and Sidon, which were seaports. The history, which tells you how they became established is very interesting, but I'm not going to share that with you now, except to say that Sidon was Canaan's eldest son. They made a name for themselves as metal workers and seafarers, but they became renowned for the discovery and marketing of purple dye, an ecclesiastical colour: often referred as Tyrian or royal purple. Those Mediterranean ports had an abundance of molluscs, and the fluid from these supplied the main ingredient for the dye. In fact the name Phoenicia was given to Tyre and Sidon by the Greeks, because it was the name they used for the colour purple. As seafarers they were able to distribute the dye all over the Mediterranean region.

It was only a matter of time before Dan's tribe integrated with the Phoenicians, through intermarriage, and because of the trading interests. The Danites would no doubt have joined them on their seafaring expeditions... remember what I said earlier about the reference in the Book of Judges, *and Dan, why did he abide with the ships.* Now, since I have gone this far, I will take you back to the Book of Genesis, where Jacob, who knows he is going to die, and is giving his final blessing to his sons. When it was Dan's turn Jacob said, *Dan shall be a serpent in the way, a viper on the path, that bites the horses heels, making the rider fall backwards.* Having taken Laish and established themselves there, they moved on to colonise other areas in that region. Eventually Israel became a kingdom under Saul, then David and Solomon; but on the death of King Solomon the nation split into two kingdoms: the northern kingdom representing ten tribes, including Dan's was called Israel. The southern kingdom included Judah and Benjamin, who had remained loyal to the Law of Moses. Of course the story didn't end there, since much later, the Assyrians invaded the northern region, capturing and deporting the ten tribes... many went to Assyria but others may have taken to the ships. In any event, that was the downfall of Dan's tribe, and if we don't move on quickly, your Mum will be evicting us from this room.' I could see Granddad looking at me as he spoke, because I was shivering, and I could feel the tears stinging my eyes. He leant across and put his hand gently but firmly on my shoulder, 'I did have good reasons for not wishing to go down that road, but as I have repeatedly said, some things are better left until you can cope with them.' His hand was very comforting and reassuring, and when I felt able I told him I was sorry, and that it was a horrible story.

CHAPTER X

RECOGNITION

'Oh! Granddad!' The words escaped before I could contain them. He had started to load his pipe, but he seemed to be more deliberate than usual in his movements, and I felt it was going to take forever. Knowing that it was a procedure, which helped him to gather his thoughts, didn't help one iota on that occasion. I didn't understand that he intended those moments to be a bridge for me.

I hadn't really thought about Nemed and Dan, but I knew that Granddad intended to talk about them, as well as about Irish Mythology and the Celts. Rather than allow my frustration and uncertainty to completely overtake me, I laid the papers and maps on the table in front of me so that I had something to focus on. Having scanned them a few times, I realised that Gomer's dispersal map and Josephus's list were holding my attention. Finally, I took the bull by the horns, and removing both papers, I placed them in front of Granddad, who had remained smiling, but still packing the bowl of his pipe, not uttering a word. I had been told that patience is a virtue, but the waiting was so infuriating.

At length he carefully placed his unlit pipe to one side and said, 'Yes, I have teased you, but I wanted to see what you would do. We can start with Gomer in Josephus's list, which says, *those who the Greeks now call Galatians but were then called Gomerites;* but we are going to use the name familiar to us, Celts. You can see that Gomer's eldest son was called Magog, and we know that he had many descendants, including a seventh generation descendant named Nemed; so you see how this man fits into our story. Now I wish to go back to Dan's family, but only to refer to the name which the Greeks used for them - Danaan. Nemed and Danaan are at the heart of Irish Mythology, but a word of wisdom before we go on.

You know learning is a life-long gift if we are so inclined, and we have talked about progress along the way. Progress is inevitable, since all beings are gifted with intelligence, with man at the highest level. Knowledge is something which is acquired, and which grows as we learn: it has always been so. So much has been written about the development in those eastern countries: about culture, language, trade, and material development. Archaeologists and scholars have been busy trying to piece together the stories concerning those times, and some of the interpretations, following discoveries, have varied according to the storyteller, or writer. Discoveries will be ongoing, and so will the varied accounts. The account I am going to relate is one which describes what we already know, and also what we believe to be the case in many circumstances.

A long time ago, there were many myths about the Fomorians, Partholons, Nemedians Fir Bolg, Tuátha Dé Danaan, and the Milesians; they all ruled Ireland for a time. You have been told or read the stories about The Children of Lir, The Birth of Cuchulain, Deirdre of the Sorrows, The Twelve Wild Geese, Dagda's Harp, Tír na nÓg, and similar tales from our ancient past. These are the stories which had been passed on by the Celtic Bards, until they were copied down by the monks in the monasteries. What is important for us to remember is that these manuscripts provide the main background to what we know about those times. That early age was divided into periods, which included the Mythological cycle, the Ulster cycle, the Fenian cycle and the Historical cycle. We haven't time to discuss those individually, except to say that they were referred to, in general terms, as representing the Invasions of Ireland. The cycles provide us with a list of the tribal invaders, including

Cessair, dated 2957 BC, who is reputed to be a grand-daughter of Noah; we know this from what was written down by J.P. Mallory in his Annals of the Four Masters. Next came Partholon, reputed to have been a sixth generation descendant of Japheth, who came from Asia Minor in approximately 2680 BC. Then came Nemed from Scythia.

Following the Nemedians, we have the Fir Bolgs who came from Greece; it's difficult to establish a link to their forefathers, and you would need to read all the history available; but we know that with each new invasion in Ireland, the outcome meant war and conflict, with some of the invaders returning whence they had come. It is believed that these were the survivors of one such tribe. After the Fir Bolgs came the Tuatha De Danaan, and they also came from Greece in the 1890's BC, providing some of the first Kings of Tara. Finally, the tribe called the Milesians, supposed to be the ancestors of the Gael arrived and continued to furnish us with Kings. They are reputed to have been descended from Gaédal Glas, who had travelled across the Mediterranean and conquered Spain.

However, if you refer to the maps, you can see that Japheth and his sons lie closest to the Black Sea. So have a glance at Josephus's list and let's reach our conclusion, as Grandma and I did, all those years ago.

There are two routes by which our mythological, Celtic invaders would have come, but of course, they weren't named Celts at that time. At the beginning of our journey I had determined to take the Danube route, and it is the one I would favour, but we will need to identify that route in our atlas.

It seems logical to assume that, until they developed bigger, more seaworthy ships, they would have chosen the shortest sea journey. We know from our reading of the early manuscripts, that many lives were lost at sea. A close inspection of any map indicates the shortest journey from Europe to Ireland to be from France or Belgium. In time though, and with bigger ships, they would have been more adventurous; it is an exciting prospect to consider that they could easily have sailed from Greece, via the Mediterranean Sea, through the Straits of Gibralter, and on to Southern Ireland.

The invaders brought with them their culture, wealth and understanding, about the real nature of things, and how it came to be provided. We spoke at the beginning about the nature of man, and now I could mention one quality in particular: imagination, which has provided us with so many mythical stories, many of which are based on fantasy, especially those which concentrated on the Underworld, or Otherworld: and one which they portrayed as a place of everlasting beauty. In order to elaborate on that, we can think about Nemed and Danaan; it is a shame that we must confine ourselves to those two. So Nemed, as we have said, was a descendant of Magog, who came after the Partholons. They had to do battle with the Formorians, who were known to be merciless seafarers. We don't know an awful lot about them, but we read in the Bible about the ruthless sea people who lived in ships; the Formorians were also supposed to live in ships, and on islands not too far away.

Nemed's descendants suffered greatly in one battle and some returned to Greece, where they again grew in number, returning to Ireland once more, as the Fir Bolgs. Then Dan's tribe, the Danaans arrived, but they had acquired an addition to their title, Tuatha Dé, which means Celtic god: they practiced magic and sorcery. It is from them that most of your scary, folkloric stories about shape changing came about. They reigned for about four hundred years, until the Milesians arrived, and defeated them. The stories go, that they did not leave Ireland, but went underground, or to islands across the water, in order to continue their supernatural existence. Now you can see how the story of Tír na nÓg originated, and it was given that title because they believed that it was possible to skip from our earthly life to that other life and back at will! Yet you know that from your story of Oisín. The real conundrum for me is the need to bring you up-to-date with reality, without destroying your own dreams and imaginings, but if I leave it here you may wonder later why I didn't give you the complete picture: just bear with me a little longer, and later on you can tell me what you think, OK.' It had to be OK, because at that moment, I had no means of telling, and I trusted him: after all, he was my mentor.

I smiled as he continued, 'Folklore is very important, because it often has more than a grain of truth in it, and we are very fortunate in having those early documents to guide us. We have just a few days left, and then your Mum will need us to clear the table. During that time I would like you, if possible, to have a quiet look at all we've got; you may want to extend your outline story after we have finished, and as always I will be around if you need me. But not before we attempt to bring the past into the present. The story is spread out before you: in those lists, maps, books, and what we have discussed. Yet, we haven't tidied up the link between those pagan times, as we call them, and what we believe today; hopefully doing so will broaden your horizon.

You can read through the Ten Commandments, which were given to Moses. You know that they are God's Laws, which are not difficult to adhere to, but then neither are the civil laws, which we have to guide us; they were all instituted for our protection and wellbeing. In both cases, we know that breaking those laws incurs some punishment, which can be painful. Although it may not have been difficult to convey the civil laws to the masses, because there would have been regional rulers who governed the people, it seemed that many rulers were very brutal towards anyone disobeying their laws. Over a period of time the rulers came to be seen as gods in their own right.

The Commandments were given to the people of Israel, but conveying the spiritual message to such a large number of people would prove to be a major problem, because for the most part, the people would reject God's Law. What a dilemma!

We have looked at the outline chart of Bible history and we know that reasonably accurate dating is only available after the death of Solomon. Therefore, if we only read the Old Testament, the early stories may appear to be fantastical; fortunately we know that the Old Testament is actually a preparation for the New Testament, with many of the prophetic accounts being fulfilled in time. As I said there is more than a grain of truth in our legendary tales. I have also mentioned that through the prophets and the Commandments, God persisted in trying to convert people to his way of thinking; and why it appeared to fail, until he sent his son.

From the beginning, from the time of Adam and Eve, it is a fact that man has questioned the very existence of God, and has used signs and portents. We know that man used his imagination and many skills to make incredible advances in so many areas; but he could not see into the future, and there in a sense lies the problem. So there were millions of people trying to give real meaning to their existence: some were good people and others were evil. Even some of the Israelites, who were trying to follow the spiritual rules, found that when times became difficult, they began to struggle with their new ideals, and eventually slipped back into their old ways.

Really there are two main points to remember here: the first you have covered yourself in your outline story, when you said that, *In the beginning God created the heavens and the earth:* the second point is that God sent his son Jesus, as his most loving gesture.

Incidentally, I know how you feel about your invisible friend, and you've said that it is difficult to understand why he would willingly give up his life for us. I am happy that you have that realisation, but at the same time I am concerned that you will be able to present a more grown up account when you are older, and now is the perfect time to start. So who really was this man who uttered from the cross, *Father, forgive them, they know not what they do.* He was a Jew who would be condemned by his own people. His life story is one of simplicity, with a very humble background: a carpenter by trade. When he set out on his special ministry, he had no home and no fine clothes: only the clothes on his back. You already know many of the stories concerning those three years, and I'm sure that you will want to read the remainder for yourself, as time goes by.

It also seems that our friend Josephus, a Jew himself: born only four years after the crucifixion, when it was still fresh in people's minds, couldn't accept that Jesus was merely human, because he wrote in his own account, *Now, there was about this time Jesus, a wise man, if it be lawful to call him a man, for he was a doer of wonderful works – a teacher of such men as receive the truth with pleasure. He drew over to himself both many of the Jews, and many of the Gentiles. He was the Christ.* Now you can see where the name originated: it was the Greek name for the Hebrew Messiah. What a dilemma for him growing up at a time of such spiritual confusion: what an enormous task he undertook, and what it cost him!

We know now that there are many faiths, or religions, with the main ones being Judaism, Christianity and Islam. Indeed there are many more, but I simply must concentrate on the Druids and the Celts: the Druids who were the ancient Celtic priests. Perhaps we can ask ourselves, where did they come from, and when they came to our shores, what else did they bring with them apart from their knowledge of iron? The Druids go back into the mists of time: they are also some of the people we have been discussing throughout these past weeks, without identifying them.

You have read the book of Exodus, where it describes God's plan for his chosen people, who were to be the forerunners in the salvation story. The children of Israel left Egypt and journeyed to Mount Sinai, where they received the Commandments, then on to Moab where Moses, who knew that he wasn't going to enter the Promised Land with them, gave them specific instructions on how to proceed when they entered the land of Canaan.

The second half of the Book of Deuteronomy records the instructions given by Moses. *When you come into the land which the Lord your God gives you, you shall not learn to follow the abominable practices of those nations. There shall not be found among you any one who burns his son or his daughter as an offering, anyone who practises divination, a soothsayer, or an augur, or a sorcerer, or a charmer, or a medium, or a wizard, or a necromancer. For whoever does these things is an abomination to the Lord; and because of these abominable practices the Lord your God is driving them out before you. You shall be blameless before the Lord your God. For these nations, which you are about to dispossess, give heed to soothsayers and to diviners; but as for you; the Lord your God has not allowed you to do so.*

No wonder the Celts were described as barbarous people, but that is the culture, which they and their predecessors brought with them; and as I have told you already, it forms the background to many of our mythical stories. However, the Druids had many admirable practices as well. Among their tribes there were learned men who, as priests, could act as judges when disputes arose. Over time two other categories emerged who were called lawyers, or *brehons*, and poets, or *filidh*; However, it is to the filidh that we owe most gratitude, because as well as composing and reciting poetry, they became a sort of mental storehouse for all our ancient mythological stories, and legendary accounts, and were often referred to as bards and storytellers.

So, next time you don't feel like memorising something for school, just remember that it took the filidh anything from twelve to twenty years to reach their particular level of expertise, since none of their information was written down, but committed to memory instead, and passed from generation to generation. That remained the case until the Monks arrived, when over a period of time, a written record was produced; but that wouldn't have taken place until after Saint Patrick arrived, and had his encounter with the Druids. You remember that at the beginning we spoke about Lóegaire, son of Niall of the Nine Hostages, who summoned Saint Patrick to his Palace, so that he could account for his actions, and you know the outcome of that meeting, which brought Christianity face to face with Paganism. It has to be said that not all of the Celtic festivals have been wiped out. Instead, many of them were adopted and Christianised. For instance, you know that Halloween, which is celebrated on the 31st October, has its roots in those early times, but we also celebrate the Feast of All Saints on the 1st November, and All Souls on the 2nd. Now a final word about the two names which I asked you to keep in mind, namely Nemed and Danaan. We have looked at Dan in some detail, but I want to conclude with a reference to Nemed, who was a descendant of Gomer's son Magog; but only to say that we established that Niall of the Nine Hostages is reputed to be a descendant of Nemed.'

CHAPTER XI

ROUND AND ABOUT

'Áine.' That was the name he used when he wanted to attract my attention; I realised that I had been looking through the window, apparently lost in my own thoughts. 'You have had a faraway look in your eyes for some time now and I am wondering whether you were listening to what I've been saying?'

I had been listening, but my thoughts had been running alongside a rather wicked idea, which had crept in as he had been speaking about all those people and their situations. Had he not noticed the mischievous glint in my eye, and did I dare tell him that with the lovely aroma of cooking still drifting into the room, I couldn't help thinking of Mum: what was she doing, and what would her reaction have been if she been through my experience with Granddad over the previous weeks, but I knew the answer to that one. Then I tried to imagine what the result might have been if she had taken all those people and put them in a huge pie; would it have been a tasty dish to set before anyone? Granddad had a good sense of humour; nevertheless, I hesitated before I said that I hoped he wouldn't be cross with me.

'Unless you tell me, I can't tell you, so let's have it,' Granddad said. His smile was reassuring, and I couldn't remain solemn, as I told him about the mixumgatherum pie. He momentarily forgot that Mum wasn't far away as he laughed loudly; then putting his finger to his lips he said, 'I don't think we had better share that with your Mum, do you?' When the merriment subsided he went on to say, 'Provided you were able to understand what I was telling you I am happy, but I did say earlier that I would ask you how you felt.' I hadn't forgotten his promise, and had been wrestling with a host of emotions; wasn't it my confused thinking which had given rise to the wicked idea.

'Yes, I have been able to follow your story because you are my patient and wonderful Granddad, and I will always remember this time. I have learned so much from you, and I will want to chase those people when I am older. I have learned so much more about the Bible too, and I promise to read it as a book because you have cared enough to share your story with me. I know I have a lot to learn, but if you asked me whether I was happier, I would have to say that my feelings are very mixed. You have taken me round in circles many times, and it was good to learn some of the background to Niall of the Nine Hostages; I will find it easier to understand our early history when I am back at school. The whole story is as you have said: inspiring, exciting, frustrating, and saddening at times. I couldn't help thinking, as you were speaking, that all those people came from the Bible Lands, but their culture was one of paganism and conflict. Yet in Ireland Saint Patrick didn't use force; he tried to convey a message of peace, compassion and understanding, and it seemed to work when people listened to him. But we still have conflict, not just in Ireland but throughout the world; and I know that because I often hear you all discussing different problems.'

Granddad nodded his head as he replied, 'Unfortunately, unless man changes his attitude and approach to life, the problems will remain, but you and I will do our best. Now, was there anything else?' Yes, indeed there was, since I hadn't shared with him the thoughts and feelings, which I had experienced since I created the pattern in the meadow. It had given me a lot of food for thought, and given rise to many questions, which I couldn't answer for myself. I had done more than create a circle; I had created a spiral, starting from the outside and working inwards to the centre. I had been thinking about the importance of the circle for all those early people, and how they came to understand its significance. I had a mind-blowing experience when I tried to identify the many circular objects, which they would have seen. Even watching Tiny, my dog, trying to catch his tail, provided an endless challenge for him and a lot of fun for me, particularly over those previous weeks, as I tried to keep pace with so much input: when I too felt that I would never catch up with myself.

Quite often on a winter's evening, when we were younger, Mum would draw for us, in order to quieten us before bedtime. She loved to draw animals, stage by stage, and we were asked to guess what the animal was, as she built up its many parts. Granddad, on the other hand, loved to draw plant life and trees. His drawings were painstaking, showing the veins on the different specimens. He loved to draw the hazel leaf, with its crinkly edge, and we often returned home from our excursions with a selection of leaves. When he drew trees, he liked to talk about how they started, and grew, developing age rings; we used to call him *our tree man with two branches*.

Of course, I was able to tell him that all his drawings and stories had helped me to imagine what those early people might have been thinking. There he stopped me to say, 'I don't want to distract you from what you're saying, or dampen your spirit, but remember that, although all plants and trees have life, they do not have spirit as we do, even though they are sensitive to many things, as you already know.' I told him about the evening I had recited the poem *Little by Little* before going to sleep, since I wasn't too happy about writing the Bible outline story next day; as he had suggested. That night I had a dream about the acorn, breaking out of its shell and beginning its journey downwards, deep into the soil, travelling at will and collecting moisture and nutrients; then upwards into the sky, becoming taller and broader year by year, and outwards in all directions, as the leaves gathered moisture and sunlight from the atmosphere. Starting with the buds in the spring – reminding us that winter had passed. Then the leaves appeared, and changed from brighter green to deeper green, as they grew and settled down for the summer; later changing to myriad hues as they prepared for the fall, when they lay on the ground until they decomposed and fed themselves back into the soil. Then the tree hibernated until the next spring, when the process started all over again.

Only a few days after my dream, Mum asked me to take lunch to Dad, because he was working in the main vegetable garden; he was happy to see me when I arrived with his meal. He had made up a bale of hay, which he could use when he wanted to rest, and it provided a comfortable seat for both of us. After he had eaten, he indicated a tree, which had been badly damaged by lightening some years earlier, saying that it was time to remove the large branch, which was partially detached from the trunk. Without more ado he disappeared into the shed and reappeared carrying a saw. I thought it would be an excellent opportunity to tell him about my dream, but sawing wood by hand seemed to be a very energetic task; he was huffing and puffing, and I decided that perhaps it wasn't the ideal time after all. I would have to tell Granddad instead, when the opportunity arose; perhaps when we were rounding up our story. When I shared my thoughts with him, I was eager to know why there were no age rings in the branches. Granddad interrupted me to say, 'That's because the branches don't have any rings, only the trunk, but you've already seen tree trunks cut into logs, and we have talked about how the rings appear.' I hoped that my agitation wasn't obvious when I replied, 'I know that Granddad, because you have told us, but I really wondered what those ancient people were thinking, when they saw the rings, and what ideas it gave them, because as we know, they were fascinated by circles.'

Suddenly the weary look vanished and his face brightened as he said, 'I see, and I am going to ask you to do something which might seem strange, even funny, but I have my reasons. Will you stand over there,' as he indicated the space near the door, 'and spin round a few times.' Strange, I'll say it was, and I couldn't be seen to laugh because he looked very earnest. It became more than a few times, until he laughed again and said, 'Oh, you can stop now: I know you love to imitate Tiny chasing her tail. The reason for my request is that there is an expression for what you were doing, which could be described as turning on your axis. Without going into detail, I can tell you that your axis bone is located in your neck, so that if you turn your head as far as you can and, keeping it in that position, begin to move slowly, you will eventually arrive back at your starting point. Do it once just to prove my point, and then describe what has happened.' I confirmed, with some merriment, that I had gone round in a circle. He wasn't to be distracted and continued, 'Now do it once more, with your arms extended out to the side, and imagine more arms extended out from your chest and back: then tell me what you think.' As I came face to face with him again, he was smiling broadly. Whilst carrying out the exercise more slowly, I had allowed my imagination to run riot. I had become an axle with wooden spokes and an iron band, like the ones on our carts and trap; I became a spinning top like the ones Dad and Granddad made us; then I became the centre of Gammie's spinning wheel, and I was the driving force for all those things. They would keep turning for as long as I was prepared to help them. They were powerful thoughts, and I needed to sit down suddenly in order to concentrate on them, and relay them to Granddad. He was pleased but he hadn't finished, 'Yes, what goes round comes round, but the main reason for this, as you have probably begun to realise, is to convey the importance of the central force: the pivotal or starting point, which more or less dictates what happens from there onwards.

I realise, from what you've been telling me, that you may have begun to understand why the Celts and their predecessors regarded the tree with awe, investing it with spirits and sacredness, they were full of gratitude for its provision. Living with and depending on nature, as they did, they took time to study everything, and the tree may have presented them with a tremendous challenge; even the roots, which lived in that underground world. But it was the trunk and its rings, which probably tested their intelligence and imagination to the limit, until over time they understood some of its nature.

You were able to imagine the wheel as you spun, and I know your Dad discussed this with you on one occasion, when he compared the wheel to a person: both having a central force. My discussion with you centres on our outer and inner journey, with the inner journey being the more important. The outer can never be complete unless the inner is whole. Now I want you to think deeply for a moment about what you need most for your inner journey. You have already mentioned it in passing, so to speak, and I don't want you to worry: just think.' Oh flip! How could I not worry, since he said I'd already said it! I remembered what he had said, but I wasn't good at remembering what I had said to him. Mum would have said, 'For heaven's sake just go back over the tree and your dream, and see if that helps you. It may have been the thought of Mum, and the fact that I was beginning to feel hungry again, which focussed my mind on food; especially the right type of food, as we were forever being reminded. I realised that in many respects the tree was just like me. I looked at Granddad sheepishly, as I replied that the right food helped to keep me strong. The guilty feeling was caused by the next question I wanted to ask, even though I knew we hadn't got time for more. Whilst considering my answer for him, I had visualised the axles in our cart wheels and I remembered Dad saying that he must grease them in order to keep them running smoothly. I told Granddad, hoping that he would tell me what the grease was made from.

Instead, to my horror, he replied, 'We must leave it there, but before we go I wonder if you could make an old man very happy by reciting the poem *Trees,* just as you do at school.' That meant head up, look straight ahead and hands behind the back, but how could I argue. After all he was Granddad.

> I think that I shall never see
> A poem lovely as a tree.

> A tree whose hungry mouth is prest
> Against the earth's sweet flowing breast;

> A tree that looks at God all day,
> And lifts her leafy arms to pray;

> A tree that may in Summer wear
> A nest of robins in her hair;

> Upon whose bosom snow has lain;
> Who intimately lives with rain.

> Poems were made by fools like me.
> But only God can make a tree.

TREES BY JOYCE KILMER (1913)

CHAPTER XII

MEMORIES

"Oh, Nan! What a change, and so quickly! It has been so warm, so bright and so exciting, but now it is so damp and cold."
The sound of Liam's voice catapults Nan back to the present. With a shiver and a very long sigh, she replies that the change has not come about rapidly: they have been lost in the mist of time and too engrossed to notice their surroundings.

When they arrived the sea had been many shades of blue; the sun was shining and the waves were sparkling and dancing as they approached the shore. There had been a large vessel out to sea, and they had briefly discussed its possible journey and destination. The vessel which, even if it were still on the horizon would not be visible, because the sea mist has crept in quietly to envelop them; a wet grey mass which has blotted out the sun. The sea although still calm, reflects the dull greyness of the mist.

How long have they been at the water's edge, each lost in time – one in time gone by and the other attempting to imagine a time in the future. Nan has been remembering her rebellion, when told that she would be moving from her beloved home in Ballinalacken to Lisdoonvarna within twelve months, a distance of just three miles, but it would seem like two different worlds as far as she was concerned. As she recalled that episode for Liam's benefit, the memories and images were all too readily available, and painful. Thankfully, the delightful sound of Liam's laughter dispels the residual sadness as he exclaims, "You have taken me on a wonderful journey of your early life, but I am now a few years older than you were then. Would you be able to tell me more, and would it be as special as those times you have already spoken of?"

It's Nan's turn to laugh now, and even though it has a hint of sadness, she is determined to match his optimistic mood as she answers, "Yes I probably could tell you lots of interesting stories about events which occurred long ago, but those memories which I have just described, were probably the most formative and impressionable ones, because in a sense they represented two tumultuous changes in my life: the first was the dreaded change in my physical location, the second was the mental and emotional change which needed to occur before the move."

"Nan! Please don't think me rude or inquisitive, but I can't help wondering if you shared all your thoughts with Granddad when, at the conclusion, he asked how you felt?"

Giving Liam a quizzical but understanding look, she replies, "How could I be completely honest with him, Liam. To have been so, would have left him feeling very deflated, even though he had said that he wished to prepare me for the future. In order to begin that journey, I knew that the child I had been must take a back seat, and create space for the adult to emerge eventually. I had told him that I felt sad about the constant strife, which existed among peoples, but I didn't share about my own sadness, and the struggles I was experiencing inside. There lay my challenge: physically I would grow at a normal rate, but mentally and emotionally he had catapulted me to the top of a mountain. I needed to climb down slowly and start the ascent at my own pace. You know, in his wisdom, I think he believed that he was giving me time to accomplish that. More importantly I think he knew, and understood, that it had to be my journey. After all he and I were at one when it came to understanding our dual journey, and we only know as much of another's inner journey as he cares to share with us; we should allow for and respect that inner space."

Liam has been listening very carefully and quips merrily, "Oh, I see! Does that mean that you don't really know what I am thinking?" Nan laughs too and says, "Well, I might think I know, but no one should assume that they really know what another person is thinking or feeling, regardless of their facial expressions, it is impossible to know. Therefore I will only know what you are thinking if you wish to tell me."

"By the way, you didn't tell me why Granddad chose to stay in this place." Liam wouldn't be happy until he knew. "Maybe that's because I hope you will work it out; but if not I'll help you. The sooner we retrace our steps back to the car the better." Whilst still talking, Nan starts to make her way across the grykes, leaving Liam to assemble and carry their belongings.

This is their favourite journey when time allows them to be together. It is situated about two miles or so from where Nan used to live. Having learned to move like the mountain goats, which roam freely in this area, they have created their own path, which takes them to the shore in the shortest possible time. That is to say it would do if they didn't need to stop every so often to examine nature's bountiful provision. Nan is no stranger to all the changes, which take place here throughout the year. As winter passes, spring seems to exclaim, look here, and here, and here … it's all around you, but you must stop, and look and listen: a pattern which continues as time moves on, and although the new season will also have its own special beauty and magic, it will be very different.

It is now late spring and Liam has travelled from the city, hoping that the weather will permit a number of excursions, and provide an escape from the business of school and city life. Here in the Burren there could be no greater contrast.

Words never seem to be adequate when trying to describe something really beautiful, because visual beauty involves senses and emotions. Finding a means of expressing these feelings in art, literature or any other medium, can sometimes be a painful struggle. So Nan was overjoyed when she first sensed that Liam had succumbed to the heavenly qualities of that earthly place. On his first visit he had declared that it seemed wild and lonely, but subsequent visits taught him to look at, rather than over the scenes, which lay before him. Gradually he began to see that the wilderness had a picturesqueness all its own. When the light reflected on the limestone hills and boulders, they became moodily, colourful scenes. The timelessness had nothing to do with the fact that it had erupted from the seabed millions of years before.

For Liam the Burren is a place of occasional respite, but for Nan it had been home for eighteen years, although eight of those years were spent in Lisdoonvarna. Returning at intervals provided an opportunity to look back and remember how important that time had been. The changing seasons simply added a different dimension to the scenery. The feeling of enchantment was there even on grey winter days, when the wet boulders stood out against the green background. The Atlantic rollers crashed with a thunderous roar onto the rocks, and the rain-laden clouds scurried across the sky: tones of grey, varying from the white of the sea spray to the grey/black of the rocks: it was all quite awesome and mysterious. This was all in stark contrast to the beauty of spring, summer and autumn, when the scenes became more colourful and vivid. There were also occasions throughout the year when the mist came down or rolled in from the sea. Those times seemed particularly eerie, even in broad daylight, because visibility became restricted, and familiar shapes became distorted. Everyone simply wished to be within the comfort of their own homes.

Nan and Liam are anxious to be back in the car, as they start their ascent from the shore. Not looking for distractions but taking care to avoid all the grykes, they are each focused on their own journey. Suddenly, there it is! On hearing the sound, Nan thinks it has to be an illusion, but no it comes again and this time more strongly, as it pierces the air from on high. Despite the urgent need to be back in the car Nan whispers, "Let's just stop and listen for a moment. My legs could do with the rest too." Liam obeys, without question, but wonders what on earth they could be listening for – the warning blast from the ship would not be heard, since it has long gone on its way. He is looking really puzzled as they sit on a flat-topped boulder, and Nan whispers, "I believe it is a skylark." For a few moments there is silence, but very soon it comes again. There is no mistaking the magical sound of the skylark. They are both intent on listening, but each in a different way. Nan, previously told him about her experience of the skylark in the meadow, as remembered by a nine-year-old, and hopes to prove that it has not been storytelling gone too far. No amount of peering into the mist is going to reveal its physical presence. They can only listen in silence, and the mist ensures that there will be no other visual distractions. They wait for two repeats, with a pause between each, and as they prepare to continue their journey, Liam says with deep emotion, "It really is a beautiful sound when you listen properly. I am so sorry I doubted you. It was difficult to imagine that sound as you told your story earlier, and even now it's hard to see it wanting to sing in these conditions: so grey and miserable we can barely see where we are going."

Nan chuckles and says, "Yes, we may feel like that down here, but the lark flies through the cloud, encouraged by the sunshine above, and later on I will tell you about another skylark, which I discovered during a later chapter in my life."

The remainder of their journey is completed in silence. On arriving at the car Liam can't resist a light hearted comment, "Of course, I would have been back in half the time if I hadn't waited for you." Nan is aware that although the statement is light-hearted, there is edginess in his voice. Nevertheless, once they have settled in she replies just as light-heartedly, "I know that's true, but you would have missed the skylark!" There was no reply.

Their journey through the mist is still uppermost in Liam's mind; the route has been very familiar but, even allowing for their brief stop, it has seemed to take much longer than normal. It has been so different without the usual scenery, and time appeared out of focus. Nan is very aware of the tension, which their return has caused. This tension seems to hang as heavily inside the car as the dense fog appears to be outside, and neither cloud is showing any sign of lifting. They have no control over the weather, but Nan needs to give Liam time to organise his thoughts before he can cope with the questions, which are juggling for his attention. In the light of their recent experience, right now could be a very good time to talk about the lark.

"Do you remember what I told you about my childhood experience of the lark in the meadow?" Despite his jumbled thoughts, Liam looks at Nan a little shamefully as he replies. "I do Nan, and I have already apologised, but I really thought you were romancing, just a bit. Now that I have listened to it perhaps you could tell me again".
Nan, wanting to hug him then replies,
"I can understand your scepticism because, as a young child I never spoke about my experience to anyone, just in case they had the same thoughts which you had earlier. Now that you've experienced just a little of its magic, it is easier for me to repeat it:

> "This is the bird that taught me about Glory and what Heaven could be like, because I associated Heaven with what I always felt was a gift from God, this bird that could fill my heart with her sense of being. I used to sit quietly in a meadow and watch the skylark rise from her nest in the grass, and as it rose it

started to sing, this to distract attention from her nesting place. The singing would become louder and more beautiful as it climbed up through the clouds, upwards and onwards until I could no longer see the tiny form but could still hear her song. I always felt a deep emotion and a sense of fear; this tiny bird must soon explode with the intensity and volume of her song, but the emotion was really a sharing of that same intensity, as my heart soared with it until I thought that my own would not cope with any more. Then there was the feeling of sadness when I could no longer hear this heavenly sound, and felt that perhaps the bird had gone to Heaven and left me behind. In the quiet as I gazed heavenwards I realized that the little form was descending, swiftly, silently and very peacefully, to land unnoticed in her nest. I felt a sense of peace and joy knowing that she was back with me.

Retelling the story allows Nan to remain focused on the present: she isn't drawn into her earlier reverie, but is happy that the story has had a new meaning for Liam.

"Well, I am happy that I have heard its song, but I don't know what it looks like. I guess it's a big bird which can fly to great heights, but would a large bird make such a sweet sound. The sound of the crow or the seagull wouldn't inspire me."

"You're right! These birds can sound almost aggressive. You know though, what a sparrow looks like and its colour helps to protect it from predators. The skylark is just a little bigger than the sparrow, and it has similar colouring. Although it is not impressive to look at, it is in the air that it manifests its real beauty, as it sings its melodious songs, whilst winging its way heavenwards. It likes wide-open spaces in the countryside or moorland regions, and as we have found today, it is not deterred by fog. Not surprisingly we are not on our own in our admiration.

I had been over the moon when I discovered that we were to

study The Skylark, by the poet Shelley, at school. My heart jumped for joy when I read the first stanza.

Hail to thee, blithe spirit!
Bird thou never wert-
That from heaven or near it
Pourest thy full heart
In profuse strains of unpremeditated art.

My joy was twofold; I had found someone who must have felt as I had, and I would be able to discuss my feelings about my favourite bird. What little I knew about the education system. My spirits were temporarily dampened when I realized that we would be studying the poem – not my feelings – and then I discovered that, having written twenty-one stanzas, Shelley was still struggling to understand how such a diminutive creature could express itself so gloriously. I could sense his struggle as he desperately tried to find words, which would adequately describe the object of his heartfelt emotions. Whilst studying the poem, I realized that my own feelings had become much easier to understand, and thereafter it was possible merely to listen and marvel.

Of course some years ago I couldn't help wondering how Percy Shelley would have reacted to the man who was convinced, that many musicians are inspired to compose music as a result of listening to birdsong."

"Who was that Nan? You know I love music, but I haven't heard about anyone making such a claim. Anyway hasn't Shelley been dead for nearly two hundred years?"

"So he has Liam, and the man I speak of was making his claim about twenty five years ago, but I would still have liked to have been a fly on the wall, observing that meeting. You see I had been watching a television programme, during which the man was endeavouring to prove his claim to a panel of judges. I was spellbound throughout, desperately wanting him to succeed. I discovered afterwards, that he had retired early, from a successful career, in order to prove his theory.

It was fascinating to watch his story unfold, and even more so to learn what he had discovered about the song of the skylark. Proving his theory involved purchasing and using sophisticated recording equipment, and going out early in the morning to capture bird song: with the exception of the skylark he was happy with the results. But his attempts to achieve similar success regarding the lark left him frustrated and deflated ... until he experimented with the playback speed. He found that ordinary sounds, including the human voice, became muddled and incoherent when the speed was slowed down, but experimenting with the skylark's song involved doing just that. In order to achieve the result he desired, he needed to slow the tape to a quarter of its normal speed. He already knew that the bird's song was so fast, and pitched so high, that it was difficult for human ears to make sense of it. He was overjoyed when his experiments recorded that not only does the lark sing approximately two hundred and thirty notes per second, but it sings approximately ten symphonies a day, with a break between each, and there was melody and variation in each harmony. As a result of his presentation, the panel of judges declared that his theories were based on sound judgement and his challenge was successful."

"How did you feel, after watching the programme?" Liam asked.

Nan, appreciating that he has been listening very intently, thinks very carefully before replying: "If you mean, how did I feel about the skylark, I would have to say that nothing could change how I feel when I hear it, because the same emotions are there each time I listen to that magic sound. That reminds me of an unfortunate habit I have developed when out walking with family or friend. If I happen to hear a lark, I am apt to hold up my hand, in the middle of a conversation, so that everyone can stop and listen … much to everyone's amusement."

Still, I felt very happy knowing that there was someone who had the courage of his convictions: prepared to make sacrifices in order to prove that nature's provision is abundant and inspiring. Maybe you could say his sentiments were similar to those of Shelley, but they each found a different means of expressing them, and I am reminded of the last line of Shelley's poem. That, together with the result of their individual experiences, taught me the benefit of listening in a wholesome way and, of course it's the only way to appreciate the offerings of the skylark.

Teach me half the gladness
That thy brain must know;
Such harmonious madness
From my lips would flow,
The world should listen then, as I am listening now.

They remain in comfortable silence until Liam becomes restless, as his eyes try to pierce the mist outside,
"Nan."
"Yes Liam." "Maybe now you could tell me about the day you moved, and how you really felt."
"Oh Liam!"

CHAPTER XIII

A LIGHT IN THE DARKNESS

"Liam, do you remember how it was when we first stood here at the very beginning of this story?"

"Yes, I do Nan, but I can't help wondering if the preparation for the journey actually helped you on the day you moved."

Nan is silent for a few moments before replying, "You're the only person to ask how I felt, and you witnessed my reaction. I have to admit that I always feel quite emotional when I return to the Burren; the memories are still very powerful a lifetime on. But since you ask, I have to say *so be it.*" Nan laughs briefly as she continues, "I am very fortunate in being an optimistic person, and creative by nature, which is probably why I relate to all that the Celts achieved. I have also learned that distressing experiences provide us with two options: to wallow in our misery or bad luck, or treat them as challenges to be overcome. The latter was to be my motto, and it proved invaluable when I became an adult tutor in craft and design subjects. However all that came later, but did my preparation help me on the day of the move, not one iota? Of course I was not the only person who felt apprehensive about that particular day: there had been two of us involved. We were kindred spirits about to be separated, unable to share our feelings just then, because we had two separate journeys.

In some respects I'm like the lark, in that I too like to be up and about early in the morning. There is always so much I want to do and never enough time. Being helpful to others was part of my early training, and I was happy and willing to be so, but problems arose when I needed to find time to dream: that eluded me. So getting up early became a game I played, except on that day. I didn't want to leave my bed: I knew that it was being moved, and that I would wake up in it the following morning. I would be in my bed, but not in the same room, or the house where Granddad lived. When I awoke and realization dawned, I had looked around the room and promptly pulled the quilt over my head, closing my eyes tightly, hoping that when I re-opened them the nightmare would have passed. After a few repeat performances I began to lecture myself, 'You have been taught to be wise, caring and wide awake to everything about you at all times, so who do you think you are trying to kid? You may have been fooling some people for a while, but you can't fool yourself.'

I heard Mum ring the bell, which she used when she wanted everyone at the table, and I suspected that there would be no time for arguments. Of course she had a lot to do, and would be relying on me to help. The move was complicated by the fact that we weren't all moving, since Granddad and Joe were remaining in the house. Mum had been making preparations for some time, yet everything appeared to be undisturbed, but that was all about to change, and as I said she needed my help. Of course! I had given it, as usual. I couldn't share her enthusiasm though, as she helped Dad to load the van, which he had borrowed for the event. Nor could I share her excitement, because I sensed that my inner flame was about to go out: my feelings were in turmoil, and Granddad was still in bed. Should I go outside to look at my favourite views, or disappear briefly to the meadow? With so many urgent chores needing attention indoors, Mum would not have understood; I couldn't blame her, but as I provided the extra pair of hands, I felt my inner flame flicker and become extinguished."

"Oh Nan I am so sorry, perhaps I shouldn't have asked you."

"No need to be sorry Liam, you see as time passed I began to realize that situations occurred for a reason, but it is only with hindsight that we are able to make sense of all that's happened, and the reason for it. So too with our situation right now, and it may be that sometime in the future you will look back and think, now I understand. What I find incredibly strange at the moment, is that we are sitting in a car, not able to see more than a few yards in any direction: like being in a cloud. What a peasouper, but I can see some of the shrubs begin to move, which means the wind is getting up, and I hope it will soon break up the cloud and sea mist around us.

I remember Granddad taking me outside once in conditions such as these: how confused I felt? I had earlier been telling him about the moonlit trip, which Mum and I had shared, and the spookiness on our return journey. He had wished me to experience that feeling of visual nothingness, because our eyes could not pierce the mist. He was wise enough to understand, and cope with my confusion. We two are in exactly the same situation now, the only difference being that we are not at home. I can fully understand what he intended at the time, but of course I don't know what you're thinking or feeling. Yet, on the day of the move, I remembered that episode with Granddad, and it certainly wasn't the only memory!

Mum had announced at breakfast, that all the packing would need to be completed before Granddad emerged. She would take him his breakfast tray as usual, then it would be all hands on deck and we should be ready to leave after lunch. I had tried to be positive, acknowledging that autumn, winter and spring had come and gone since the bombshell was dropped concerning the move. I had returned to school feeling much happier about all that lay ahead. My resolution to note the seasonal changes remained uppermost in my mind, and the time sped by. During the winter months I had gone back over my journey with

Granddad, and sometimes we chatted about those things, which had perplexed me. I certainly spent a lot of time thinking about how those nomadic people would have felt, particularly in the light of my own move. Granddad avoided telling me that their situation and mine bore no comparison. After all I was only moving three miles, and to a lovely modern bungalow. However, he knew how I felt, and he didn't need to point out the obvious.

By the time summer arrived, the new bungalow was nearing completion; Mum had bought the fabric and was in the process of making the curtains. As Granddad had said, she was a wonderful homemaker: a very excited one because, according to her, it was her own home. Being a small rural area, everyone was acquainted, and wished to know what everyone else was up to. It was inevitable, that after Mass on Sundays, different people asked when the move was to take place. I grew accustomed to the comment, *Sure won't it be lovely to be here, with all that's going on, and you won't be needing to travel so far to Church.* Thankfully none of the statements were directed at me, bar one, *And of course, you'll be at a new school, won't you?* To which I replied *'Yes, but it's no nearer than Ballinalacken school, and I like it there,'*

Of course there is nothing whatsoever wrong with Lisdoonvarna: a small town with a history of its own. I remember visiting the Spa Wells with the whole family when we had been younger and Grandma was more agile. As I've told you, Uncle Ben and Aunt Alice stayed at what was called the Queen's Hotel, but now called the Hydro, when they travelled from Dublin for their annual holiday. During their stay, when the weather permitted, we all congregated at the Spa Wells, but only after we had enjoyed tea and scones at the hotel with Uncle Ben and Aunt Alice. At the Wells there was a large platform area in front of the main building, and across the river a bandstand. It was a very popular venue for visitors, who came to drink the health giving mineral waters, then relaxed as they listened to the music. The hotel was situated on the hill overlooking the Spa, where it was possible to hear the band. After tea we journeyed down the hill to join in the merriment. The lively music was an incentive for many to get up and dance, taking care not to fall off the edge of the platform into the river, which ran alongside. Dad loved to tease me on those occasions, as he encouraged me to dance with him. It was supposed to be a serious attempt, since he hoped to teach me proper dance moves, but it usually dissolved into chaos, partly because of our disproportionate sizes. I think it was mainly because I wasn't ready and couldn't control my laughter. Mum usually saved the day by joining us, when Dad would pick me up in his arms and continue to dance with Mum; after which I usually took off in search of my brothers, who would be larking about in the wooded area over the bridge. We had been told that Granddad had helped to plant many of the trees there, and that he had also been involved in the setting up of the Spa Wells complex. It was a very happy, memorable time, but far from my thoughts on the day of the move.

Lunch that day became an occasion I would choose to forget, but since it was part of the experience, I couldn't do so. I had been dreading Granddad's appearance because, in my disheartened state, I wouldn't have known how to cope. For the first time I wouldn't have felt able to tell him why; that would have seemed like an insult, since he had spent so much time and effort preparing me. Nevertheless I became concerned when he failed to appear at his usual time ... until I heard Mum whisper to Dad that he had seemed very dejected when she had taken his tray in. When he finally emerged, shortly before lunch, I realised that whilst he had made a supreme effort to look and behave in a cheerful manner, his shoulders remained hunched: just as they had done after Grandma had left us ... and I felt helpless.

With the exception of my eldest brother Tom, we were all there.

Dad and Mum were pre-occupied with all they needed to think about. My older brother Joe, who was very philosophical, just accepted what was, and Patrick on that occasion was very well behaved, probably because Dad had told him that he would be travelling in the passenger seat of the removal van. Poor Granddad was required to listen to some do's and don'ts from Mum, whilst he answered her in a despondent manner. I noticed that he wasn't eating much food, and was thankful that Mum didn't comment; neither did she mention my failure to make an impression on my food. Naturally Dad and Mum had no misgivings about the move: it had to be, and they had faced a much more difficult move just after I was born, when they had to abandon their home in Dublin at the beginning of the Emergency. There was to be daily contact, since Dad would be visiting Rockville each day, because the farm, still needed to be managed. He would also take a main meal for Joe and Granddad, who were to join us on Sundays after Mass, bringing their laundry for Mum to organize. Naturally, we children would be able to go up to Ballinalacken regularly. So it would almost be like old times, Mum had said, as she looked at Granddad adding, 'But I wish you had decided to come with us.'

So that was the problem, he couldn't drag himself away. I longed to cry, as we made eye contact for the first time since we had seated ourselves around the table. He knew me well enough to understand what I was thinking, 'Oh Granddad you can't drag yourself away, but I have to go!' I didn't rush from the table, but excusing myself quietly I retreated out-of-doors, hoping that on such a beautiful sunny day I might find anything to light a spark. But the brightness and warmth of the sun could not penetrate my inner being. It was as though someone had drawn a veil over my eyes, and I couldn't see through the mist, so I returned indoors, disconsolate. Mum was already washing the dishes, and I found a tea towel and helped, as usual.

The arrangement was that Patrick would travel with Dad, but Mum and I would walk the three-mile distance, using the lower road, because Rooska was situated at that end of the town. There were to be no awkward moments as we parted company, because Mum had already put her case as she saw it, but I couldn't look at Granddad as I hugged him, and began to turn away. As I did so, he took my hand and placed a brown paper package in it, 'This one is very old and dog-eared like me, but I hope it serves you well.' A quick look inside the package confirmed that he had given me his personal Bible. Then I looked at him, handed the parcel to Mum and fled.

By the time Mum and I arrived at the bungalow Dad had already emptied the contents of the van, being ably assisted by Patrick. As I said earlier, the move had been complicated because Granddad and Joe were remaining, which entailed purchasing many necessary pieces of furniture and fittings. That had all been accomplished well in advance, and Mum had talked animatedly from the time we had left Rockville; she had lots of plans for the future. The worrying consequence of the move for Dad and Mum had been that, whilst we lived in Rockville, our living expenses were covered by the farm and Granddad's pension, but the move meant being more financially independent. Dad had been very fortunate in finding work when we had arrived in Ballinalacken. There had been a shortage of phosphate, which was considered to be a very useful mineral, in the production of fertilizer. Since a phosphate mine had been discovered in Doolin, there was a need for a manager, and he was offered the job. When the mine closed after the Emergency ended, there was no further employment for him. Mum realised that, after we moved, she would need to set up her sewing business; and she was eager to get it under way. She didn't need to advertise that fact, because many people already knew that she was a gifted needlewoman. The practicalities of achieving her goal had been uppermost in her mind, as we had walked the road to Lisdoonvarna, and I realised that she would be in need of as much help from me as possible, but I didn't comment, I merely listened. Fortunately Dad had anticipated our weariness and had put the kettle on.

I had been to the bungalow on a number of occasions, identifying what would be my bedroom, and noting the surroundings outside, but I had been reluctant to dwell on either. I hadn't actually been with Mum, as she carried out the finishing touches. It was a lovely bungalow, which looked bright and fresh, with a smell of newness: it was my new home. We were all very familiar with the expression *home is where the heart is*, but although I loved my parents and brothers, my heart was elsewhere.

The day had begun with an inner argument, which was to continue for some time. As soon as we had finished our tea I washed up, so that Mum could concentrate on the unpacking, and then went outside, to argue some more. In the field across the road from the bungalow, a donkey stood motionless, almost as though it was asleep standing up. I crossed the road and began to talk to him. Maybe he thought I was about to offer him some food, because he opened his eyes and wandered over to me. A brief sniff of my extended hand confirmed that it was a wasted journey, and with a flip of his tail he wandered away. I resolved next time to bring a carrot. Although I had had a long walk with Mum, I still desperately needed time to think, and walk by myself; the problem was where, since I didn't know the area, and was too young to explore unaccompanied, probably just as well because I would have retraced my steps back to Rockville. Had I been allowed to bring Tiny, our Jack Russell terrier with me, I could have walked further, and she would have been a source of comfort! Finally I decided to walk to the bend in the road, which wasn't far, at least not far enough for any meaningful thoughts to develop before I needed to return. As I did so, the donkey began to bray, and the sound of the hee-haw accompanied me. Initially the braying seemed to frustrate my efforts to think, until I decided that he had won; and had the right to be himself. As I listened to the rhythm, I remembered that donkeys had been around for a long time; being domesticated animals in Egypt and Mesopotamia for thousands of years, and they were often mentioned in the Bible. As I came abreast of him, I noticed a boulder in the field, tucked up against the hedge; it wasn't difficult to find a way in. The donkey raised his head as I made my way across to the stone.

Incidentally, we were constantly advised that when moving through fields with animals in, we should always keep a watchful eye on them. Remember the story I told you about the bull chasing us, when we were out hunting with Dad: we reached safety, but only just in time…that was one of my scariest memories. Needless to say, Dad didn't need to warn us again, and it became something which we did unconsciously. There were hidden dangers, when travelling through the countryside, and the motto was *look where you are going and be watchful at all times.*

I observed the donkey's movements, as I made my way across to the stone, but he wasn't in the least interested. He had stopped braying when I entered the field and proceeded to munch the longer tufts of grass. Having settled myself on the stone, I continued to observe him, whereupon he stopped eating and focused on me. How much did I really know about donkeys? Well, not a lot, apart from what I had read or been told, but I had often observed them when we were moving turf at the bog. Because we had a pony and a horse, there didn't appear to be a need for a donkey as well. However, on one occasion Dad had described the nature of the donkey, as we journeyed home with our load of peat … we had earlier observed the donkey's stubbornness when, having had the paniers on its back loaded with peat, it had refused to budge. We hadn't waited to see the outcome of that episode, but I wished to know why, since our pony was very cooperative; of course the pony was pulling a cart and didn't have those baskets or paniers on its back.

Dad explained that the donkey was a pretty ancient animal, being a member of the horse family, although completely different. It had a notorious reputation for stubbornness, but with proper treatment it was very friendly. Whereas horses could be skittish at times, and easily startled, not so the donkey, and it was not possible to frighten or persuade it to move, if for any reason of its own, it considered it unwise to do so. However, we know that it is often considered the most suitable animal for taking children for rides, when it has been properly trained. Of course they have often been referred to in a derogatory manner, when people sometimes use the alternative name, and I wondered if the farmer in the bog called the donkey a silly, stupid ass, or worse. I had asked Dad at the time, if the donkey might have felt over loaded, since the paniers were piled high with peat. Dad had agreed, but said that the man would need to discover for himself who the silly ass happened to be. Surveying my solitary companion, I thought, 'I have a fair idea about your nature, but we need time to get to know each other. I know the story about the cross on your back, and true or not, it will keep me going for now,' whereupon I took myself indoors. It had been an exhausting day for everyone, and when order had been restored after tea, Dad and Mum sat listening to the radio: Patrick had his comic, and I surprised them all when I told them I was going to bed with my book.

Attempting to relate to the story, which I had been reading, would have been impossible. Although I was in my own bed, I was a different me: I didn't know that person and I didn't know how to go about finding the old one. As I closed my eyes, whilst trying to shut out the bedroom, I had a recollection of the donkey in the field; seemingly completely undisturbed ... I let my thoughts dwell on him. Granddad had said that they had emerged in the east, and that they were invaluable as a means of transporting goods in the Eastern countries before and during the Bible era. They could carry loads on their backs, pull carts or carriages, and they were prized as much as horses. Our first Bible story had been the one of Joseph, Mary and the donkey arriving at the Inn in Bethlehem as Jesus was about to be born; our manger pictures depicted the donkey as well as the ox and the sheep. Then he featured again in the story of the Flight into Egypt: a story which left me feeling very indignant when I first heard it. There was also the story of Jesus riding on a donkey as he arrived in Jerusalem for the Passover.

Those were our main stories as I recalled them. I resolved to unpack my books next day; maybe I could focus on other Bible stories, since there was a sense of timelessness about them, and they might be a bridge between the old and new me. Unfortunately they were also a reminder of all that the displaced people must have suffered in their wanderings. I knew that there was no comparison between their situations and mine: at least in a physical sense ... outwardly everything in my life was fine, and I had so much to be thankful for. Still my sense of wholeness had been blown to smithereens: where was my invisible friend? Was he in the pit inside me? I had read the story of his last night, before his crucifixion, when he was imprisoned in the pit, which lay underneath the house of Caiaphas. I didn't want to think of that story too much. I only wished that I could sense the feeling that he was there, but I couldn't. I felt consumed by a sense of longing for all that seemed to have vanished. Only then did I have an inkling of how all those ancient people may have felt, as they longed to belong.

My last thought was of Granddad and his new situation, but it became too much to bear. Because I hadn't closed the curtains, the room was still bright, which reminded me that my inner light had gone out in the morning, but the sense of longing remained for the sisters I hadn't known, who might have been able to help me, because they would have been older; although I had to accept the fact that they may not have shared my feelings. Would they have felt the same about feeding the hens, whilst listening to their squabbles: the corner of the Burren which was like paradise to me, and Granddad who had proved that he shared those feelings, because he couldn't persuade himself to leave there. I realised why he had made such a valiant attempt to prepare me. The Celts had been the means by which he took me through the Bible events, and taught me his own philosophy. Dad and Mum had said that we would be able to go back any time we liked, but Dad usually cycled the journey and would be in a hurry to get on with the chores, so that wasn't going to be an option. Anyway, I had moved and there was no going back. There was simply the longing for that other presence … even though Granddad had said that I must develop a more adult method of describing him, he was my invisible friend and I needed him to ignite my inner flame, but when and how? What could I do? I was only ten and even the tears had dried up.

The sun was bright when I awoke next morning. Normally I would have leapt out of bed and crept outside to soak up the atmosphere, which was so intoxicating … simply watching the world waking up around me made me want to sing and dance, even though everything about me appeared to have more sense than I had. For instance, in the henhouse, the cockerel crowed but didn't move; the noise woke the hens and they clucked loudly, but nothing more. The dog opened one eye, had a quick look at me and then closed it again. The birds began their preening exercise: preparing for a new day, but they didn't emerge from their nesting place, unless startled. The bees and insects remained in hiding until the sun began to dry off the moisture on their favourite plants; the flowers, which had folded up their petals in the evening, were in no hurry to open them.

The sea in the distance, and the terrain all around had a gentle overall haze, as the sun began to soak up the moisture. It was a new day dawning and it had a magical sense of mystery.

However, as I woke to the reality of my new situation, there were none of the usual incentives, but I still needed to prepare myself to cope with Mum, in her new surroundings. Dad had already breakfasted, and set off for Ballinalacken, when I joined her in the kitchen. Patrick was eating his breakfast, and Mum was giving him a list of simple chores, which included filling the basket with peat to fuel the range. She smiled as she told both of us that we would need to do the shopping, and she had prepared detailed notes for the butcher and grocer, but we didn't need one for the newsagents, because we knew the paper Dad read: Patrick didn't need anyone to tell him which comic to buy, and I was allowed to read Mum's copy of Ireland's Own. We were to be the messengers, but we must look after each other.

Our bungalow in Rooska was situated on the outskirts of the town. Walking at a reasonable pace would take us to the shops in the square in approximately ten minutes, but for dawdlers it would take much longer. We hadn't been told to hurry, and it provided a good opportunity to check our new surroundings. Of course the shopkeepers knew us from previous visits with Mum, when we travelled from Ballinalacken, and they were eager to know when we had moved; and I wished that they didn't talk about moving. In any case I left all the talking to Patrick, hoping that we would be on our way as quickly as possible. There were no self-service shops in those days, and commodities such as sugar and flour were stored in large hessian sacks, and weighed into brown paper bags according to requirements. Most items were stored on multiple shelves behind a long counter. The serving procedure could go on for some time, if the shop wasn't busy with customers, and the owner was eager for news!

The return journey was much quicker, and we were happy to offload our purchases, but it didn't end there, because Mum was also eager for news: who we spoke to and what they said, but I left the update to Patrick. Fortunately Mum had picked up her magazine, and there were no more questions; it was an ideal moment for me to escape. I had surreptitiously removed a carrot, which I broke into pieces, taking it with me as I visited my new friend across the road. He was like a lifeline, and the only animal around. I could tell him that I really didn't want to be there. Perhaps it's just as well that he couldn't reply. He might have reminded me that he was there, and that I should count my lucky stars. By the fourth day I had learned to say, 'Perhaps I should count my lucky stars, and hopefully it will get easier as time goes on.'

The routine became easier and school commenced two weeks after the move. There were new classmates to become acquainted with, and new teachers, and learning methods to get used to. There was homework in the evenings, but I also had my chores at home. The time passed quickly and I carried on mechanically. After Mass on Sundays our previous neighbours would chat briefly, wanting to know how we were settling in. Granddad and Joe joined us for lunch, as promised, but it wasn't possible for me to spend time alone with Granddad; in fact, it was probably a good thing, because I wouldn't have known what to say, and I couldn't have burdened him with my thoughts. Mum had acquired quite a lot of work and life was busy.

The school was situated a short distance beyond the Church, and I had noticed when I passed by that the door was always open; it seemed like an invitation to enter there. One day, on my way home from school, I observed a lady going into the Church and I quietly followed her inside. When I arrived she was already seated on one of the long pews. I sat a few rows behind her and waited. She didn't remain long and when she left I followed her outside: needing to ask her if it was OK for me to go in by myself. She smiled as she replied that it was fine, if the door was open, and so it became a habit, over the following months for me to pop in occasionally, when I merely sat and looked at the whole scene without any degree of concentration. I didn't think about anything in particular, and at times it felt almost as mechanical as everything else I did, almost but not quite. Although I couldn't pray, I began to feel more comfortable. I had always felt happy to be in Church before we moved, and I desperately wished to feel that same sensation again. I knew that the change was in me because everything else remained the same.

The period from the beginning of December to Christmas is known in the Church as Advent, or preparation for Christmas. The Sunday readings focus on what has been foretold in the Bible, and it had always been a joyful time for me. As the Advent weeks passed by I began to feel desperate: was I ever going to know those deeper feelings again. Such was my dejection when I next entered the Church. A previous visitor had been in and lit a candle, placing it in the stand which was next to the statue of Mary, holding the infant Jesus."

Nan stops talking abruptly, causing Liam to turn in his seat and stare at her. They are still in the car looking into the mist as she relates the experience, which she is apparently reliving for the sake of her young friend, even though she is apt to be unaware of his presence, from time to time. Liam is a lively, witty, fun-loving character, who also has a deeper side to his nature. He senses that Nan is beginning to falter, but nevertheless he whispers, "Go on, if you can Nan."

Then she looks his way and smiles, "I was trying to remember what I told you about Grandma leaving us. There was that experience I had with the candles, when I had crept back into her room, which had been placed on either side of the bed. As I tried to come to terms with her going, I had remembered one of our

Sunday Mass readings, where the Priest quoted the words of Jesus, *I am the light of the world. Whoever follows me will not walk in darkness, but will have the light of life.*

"Yes I do remember," Liam said. "Well that was the memory which I couldn't obliterate, as I sat in the church looking at the candle and the statue. I tried so hard to wipe it away: almost as one would wipe an image from the computer screen, but I am not a computer and the image wouldn't go away. I had wanted to dash out of the Church, but my legs didn't seem to want to move. I didn't wish to dwell on those earlier times, but simply to go on being mechanical; doing all the things which were expected of me. But hey ho, we all know that mechanical things don't have feelings: they are not beings, since to be a being in the real sense one must have feelings. I realised that I had been trying to be OK for everyone else's benefit, but I was shutting out the real me, the inner person which kept the outer person ticking.

I continued to gaze at the candle flame as the realization flowed over me. Suddenly I knew that I was crying, but it didn't worry me; it felt rather like a stream rushing over a dry river bed, which had become parched in the drought, but was about to come back to life, so that even the lifeless stones would sparkle in the sunlight. Like the stream, which had its source deep in the earth, the tears led me to what had become my pit, where they had been bottled up. The tears flowed out and the memories flowed back, but my gaze remained fixed on the candle flame, the flame which helped to light my journey backwards to my inner being. The candle had almost burned out before I realised that I had been in Church a long time, and heavens wouldn't I be in trouble when I arrived home. It didn't seem to matter, because I had found the pearl I had lost, and together we would cope with whatever came our way. I told the donkey that everything was going to get better from then on: it was just a comment, as I sped past him, he merely flipped his tail and continued to munch peacefully. Mum had a client with her when I arrived, and commented that I was very late. Believing that there would be more about that later, I gave her a happy smile and whispered that I had been delayed by a friend. Meanwhile I had an urgent, unfinished task of my own: there was the friend who deserved a special reward.

I broke the carrot into several pieces before entering the field, and made my way across to the stone, because that was the most private place. It may have been my purposeful walk which alerted him, but for the first time he followed me ... it didn't make me nervous, as it would have done at the beginning. As I gave him a piece of carrot, I began to reflect on my first visit: the beginning of my journey with him who was to be my silent listener. I didn't know his real nature then, but I was glad of his presence. As time progressed I remembered more of the stories concerning him: the Bible became my storybook as I tried to discover how many times the donkey was mentioned, but gave up counting, becoming lost in the stories instead. Gazing into his eyes, as he waited for the next piece of carrot, I decided that the donkey's mission in life was a very humble one indeed, and it could only be so because he was humble by nature.

I was certainly very grateful for the one that decided enough was enough, as he began to nuzzle my hand, where he knew the carrot was concealed. Hearing my laughter he nuzzled deeper, even though I reminded him that sometimes we have to wait; although my wait for that afternoon's revelation had seemed like an eternity. Yet as I stroked his nose, I knew that I was about to begin the next chapter of my life. I thanked him for being a real and silent presence during those awful days.

Hearing voices close by I realised that Mum's client was departing, and I should be getting back indoors. Sensing my haste, the donkey curled his lips backwards, as he opened his mouth and started to bray loudly. I was still laughing when I arrived in the kitchen, wondering what questions I would need to answer. Mum looked at me searchingly for a moment, before saying, with what appeared to be a sigh of relief, 'Well my goodness, if that doesn't sound more like the real you!' How well she knew me."

CHAPTER XIV

WHAT IS REAL

"What is REAL?" asked the Rabbit one day, when they were lying side by side near the nursery fender, before Nana came to tidy the room. "Does it mean having things that buzz inside you and a stick-out handle?" "Real isn't how you are made," said the Skin Horse. "It's a thing that happens to you. When a child loves you for a long, long time, not just to play with, but REALLY loves you, then you become REAL." "Does it hurt?" asked the Rabbit. "Sometimes," said the Skin Horse, for he was always truthful. "When you are REAL you don't mind being hurt." "Does it happen all at once, like being wound up," he asked, "or bit by bit?" "It doesn't happen all at once," said the Skin Horse. "You become. It takes a long time. That's why it doesn't happen often to people who break easily, or have sharp edges, or who have to be carefully kept. Generally, by the time you are REAL, most of your hair has been loved off, and your eyes drop out and you get loose in the joints and very shabby. But these things don't matter at all, because once you are REAL you can't be ugly, except to people who don't understand.

From: The Velveteen Rabbit, by Margery Williams.

"You know, Liam, that we are always real to others, whatever guise we use, but what makes us real to ourselves? … that is the question and life's quest: how to be real and wholesome."

As Nan has predicted, the mist is beginning to clear, and it will soon be time to move. In the meantime she hopes to establish what Liam's thoughts are, and if possible answer any questions he may wish to ask. Although they are glad of the shelter, she realises that they have been cooped up in the car for much longer than they had hoped. It hasn't escaped her attention that whilst Liam has been listening, he hasn't been able to resist fiddling with the car instrument panel in front of him. Of course he would soon be learning to drive, and exploring the panel wasn't merely an aimless pastime; there would be questions to follow, no doubt.

"Can you tell me how you feel now?" Nan asked, "I haven't failed to notice your interest in the car gadgets, and we can talk about those later, if you wish. For the moment I think it would be good to parcel up some of the stories, and I need your help in order to do so. I would like to feel that I may have passed on a few worthwhile thoughts for the future, as well as given you a glimpse into the past."

"To be honest with you Nan, I have felt just a bit unnerved sitting here, gazing at nothing but the car instruments. I have been grateful for the absorbing details, which helped me not to dwell on my own feelings, and I can begin to understand how you must have felt when you stood outside in the mist all those years ago. I don't suppose, for one moment, that it would be a problem for you now, would it?" Liam was looking at Nan as he spoke, but he couldn't resist a giggle as he continued, "I mean at your age and with so much experience, I can't imagine anything disturbing you."

Although she felt able to laugh along with him, Nan gave him a wry look, "Sorry Liam, I really shouldn't laugh, although I can see why you might assume that by now I should have all the answers. Of course, there may have been the odd occasion when I thought I was doing well, until the next problem arose, which soon convinced me that no two problems are identical. All I can say is that although the problem-solving experience probably helped me to cope slightly better, it didn't provide all the answers. Actually, come to think of it, there was one particular experience, which might explain better what I am trying to say, since it appeared to threaten all I thought I knew. You know this area was my hunting ground, during good times and bad; I believed I knew it almost as well as I knew myself.

So it was with confidence and some excitement that I set out with a friend one January morning just a few years ago... I was going home! Our journey commenced in mid Wales, where I now live, and the coastal route took us to Holyhead in Anglesey. It was a beautiful crisp, clear, January morning, and we had two hours of pleasant motoring, with wonderful scenery. The boat, which was destined for Dun Laoghaire, departed on time: the Irish Sea was as calm as a millpond. With such perfect conditions it promised to be a mini cruise, and so it was until we sailed into fog, which accompanied us at intervals, until we arrived at the port. We hoped that it might simply be sea mist, and that when we resumed our car journey, the onward drive would have been as pleasant as our early morning trip, some hope! With the exception of a few short intervals, the low cloud remained with us for the duration: a distance of approximately 160 miles. It had proved difficult for us to accept that, each time there was a break in the cloud, it would be so short lived. Later a kind gentleman at the Met Office confirmed that, in fact, visibility had been reduced to between 200 and 300 hundred metres across Ireland.

It was a tiring journey, but I remained full of anticipation until we approached my old familiar territory, where my problems really began. Surely I would be able to recognize my favourite places: I didn't... I strained my eyes as I tried to orientate myself, but to no avail. I can laugh now, as I remember, but at the time it was such a shock to my sensibility, because I couldn't identify any familiar landmarks. We travelled the length of the coastal area, but I didn't recognize anything, everywhere was shrouded in mist.

I had completely lost my sense of perspective, and knew that had I been the driver, I would have wished to stop the car and get out. I felt so claustrophobic in the car, and quite idiotically, I wanted to spread my arms and wipe away the mist: an idiotic concept, which was really an emotional cry. Ironically we were only two miles from our destination, a holiday cottage halfway up the mountain, only a little further up from where we are now. As we began to climb, we left the fog bank behind us. We arrived to witness a glorious sunset, but gazed in amazement at the bank of low cloud below us. It would have made a wonderful picture for the record had we had the presence of mind to capture it on camera. Not that I needed to be reminded ... some experiences are unforgettable. So in answer to your question, I have to confess that my previous experience had probably allowed me to assume too much. You know, it is possible to imagine what Granddad would have said, 'Well my dear, and what a valuable lesson you learned,' of course he would have been right."

Looking at Liam she said, "I hope you won't mind if we step outside for a few moments ... I need to stretch my old bones." Although visibility was not yet as good as Nan wished before moving on, it was refreshing to stand outside. Liam was in the process of flexing his muscles and hop-scotching nearby, but he still managed to comment, "You haven't yet told me how you eventually came to feel about your new home and life, and how often you returned to Rockville."

Watching his lively antics, and remembering how it used to be for her, Nan retorted, "No, not yet, but I am inclined to think of two very pertinent words right now - *moving on* - because we do need to think about moving on shortly.

Moving on also became my formula, after that very enlightening afternoon in the church, but I had made a new resolution: I would never again try to leave the real me behind. So, for your benefit I will repeat Granddad's comment to me, as he spent those summer months doing his best to pass on his words of wisdom, 'There may not be another opportunity like this one.' I have never forgotten all that he taught me, even though at times I became a restless listener, and I will remain eternally grateful to him, because he taught me how to be real. If you remember, I told you about the morning we moved: I thought that I could deceive others, but I could never fool myself. Yet that's exactly what I tried to do.

In that sense I had let both myself and Granddad down. Despite all that I had shared with him, I hadn't really understood that it isn't possible to separate the two journeys, the inner and the outer, and remain whole, since they are interdependent. But I had become a mechanical being and without substance. That realization was a sort of catalyst, since despite my age I knew what it had felt like to be whole and real before the move, and I had a real need to feel whole again. The need itself became my motivation, but it meant accepting the fact that I could never run away from myself, but take all the baggage with me. Initially that acceptance made my journey more difficult, and at times I ached to be back in Ballinalacken...but did I go back? The answer is no, although I occasionally attempted to do so, and would set out rebelliously, only to turn back when overcome with guilt, or a sense of fear, which in turn made me angry. It may seem strange to you, even funny perhaps, but I did learn from that, because when I turned to retrace my steps I was also turning back on my emotions and learning to challenge them. Had I not done so, I would have indulged in self-pity, which I didn't think would ever have helped me to feel whole or real?

I was lucky in that I loved nature and space: a combination which provided an excellent environment for reasoned thinking, and by the time I returned indoors, I was usually at peace with myself, and fit to resume whichever task had given rise to my outburst. This was occasionally the case when I needed to help Mum, if she happened to be overburdened with sewing? Actually, it wasn't the sewing itself which caused her problems; but rather the rare occasion when she had to turn a coat!" Nan began to laugh as she said, "Now I don't expect you to understand the term *turning a coat*, as we did it; it is not turning it inside out, with the lining on the outside! You know we didn't live in a throwaway society then; there was still a high degree of poverty, with a need to make-do-and-mend. Still, Mum really dreaded the occasion when someone would say, 'You know Annie, this coat has a lot of life in it yet, but it is so faded, although the inside is as good as new! I wonder if you could turn it for me.' Mum's kind heart wouldn't allow her to say no, and on those occasions, I simply wanted to leave home."

Nan was still laughing as she tried to describe the preparation for the dreaded exercise. Nevertheless, Liam detected a change in her tone, as she continued, "I couldn't forgive Mum for taking on such a loathsome task, and believed that had the owners of those garments even the slightest inkling of what it entailed, they would have been mortified! It was a case of ignorance being bliss, and they assumed that it was easy. Despite my objections I did learn quite a lot about construction techniques, as I carefully removed the sleeves and collar, stitch by stitch, with the aid of a pin. Mum hadn't considered that I could be trusted with a razor blade or the scissors, which she used and which made the task much quicker. Although I could accept that she was right, because a cut in the fabric would have been disastrous, it didn't help the way I felt about the whole operation. To make matters worse, Mum's method of cutting the stitches produced hundreds of individual threads, which then needed to be removed by hand. That stage completed, it was over to Mum who carefully pressed all the pieces, but for me there was only one redeeming factor: the original quality and colour of the woolen fabric, which was so evident. Even so, reconstructing a garment is much more difficult and time consuming than making a new one, because of the nicks and tucks which make for ease of assembly, since the pieces don't always match quite so well the second time round. Mum usually breathed a sigh of relief when the task was accomplished.

Aside from that, there were many occasions when we chatted contentedly as we worked. Mum talked about the shop she had in Dublin before getting married, and how she enjoyed meeting all the customers and loved her work. When I asked if she ever missed that life, she had replied that it didn't do to dwell on the past, it was better to learn from it, concentrate on the present and consider the future. I was learning the tricks of the trade, which were to prove invaluable throughout my life. I was eager to practice all the techniques involved in making garments, since I hoped to be able to make my own one day. But my enthusiasm completely deserted me when she needed to make hats, probably because I couldn't abide wearing anything on my head, and preferred the freedom of the elements. I had one other aversion... mending: mending anything, because it never looked as good as new. However, as I said, those were days when it was vital to be able to make do and mend: a stitch in time was also a valuable motto. Girls were taught how to knit, sew and carry out repairs from an early age, both at school and at home. Still, none of that knowledge could alter my thinking with regard to hats, however beautiful they may have looked on completion. Of course I had to cover my head when the weather demanded it, but I had knitted hoods, which weren't as rigid as hats.

I felt very grown-up when Mum taught me to use the sewing machine. It was a treadle type, which could be converted for hand usage, and initially I had to be content with that. Unfortunately I needed to be taller, because in order to operate the treadle I would have to be seated, when of course my feet could touch, but not manipulate the peddle. However, that didn't deter me from using the hand version, and it didn't take long to master straight lines; there were lots of remnant scraps for practicing on. I was over-joyed when Mum produced one of her favourite pieces of fabric, and holding it in front of me, she commented, 'Now, I know that you have long admired this design, so would you like to make a bolster cushion for your bed!' Would I like! Yes, I certainly would. I had cherished that piece of fabric, which she had said was a William Morris design. It had a pale blue background colour, and the design included small delicate cream flowers, with lots of dots and squiggles. Oh, I felt so grown up... I would have a new cushion on my bed by bedtime. But the fun had only just begun.

'You must go to your room and decide how long you want your cushion to be,' that wouldn't be a problem, 'then you need to decide how fat and round you would like it to be.' That was a problem! Putting my arms in the air to create a circle didn't help either. 'No, this is your decision, and you must work it out, cut it out and make it up: I will help you, but not do it for you.' I realised then that there was a lot more to being grown up than I had imagined, as I trailed about the kitchen, looking for round objects, which might give me inspiration. Of course there was a much more sophisticated method of arriving at my circle, but I hadn't begun to do geometry at school, and it was obvious that Mum was relying on a simpler method, but she wasn't telling me what that was. What a pity she hadn't suggested a square or oblong cushion, when I could have managed with a tape measure.

It was time to visit my four-legged friend, who was accustomed to listening to my grumbles, as I fed him his carrots. I had discovered that there were occasions, when I spoke to him, that the answer became obvious. Mum was busy with one of her hats when I collected the carrot. The donkey was at the far end of the field, which was wet, and after a furtive check to make sure that no one was within earshot, I whistled. Of course that was something which girls simply didn't do, but my brothers had done a good job of training me, even though they had to condemn my attempts as useless; their attitude being that it was fortunate that I didn't need to. However bad it was, the donkey had learned to recognize it, and respond … which he did, but it was going to take him forever to reach me. As I surveyed his measured, approach I remembered that patience is a virtue, and I concentrated on my own problem. Why, oh why had Mum asked me to use a circle? Was it because of my endless chatter before we left Ballinalacken, when I talked at length about the Celtic circles; but she often used circular patterns herself, when she was making hats. Oh fiddle-de-dee, why hadn't I taken more notice when she made hats! Wasn't that the reason for my escape: she was pre-occupied with the hat she was working on. To my horror I realised that I had marched out with her tape measure still round my neck. As luck would have it, the donkey had just arrived and I hadn't broken his carrot into pieces in readiness. Telling him to eat slowly, I popped it into his mouth and dashed back indoors.

Mum didn't appear to notice the tape, but she gave me a strange smile, the way people sometimes do when someone is *on the spot* so to speak. I hadn't worked out the size of the circle, but I noticed the selection of round patterns standing by, and asked sheepishly if I could borrow them. As I disappeared into my bedroom she said, 'But why are you taking them away?'

I turned to answer, 'I am going to do battle with my pillow,' she looked very intrigued. It didn't take me long to squash the pillow into a roll and rest the end on the different patterns. Having found the best size, I returned the patterns to Mum, asking if the chosen one was OK. She confirmed that it was fine, but she hadn't worked out why I needed the pillow.

She merely continued, 'Well! now you can make your own pattern from mine, and there's plenty of newspaper for that purpose: not forgetting to add on seam allowances. Then you can use some of the old sheeting to make the inner bolster which you can stuff; it will be a practice run for you.' Oh, stuff and nonsense, but the vision of a lovely bolster on my bed would help to keep me motivated. Drawing freehand circles was one thing, but working out a pre-determined size was a whole new ball game. Having given me my instructions, she decided that it was time for her break, and she was eager to look at one of her latest magazines.

She had a really interesting collection, some of which had been sent by my aunt in the United States. When she opened her latest magazine she became very excited, as she exclaimed, 'Well, here's a piece of information which should make you very happy.' Her excited tone interrupted my concentration, and I knew I had to give her my full attention as she carried on, 'you know that fabric you are about to use.' When I nodded, she continued, 'Well this is a description of the man who designed it, William Morris, himself. However, I don't want to stop you working now … you'll enjoy reading it for yourself later. Still I can tell you that he was a wonderful man, who worked very hard for under privileged people, and he became known as the father of the Arts and Crafts Movement.'

Yes, I could look forward to reading the article in the evening, but as I continued to work I began to think of another person who believed in the rights and needs of others, and I had an inkling as to why he had spent his time in Ballinalacken.

I was reminded of William Morris, as I wrestled with the interior of the bolster cushion; if the inner bolster was a practice run, then I should do everything possible to make it worthy of the of outer fabric, and learn a very constructive lesson in patience as I worked. I began to dream that maybe one day I might be able to explore fabrics and design! It was some considerable time before that was to happen."

Liam's voice interrupted to ask, "When did you find the time, Nan?"

She smiled and replied, "Not until my own children reached University age, when I discovered a particularly interesting course for mature students, and decided it was a now-or-never opportunity. Part of the selection process, for admission to the course, was based on the life experience and interests of the student. The course opened so many doors, which presented its own challenge as to which doors I should enter, and it was a case of putting many options on the back burner for another time. My sole aim, when applying, was to obtain a certificate which would enable me to pass on my chosen subjects to others, being aware at all times, that I was no more than an enabler, since the concept of creative design is about self-discovery and self-worth.

That had been my dream, as I struggled to produce a perfect circle to form the ends of the bolster cushion; a process which meant some unpicking, when the needle wandered off-course, but the second circle was much easier than the first, because I learned that some things cannot be rushed! Mum managed to make every process look easy, as she deftly manipulated the materials she used. I tried not to despair, as I endeavoured to copy her movements, but I had to admit that I felt clumsy, with fingers which didn't want to co-operate; even the silver thimble, refused to stay on my finger. That thimble was very precious because it had belonged to my grandmother and Mum wished me to have it.

How often I thought of Granddad's poem, *Try and try again boys, And you'll succeed at last.* Mind you the boys didn't have to bother with thimbles. Years later I found it very reassuring to look back at my first effort, if only to remind myself that beginning any subject, at any age, is not necessarily going to be easy, but our becoming, and feeling of self-worth depends, to a large extent, on how we manage the journey.

Indeed the first year after the move proved to be one of discovering what was, and was not possible, as I adapted to my new existence. During that summer, I experienced a need to find an out-of-doors secluded place; the Twin Wells was the answer, as it wasn't too far from home.

I should mention that Lisdoonvarna is renowned for two things: it is Ireland's premier spa, with three main wells. The town doesn't appear on the 1840 Ordnance Survey map. In fact it didn't begin to emerge as a town until the Gowlaun/Sulphur spring was discovered around 1852, when some of the local people located other mineral sources in the area. Over a period of time, the various analyses carried out revealed that the waters contained three times more hydrogen sulphide gas than the popular Harrogate Spa in England. All the waters were found to include iodine, which was very therapeutic. But I said that the town was renowned for two things: the second was its popularity with matchmakers; that news quickly spread over a very wide area. Initially the town was frequented by the elite, who came to take the waters and soak up the splendid atmosphere. Enjoying the baths and drinking the health-giving waters was interspersed with listening to music or dancing. Due to the success of the entertainment a Pavilion was built in the park, which is situated not far from the Spa. There were many changes during the Victorian era, and over time politics appeared to change people's perception of what the middle classes should be able to do. This resulted in the more successful farmers turning up en masse during the month of September, after the harvesting. It became a traditional time for matchmaking, which was a widespread practice amongst the farming fraternity. It actually developed into a thriving business, organized by one man, who sought to encourage the matchmaking process for those who were too shy to conduct the procedure for themselves. It remains a thriving business to this day, as people flock to the town; it could be said, that if the accommodation hasn't been pre-booked, it is unlikely that a room will be found during the month of September. So the Spa, or Sulphur Wells, became the hub around which everything else developed. As I told you, there are two other wells: one known as the Magnesia and Iron Wells, which was situated close to the Roadside Tavern – an Inn which had been built about 1865, and to which many visitors adjourned in the afternoons. The other is the Twin Wells which is situated by the river Aille, and which became my favourite haunt."

Giving Liam a wistful smile, Nan continued, "You know I don't often wish to be young again, but right now I wish I could set off from here and travel up the Knockauns Mountain, just as my brothers and I did when we were young, but this time taking you with me. I remember that, in order to get us out from under Mum's feet, Dad would occasionally elect to get us togged out – as he put it – and take us up the Burren Way, where even on the coldest days, the scenery was breathtaking. He never missed an opportunity to talk to us about the early people, who had survived in what sometimes appeared to be a very inhospitable area. We know they did survive, because of the legacy they left behind. On those occasions we passed below Slieve Elva. After the move to Lisdoonvarna we were living to the south of that mountain, which was in fact the source of the minerals, and the source of the Aille River. However, I wasn't aware of that until I told Granddad where I usually escaped to, and he reminded me that the river started its journey in the mountain, up the road from Rockville, and from there it cascaded or meandered down to the Spa Wells, where it was joined by the Gowlaun river, and continued through Rooska, past the Twin Wells, under the famous Spectacle Bridge, and on to Doolin where it flowed into the sea.

When time and weather permitted I took myself and my book to the Twin Wells, where the sound of rushing water was very peaceful, but it was also a source of mystery and fascination, since the Twin Wells is so called, because the two springs issue from the rocks within centimetres of each other. Granddad said that it had been exceedingly popular at one time, when it could be accessed by strolling from the Spa Wells, through the park, past the pavilion, along the raised river bank, to a point where one needed to descend a long flight of steps, before arriving at the spring, and people were thankful to help themselves to a refreshing drink, as they sat on the benches which were provided. Actually there is a second entrance to the Park and the Wells, situated near the Tavern. I guess there was a choice between the man-made refreshments, which didn't require any footwork, and the natural waters, after a promenade through the park! Anyway, the third entrance was my best choice, being closer to home, where there was a short flight of steps. The well was surrounded by a simple structure, with slate top and sides. There were two white enameled jugs in place to collect the water, as it trickled through. The interior of the jug, containing the iron water, had changed to a rich brown colour with long use. The drinking containers were placed on a ledge, but the utensils were only available during the summer months.

Surrounded by trees and vegetation, there couldn't have been a more secluded spot, not often visited by the time I discovered it.

I took a small cup along with me, but my refreshment was confined to the iron water: one taste of the sulphur water was a complete deterrent, despite its reputed health benefits. Mind you I wasn't in need of any therapeutic help in those days ... perhaps we could pay a quick visit before we leave the area!"

"Do you think that I might like the sulphur water Nan?" Liam ventured.

Nan laughed as she added, "If you hold your nose as you drink, you might."

"Whatever for, Nan, surely it is the taste that matters!"

"Oh no, Liam, not if you can smell rotten eggs!"

"Yuck, I see what you mean, so why do they use it?"

"Because they believe in its special curative properties, and at my age I believe I know what that means! There isn't time for me to list all the benefits derived from drinking the various waters, but as I have said, very extensive tests were carried out, and the number of people who flocked back year after year, was proof enough. However, I shouldn't leave the subject of the springs without telling you that it was the obnoxious smell of the sulphur water, which first attracted the attention of a surgeon from Limerick, whose name was Sylvester O'Halloran, and that was as far back as 1751.

As I sat on the edge of the platform with my legs over the side, listening to the flowing water in front of me, and the trickle of the springs behind me, I felt very thankful for all those people who had spent so much time conducting experiments on the spring waters. I was also truly grateful for others who had used the information they had been given, in order to provide the means whereby it could be used for the benefit of mankind ... and provide me with an escape haven, as well. As I gazed into the tumbling water, I recalled one of the verses from the poem, *The Brook* by Alfred Tennyson, which I had learned in Ballinalacken School:

I chatter, chatter, as I flow,
To join the brimming river,
For men may come and men may go,
But I go on forever.

Like the water itself, the poem has a beautiful sense of rhythm and timelessness, and I couldn't help thinking of those people who had obviously worked so tirelessly to develop the Wells: they had come and gone. Neither could I forget those who lived long before that time, long before Lisdoonvarna had existed, even back to the Celts! Oops! I know you are going to say now, 'There you go again, Nan,' but in my own defence, this time I have to say that it can't be helped, because the name of the town takes us back into the past, since Lisdoonvarna is translated from Lios Dúin Bhearna: Lios means fairy mound,; Dúin means fort, and Bhearna means gap, so it is commonly referred to as fort in the gap. We always referred to the fairy mounds as Lios, and no one dared interfere with them. You remember my telling you about the Tuatha De Denaan, who agreed to go underground and become the fairy folk, when they were beaten by the Milesians: a mythical tale with a grain of truth. There are so many sites in the area which can be dated from the Iron Age, and the discovery of a Bronze pot, about 500 yards from the Sulphur Wells, confirmed the existence of early habitation there.

Still my respite on the riverbank was not often an occasion for dipping into the past, but more one of preparing for the future, by coping with the present. Our circumstances at home were about to change dramatically when, after two years, Granddad developed pneumonia and came to stay in Rooska, whilst he recovered. By the time he was declared fit once more, Mum had persuaded him not to return to Ballinalacken; of course, she was also missing Joe, who had remained behind to keep him company. By this time Tom was living seven miles away in Ennistymon, where he was apprenticed to a Men's Outfitters and attending night school. His abiding passion was Gaelic Football, which he played at the week-ends, but we saw him at intervals. Granddad's decision caused a number of upheavals, and Mum needed to drastically reduce the amount of sewing she was able to do. About the same time I transferred from the Primary School to the Convent Secondary School, where I formed my first real and lasting friendship outside home. Geraldine epitomized all those qualities, which Granddad had declared essential in order to become a real, lovable being."

Liam interrupted to ask quietly, "How did you feel when Granddad elected to stay in Rooska?"

After a moment's careful consideration, Nan replied, "Well, for selfish reasons I was overjoyed, but we were both aware of what the severance meant, even though we were united again, and there was one huge difference: I was focused on moving forward, whereas Granddad needed to be content with his memories, and the fact that he was being very well cared for. There were times when we both experienced an acute wish to be back in Rockville, and strange as it may seem, it happened more often during the bleakest winter months. Most places have a certain bleakness at the height of the winter, but that could never be said of Ballinalacken, since even during those particular times the rugged, timeless beauty of the region, was its own reward. Despite that, we shared another five years, being ourselves. The locals became accustomed to seeing him walking into town, carrying his stick: which was mostly a precaution rather than a necessity, since he remained upright and very alert. He had more visits from his friends, because he was accessible in Rooska, and they spent many happy hours reminiscing. His health remained very good, until he developed a second bout of pneumonia, which sadly he did not survive." Nan was rummaging in her handbag as she was speaking, and finally produced a small plastic bag with a rather battered piece of paper in it. Showing it to Liam she read the obituary which had been printed in the County paper, and which was a testimony to his time in the Burren."

The death has occurred at the County Hospital, Ennis, of Mr. Thomas Chambers, ex-N.T., at the age of 86. He was a noted educationalist and taught in North Clare as an assistant in Kilfenora N.S. and as principal of Ballinalacken N.S. In the days when secondary education was not within the grasp of many, he very successfully prepared pupils for teaching, civil service and bank examinations. He was a noted athlete and sportsman, and a great student of nature. Up to a few weeks before his death his erect figure could be seen tripping lightly over moor and bogland. The immense cortege which followed the removal of the remains to Corpus Christi Church, Lisdoonvarna, on Monday evening, and to Holy Rosary Cemetery, Doolin, on Tuesday, testified to the high esteem in which he was held by his ex-pupils and a large circle of friends.

"You see Liam, love is real. We live on in the memory of those who love us, and we remain in perpetuity through the stories told about us… and here comes the sun, so let's get moving."

CHAPTER XV

THE LEGACY

Money will buy:

Money will buy a bed but not sleep;
books but not brains;
food but not appetite;
finery but not beauty;
a house but not a home;
medicine but not health;
luxuries but not culture;
amusements but not happiness;
religion but not salvation;
a passport to everywhere but heaven.

"You know Liam that poem was given to me by a retired Schoolmaster who introduced me to the Welsh language. His name was Les Williams: sadly he passed away a few years ago. Our village is situated in the Dysynni Valley, in the heart of the Snowdonia National Park. It has its own distinctive, captivating beauty, which is very different to the beauty of the Burren. From a social, historical and architectural point of view they have many similarities, including evidence of the Celts, but here comes the sun. It really is time to move, because there is one other place I wish to show you before we leave the area."

Nan was heading back to the car, as Liam's plaintiff voice caught up with her,

"Oh Nan, you haven't answered my most important questions yet!"

"Haven't I? Well, you just hold on to that thought for the time being. You know I can't drive and think of serious issues at the same time ... just hop in, belt up and we'll be there in no time."

She is true to her word and it isn't long before she is parking the car by a turn gate, which opens onto a narrow path: a path which disappears from view almost immediately.

Although they have left Ballinalacken in hazy sunshine, it certainly hasn't travelled with them to Lisdoonvarna, and she begins to doubt the wisdom of her choice, as they get out of the car. Liam gives her a questioning look, and she has to admit, "Yes, I am also wondering, but let's go and see." Within minutes they are through the gate, heading along the path and down some steep steps, with Nan in front and her grumbling companion bringing up the rear.

"Whatever are we doing here, Nan ... it's so spooky and the droplets from the branches are trickling down the back of my neck."

Before he has time to reinforce his argument, they arrive and are standing on the platform edge, looking at the tumbling river – the Áile – as it pursues its journey to the sea. Of course Liam can't see very far, because the mist hangs heavily amongst the trees. Nan, momentarily lost in the past, forgets one of her own rules, *always try to see things from the other person's point of view.* Then, noticing Liam's miserable face, she rushes up to him, giving him a big hug before turning him round to face the rocks, which he should have noticed when they arrived; had he not felt so dejected. She looks at him as she points to the rocks, "You see the water is still trickling through and, yes, this is the Twin Wells. You were wondering what the sulphur water tasted like ... now's your chance, but you'll have to scoop up the water in your hand."

Gone is his fit of the blues, as he becomes caught up in the experiment, whilst declaring that the taste isn't too bad. Holding a cupped handful of water out to Nan he laughingly says, "Like to join me, Nan?" but she light-heartedly declines to do so. It is so good to hear him laugh as he continues to sample both the iron and the sulphur waters. However, Nan, who has been biding her time, decides to wait no longer. Turning to face the river once more, she invites him to join her. "I wouldn't have chosen weather like this to bring you here, but it does seem very apt, in the circumstances … you see, this was where I came for a final outing before leaving for England with Mum, when we were going to join the rest of the family in Preston.

There was no major packing to be done, because Dad and Mum intended to return at some point. I should say that when Granddad came to live with us, it was decided that the farm should be sold. Tom had left to work in Preston, and when he was comfortably settled, he suggested to Dad that it shouldn't be difficult for him to find work too; and so it proved. Joe and Pat followed later, leaving Mum and I holding the fort: looking after Granddad. However, before the menfolk returned to Preston, following Granddad's funeral, Dad had made arrangements for us all to be re-united over there.

So it was … one afternoon in September, 1957, I came here for one last visit. It was a glorious afternoon and I remember trailing my feet through the fallen leaves, as I came down the path, and being conscious of the wonderful variety of colour. On arrival I stood, as I so often had, just gazing into the flowing river. There are many stanzas in the poem I mentioned earlier, and there always appeared to be one which suited my mood on the day. On the whole the poem, *the Brook,* seemed to represent life's journey. On that particular day I recited all of them; I didn't know what else to do. I realised that I was supposed to be finding a sense of perspective to guide me forward, but how on earth was I to achieve it. I knew that Dad and Mum would return, but just as I realised when I left Ballinalacken, I wouldn't return to live there, and I also knew that I wouldn't return to live in Lisdoonvarna either. It was an overwhelming thought and, despite the beautiful weather, my initial feelings were a better match for today's miserable scene. That was my problem, and my challenge: how to reconcile all that I had learned, but more importantly, all that I had experienced. So many pictures flashed through my mind. I thought of Dad and my brothers, who had already gone; and Mum whose siblings had emigrated at an early age, and with whom she had such little contact thereafter. Naturally she wanted all her children to be near her, if that were possible. I thought of Grandma and Granddad who had spent all their married life in Ballinalacken.

Yet it was Grandma's travels and wealth of knowledge, which had been responsible for the journey that Granddad and I had taken together. It was to be a story which accompanied me on my own journey. As I've already said, I was grateful for their legacy. But life was never going to be the same for me after Granddad left us; ours had been a deep, abiding love and friendship, and on occasions I simply wished to flee from here, but only to separate myself from the pain of his loss. Of course he would have been the first to remind me that life is about change, and change is not always easy or comfortable. I remembered the promise I had made myself when I reconnected with the real me in the Church: never again, *this time you are moving as a whole person and with all your emotional baggage.*

As I continued to gaze into the water, I realised that I had to be one of the luckiest people alive. Yes there would always be personal problems, because that's part of my make-up. The realisation was a valuable lesson, but I had learned an invaluable one too: even on those occasions when I might be on my own, I would never feel alone, unless I chose to ignore my invisible friend. That knowledge was to become more than invaluable; it became priceless. Of course I eventually found a new name for the source of my strength, in accordance with Granddad's advice ... I called him The Carpenter; after all he had been a carpenter by trade until he began his ministry at the age of 30, and I couldn't think of a better name for someone who was so adept at putting me back together whenever I seemed to fall apart, spiritually or emotionally. This was the reservoir that I could tap into at any time, but like the water coming from the rock behind us, I have to collect it for myself. It is free and life giving."

"I love you Nan, and thank you for sharing with me, but you still haven't told me why Granddad moved to Ballinalacken, and where from." Nan looked at Liam and began to laugh,

"My goodness, you seem to have inherited my persistence when it comes to asking the same question over and over again ... however, there are a few extra snippets which I want to share with you, now that I recall them. Once we leave this place, I will be putting the past to rest again. I've taken you on a sojourn, just as Granddad took me. Of course much of the past is the stuff of history, recorded by many people from different perspectives and it becomes a fascinating topic for discussion."

"Nan."

"Yes Liam."

"I am wondering, since you won't yet tell me about Granddad, could you at least tell me which part of the Bible had the greatest impact on you. You know I've tried reading it, but I have to admit that I don't find it easy?"

Nan takes so long to answer that Liam almost regrets asking; finally she smiles, "Wow Liam, that's a loaded question, and I wonder where it came from. Over a period of time I learned to understand and value many of the stories. Still if I had to select one story in particular, and say that it had a profound effect on me, it would have to be the story of Saul, or Paul as he came to be known."

"Perhaps if you tell me about Paul, I could try reading it for myself."

"Very well Liam, I feel sure that you will, on occasions, have listened to somebody who speaks with authority on a subject, making it easy to understand, so that you want to learn more; you could say that person was an eloquent speaker. So too with hand skills: watching someone quietly but dexterously manipulating materials in order to produce something useful and interesting, has always intrigued me. Of course Mum was my first source of inspiration in that respect. You know, as I grew I learned that if I ever had an awkward problem, which I wanted to discuss with her, it was better to bide my time until she was comfortably seated with her handwork, and seemingly at peace with herself and her surroundings; that aura of peace seemed to invite me in. However, as a teenager, I couldn't help but compare the difference between her approach, and that of Granddad, which was very intellectual and eloquent. The reason for sharing that with you is that Paul was a person who combined all those qualities: he was both eloquent and skilled with his hands.

Now here we go with our name-changing again, since Paul became the new name for Saul. One could say that Saul, the adversary, became Paul the advocate. He was born in Tarsus, the capital of Cilicia, being a very devout Jew, as well as a Roman citizen: a combination which was to prove very useful later on. He went to Jerusalem, where he trained to be a Master of the Law. Despite his academic qualifications, he was also expected to learn a trade; this was customary from an early age, and children were usually taught that by their parents: hence my reason for choosing the name Carpenter for Jesus, who had learned from Joseph. Paul, on the other hand, became a tent-maker and that would later support his ministry.

However, Saul had not witnessed what happened in Jerusalem, and he hadn't known Jesus beforehand; he could not accept all that followed, nor could he tolerate the new Christian movement which developed. He determined to wipe out all those whom he regarded as a threat to the established faith, and went to great lengths to obtain letters from the high priest, giving him authority to do so.

There is the moving story of Stephen, who had become an ardent follower of the movement. He had been elected, with six others, to look after the needs of the people, allowing the disciples to concentrate on their teaching mission. Stephen was to become the first martyr. Those involved in stoning him removed their outer garments, placing them at the feet of Saul for safe keeping. He had asked for letters of introduction to the synagogue in Damascus, so that he could round up any followers of the Way, and bring them back to Jerusalem for the prosecution. It was on this fateful journey that he was to have his life-changing experience. For, as he approached Damascus, he was stricken by a blinding flash of light. As he fell to the ground he heard a voice saying to him, *Saul, Saul! Why do you persecute me?* When he asked, *Who are you, Lord,* the voice replied, *I am Jesus whom you persecute, but get up and go into the city, where you will be told what to do.* Those who were with him heard the voice but couldn't see anyone. They took Saul by the hand and led him into Damascus, where he remained blind for three days."

Nan was looking at Liam's intent face as she continued, "From adversary to advocate, but what a missionary he proved to be. I think if you read the full story, which you will find in the Acts of the Apostles, and Paul's own letters to the other disciples and Churches, it will take you into the heart of the Bible."

"Oh, how I wish you could tell me more." He was hopping from one foot to the other in an attempt to warm himself; the mist had a chilling effect. He laughed as he continued, "You needn't answer that, because you have inspired me to go read for myself."

Nan shared his mirth as she replied, "Oh good, because that wasn't what I had chosen to share with you. Of course, I was very fortunate in that my childhood understanding of the Bible was based on the simple message as spoken by Jesus himself. It was a good starting point for me, but I did read the whole Bible many times: I had promised Granddad that I would.

I have to admit that, as a teenager I once read it simply as a story, because I had become interested in imagery, mythology, symbolism and that sort of thing. By then I had found other favourites also: blockbuster stories of the Wild West, the Apache Indians, and of course detective stories. The whodunit really captured my imagination; they were escapist books where the good guy always wins! There had to be a blockbuster element to hold my attention: it was from that perspective that I decided to re-read the Bible. Already secure in its spiritual message, I needed to know how else it could be interpreted. There is no real parallel to compare with it; where else could I find such length and breadth of written material, which so perfectly describes the human person from the beginning. It includes so much drama, frustration, exhilaration: with a mixture of power versus humility, hate versus love, hope versus despair, barbarism versus civility, self -sacrifice and compassion.

I had another reason for reading the Bible in that manner, since I was already captivated by the writings of J.R.R. Tolkien who hadn't lived in the Bible era. In one respect he helped to seal my reverence for, and approval of the Bible in its entirety."

Liam, still trying to offset the effect of the penetrating dampness, suddenly stops in front of Nan - completely agog.

"How on earth ...?

Nan, holds up her hands and says, "No more, until you take my keys and retrieve our jackets from the car. The run will do you good, and give me a few moments to myself."

Indeed, it doesn't take him long, but it is sufficient for Nan to be, once again, that person about to set sail into the unknown, leaving Ireland to join her brothers in England. She had a flash back to packing her suitcase, which involved so many painful decisions, because there wasn't enough room to take some of the things she really wanted. She wasn't to see again the childhood books, her doll or some of the things she had made. She hadn't realised then that she wouldn't be re-united with those precious, personal items; but it wasn't to be the limited contents of her suitcase, which would become her greatest asset. Nevertheless, she has time to reflect on the thought, which she'd had all those years ago: *how fortunate she was then and is now.*

Liam had disappeared like a puff of wind, and now reappears wearing his jacket. Handing Nan her garment, he is eager to tell her that the sun is shining. However, there is a mysterious, eerie quality to the information she wishes to share with him, and their present environment is ideally suited to that. She smiles as she reminds him, "This is a good place to talk and what I want to tell you and it won't take long."

Liam gives one of his lopsided grins saying, "Oh good, because now I am intrigued. Does this involve Tolkien and the Bible?"

Nan grins back at him as she continues, "Yes, but sadly once again time is not on our side, and I have a boat to catch soon. I am reminded of Granddad's oft repeated comment, *if only there was more time,* but let's see why I often thought of Tolkien when I read the Bible. It was he and his close friend C.S. Lewis who intrigued me: one born in Africa and the other in Northern Ireland, but what was the bond they shared?

Actually it was Aunt Alice who lit the first spark, when she and Uncle Ben came from Dublin for their annual visit. She had always brought me something special, and teased me unmercifully whilst I opened it. I knew when it was going to be a book because of the shape, but as I unpacked that particular book, I listened to her comments, which were so different, she wasn't teasing as she remarked, 'Now here is someone who will fire your imagination. We've already met him briefly in Dublin, following the publication of his story *Leaf by Niggle* in the Dublin Review, although that particular one will only be suitable when you are much older; the one you are holding will be just right for now and so was she: just right I mean, because I didn't want to put it down. On finishing the reading I wished for more, so I read it again. *The Hobbit, or There and Back Again* was a perfect book for encouraging imaginative thinking, it caught and held me; being full of different imaginary creatures: hobbits, dwarves, giant spiders, goblins, elves and different faeries. The description of Bilbo Baggins was very endearing, as was his home.

However, the first few chapters did nothing to prepare me for Bilbo's eventual meeting with Gollum: then my imagination ran riot. I wasn't enthusiastic about Gollum's appearance, or his abode in the dark slimy cave; it made me shiver, and I wouldn't have wanted to encounter him, as I would Bilbo. Anyway, those nasty pictures I had conjured up were soon banished, as I read about the encounter between Bilbo and Gollum. Gollum's mode of speech appealed to my wicked sense of humour. His reaction when he first encounters Bilbo is described by Tolkien, *Bless us and splash us, my precioussss! I guess it's a choice feast; at least a tasty morsel it'd make us, Gollum.* Apparently when he said *Gollum*, it emerged as a weird gurgling sound. The riddles which followed were quite exciting, but it was his habitual use of ssss which constantly reduced me to giggles, and I practiced my own words on anyone within earshot, driving poor Mum to distraction, but causing much laughter amongst the guests.

However, my light-hearted reaction was merely a prelude to what was to become the main topic of conversation for the duration of Uncle Ben and Aunt Alice's stay. Fortunately it provided a distraction from Grandma's deteriorating health. They were all intent on sharing their accumulated knowledge regarding C.S. Lewis and J.R.R.Tolkien, and his inspiration for *The Hobbit.*. Now, in case I forget to mention it later, my copy had a very happy parting between Bilbo and Gollum, when Bilbo was allowed to keep the ring because he had won it fairly during the riddle session. So, I was sad to learn many years later that, in order to satisfy the Publisher's request for more of the same, Tolkien needed to revise the early copy in order to produce The Lord of the Rings. In the revised edition Gollum concludes, *Thief, thief, thief! Baggins! We hates it, we hates it, we hates it forever!* I know I would probably have felt the same about that ending, when I first read it. However, the name Gollum, and the inspiration for the story was what formed the basis for all the adult discussions.

You remember, when I was reminiscing earlier, I told you that I wished to be young again so that I could take you up the Knockauns mountain, as Dad used to take us children. I also said that we skirted Slieve Elva, when Dad talked to us at length about the geology and past history of the area; and the need to keep our eyes open at all times. It wasn't merely an excursion to get us out from under Mum's feet! Dad enjoyed sharing what he knew, and Elva, which is associated with the Tuatha de Danaan, is fascinating, if only for the fact that caves there formed an underworld maze. For instance, he mentioned Poulnaphouca, which he said was supposed to be associated the Pookas – ill-minded faeries intent on causing chaos. That was really a myth, but not so the advice he gave us regarding Poul na Gollum. We had been warned to beware of potholes at all times. In fact, there was a local story about the man who discovered the Aillwee caves - now a major tourist attraction – when his dog disappeared through a pothole whilst chasing a rabbit. The farmer didn't venture too far into the cave, and it was thirty years later that he happened to mention it to some cavers.

Dad told us that Poll na Gollum was not safe for us to visit. Although he and our uncles had visited there after reading an article by the noted archaeologist, T. J. Westropp. He referred to the *great pit called Paul na Gollum,* so called because it had been the home of the rock dove. Westropp ventured only as far as the first main junction within the cave: that was in 1880. By 1912 others had taken up the gauntlet, and eventually the real extent of the caves was revealed. Being approximately 10 miles – the longest in Ireland – it has numerous streams, lakes and passages. In fact, a number of entrances were later discovered, but the one Dad described to us was the first and largest. The entrance pit is very deep, and the caves can only be accessed by using a rope.

I had difficulty imagining the cave, but I remember pestering Dad about the doves, and what they might look and sound like? When my brothers and I went into the castle, I had been spooked by the bird noises there; they sounded lofty, unreal and unfriendly. When I mentioned my experience to Dad he said, 'Well, that's because the castle walls help to cause a spacious vacuum, and the noise becomes distorted and loud, reverberating off the castle walls. Actually, it was a similar noise which had indicated the extent of the underground cavern at Poll na Gollum. Dad also said that the rock dove is different to ordinary doves which make a coo-coo sound: the rock dove being more like a pigeon, with a more guttural sound, which is not pleasing to listen to. He had proceeded to give us a demonstration on the difference; and was then subjected to a chorus as we all practiced together, until he clapped his hands over his ears, 'Well I think you've all got that one, so let's leave it there.'

Still, it was Dad, Uncle Ben and Granddad's input during their animated conversation, which had electrified me, as they began to discuss the early childhood of Lewis and Tolkien. Being young myself, I felt a deep sadness for both the young boys, as I became absorbed in their plight.

J.R.R. Tolkien, was born in Africa, but when he was only three years old his mother returned to England with him and his younger brother; they lived near his mother's family in Birmingham. He was not to see his father again, since he died the following year after a short illness. A few years later his mother, who had been an Anglican, converted to Catholicism: the family became very devoted to the church. His mother died when he was only twelve, but the priest at the Oratory in Birmingham took the boys under his wing, although they lived with their aunt. He remained grateful to his mother and the priest for all that they had done for him. He had a very keen interest in nature, botany, history, literature, language and fantasy; even inventing his own private languages. He later became a Professor of languages at Oxford University. It was there that he and C.S. Lewis first met in 1926. He was 34 and Lewis was just 28.

C.S. Lewis was born in Belfast, and was to lose his mother when he was only ten years old. He was immediately dispatched to a boarding school near London, that must have felt like losing two parents. After a short spell attending a college near his home, he returned to England to study. He was then thirteen years old: so young to be shunted from one country to another. I wondered if that became his reason for rejecting his Anglican faith, he felt rejected himself. However, he proved to be academically gifted, and later became a tutor at Magdalen College, Oxford, where he was to meet Tolkien before long.

Losing parents, at such a young age was likely to create an immediate affinity between them, and it became stronger as they came to recognise the extent of the creative interests which they shared: they were both writers. It wasn't long before Lewis rediscovered his faith, and it was to him that Tolkien gave the unfinished proof copy of The Hobbit to read in 1932. For me, the intriguing aspect of the adult's discussion was how Tolkien came to be in the Burren, and captivated by its landscape.

It always amused me to see men suddenly stick out their chests, when they occasionally spoke with pride about an achievement, or someone they knew. Even Granddad! He was so keen to tell everyone that Lewis' father was a Cork man, just like himself, but that he had travelled from the south to the north where he eventually became a county solicitor. We already knew that two of Granddad's brothers had travelled to Belfast about the same time. Of course Cork was one of those districts which had suffered greatly during the time of the famine, and for a long time afterwards. Did Granddad's brothers or Lewis's father travel through the Burren en route for the north? Almost certainly, according to Granddad; but he himself had decided to remain in that area, and was fortunate in finding work which allowed him to do so.

Lewis would have been keen to introduce his friend to all those things and places, which he knew would have been of interest to him. One area of profound interest would have been the ancient

Irish manuscripts, such as the *Annals of the Four Masters* and the *Lebor Gabála Érenn* (otherwise known as the Book of Invasions), which included the pre-history accounts of Ireland's past: full of mythology and folklore. Following that inspirational summer interlude with the adults, and already deeply immersed in the myth and fantasy of the Hobbit, I occasionally wondered what else those two writers did.

Twelve months later, when Granddad was taking me on our own inspirational journey, I visualised Tolkien pouring over the Old Irish Manuscripts, whilst comparing their contents to those of the Bible; Granddad had outlined the historical link, but Tolkien was to develop the mythological link. Whilst Lewis, who had re-discovered his faith, concentrated mainly on spiritual material, Tolkien opened up a world of fantasy, with a spiritual thread running through it: never losing sight of the power of good over evil."

Nan couldn't resist laughing, as she said, "Of course I had also acquired a new ally; there were occasions, when I arrived back from school feeling cold, wet and hungry, that Mum would say, 'Could you just feed the fowl before you take your coat off.' Then, it was easy for me to reply, *I hates it,* and get away with it." Liam joined in the laughter, adding, "I will remember that one!"

"We really must be on our way now Liam. Needless to say I can't race along as you did; so I am going to give you a riddle, which you should have solved by the time we reach the gate."

"OK! I'm ready go ahead."

"This thing all things devours:
Birds, beasts, trees, flowers;
Gnaws iron, bites steel;
Grinds hard stones to meal;
Slays king, ruins town,

And beats high mountain down."

By the time Nan had repeated the riddle twice, they'd arrived at the wooden gate, which Liam was holding open. Looking at the gate, and then at her companion, she said reminiscently, "There used to be an old iron gate here, but even then it was rusty and creaking at the hinges."

"Oh Nan, you can't catch me with that one! As I told you, I love Tolkien's books, including the Hobbit; after all you told me at the beginning that *time waits for no man*, but it would appear that it leaves its mark on everything; including the old gate."

"Yes Liam, you're right, *time is of the essence*, and of course it is the answer."

Nan, had resorted to her Granmaric tone as she declared, "Right! Into the car … time and the damp conditions down there are no friends of old bones." Within a few minutes of seating themselves, they were shedding their jackets and Nan was more comfortable.

"Nan"

"Yes Liam."

"You know there is something you haven't told me? I'm not thinking of Granddad this time, because I believe I've got a pretty good picture of him now. But I remember how emotional you were when we arrived in Ballinalacken; you said then that no one had ever asked you how you felt when you left there. I remember also, that you said I should ask questions if I needed to. Well, you have given me so much to think about when we leave here. Yet, you haven't told me about the day you left Lisdoonvarna. Just now you were telling me about your last visit to the Twin Wells, but I need to ask the same question which I put to you concerning your departure from Rockville." Liam laughed nervously as he continued, "I'm not really sure whether I should be asking you, but it would help to complete the picture if you were able to tell me. Did the thoughts you had by the Wells help you to cope with the move? "

Nan sensed that Liam was nervous, and that it had taken considerable courage to broach the subject. She could choose to be Granmaric again, (that was a word she had invented, when she didn't want to argue or have a scene), or she could reflect on those first moments which they had shared in Ballinalacken, when he had thoughtfully asked, '*How did you feel when you moved to Lisdoonvarna?*' She knew that she really didn't have a choice, and simply said, "I wouldn't actually choose to go there Liam, but your initial question, which was one of love and concern, opened up those early chapters of my life. Now, I believe that I should love and respect your wishes, and revisit that last morning, like it or not! As you know, the bungalow is just around the corner so let's go there. It isn't strictly possible to compare my departure from Ballinalacken to that of leaving Lisdoonvarna; the first event took place when I was ten years old, and I was seventeen when we left Rooska."

They had arrived outside the bungalow, where Nan parked the car, but made no attempt to leave it. They sat in silence for a few moments until Liam said, as he had done previously, "You don't have to, if you think it will be too upsetting!"

Nan took his hand and squeezed it as she continued, "Do you remember what I told you about my visit to the Church, when the candle flame kept me transfixed until I opened up to its healing light. Well you, Liam, are rather like that candle, with your inner glow: an attentive and thoughtful listener, so I will do my best.
The morning we left was strange to say the least; it being a *fait accompli*, so to speak. The packing had been done the previous

day, and the only remaining task was to ensure that the bungalow was secure. One of Mum's friends, who lived nearby, had a spare key; she was also taking charge of Tiny, our Jack Russell terrier. You know I said that on the day we moved to Rooska, I really missed Tiny because she could have accompanied me on my walks, but she actually belonged to Joe, who used to take her rabbit hunting. In fact, apart from school and church they went everywhere together. When Joe left for England, Tiny remained in Rooska, and she quickly attached herself to me. She was a very playful character, always aware of my movements; and in her element when I put her in the basket, which was fixed to the front of my bicycle. I always imagined that her upright, forward-leaning posture meant she felt quite exhilarated by the wind rushing past her, as we sped along.

I know that animals have what is called a sixth sense; it was so evident on that particular morning. After all, Joe had packed a case, and disappeared; would she have sensed his changed attitude to her before he left? Had she done so, she would have been getting similar vibes from me. Normally she remained indoors when Mum and I needed to be elsewhere.

However, Mum's friend arrived in good time in order to collect Tiny's belongings, and having done so, decided that she and Tiny could wave us off. Mum and her friend chatted whilst I held Tiny's lead; it was the first time she had worn a collar, and she wasn't happy. As I tried to reassure her, I couldn't help noticing the look of fear and uncertainty in her eyes, which seemed to say, are you leaving me too? I did wonder whether it would have been better for her to have remained indoors until after we'd gone: for her sake and mine.

It had only been four weeks since we had lost Granddad, and although I could and did often remind myself that I was indeed a very lucky person, reassuring Tiny made me very conscious of my own feelings. I was still grieving for Granddad, but whilst I remained in the bungalow, I could sense his presence there. I hadn't allowed myself to dwell on the fact that leaving would be a final severance until that moment. The bus had arrived and it was all activity: the driver had alighted to put our cases in the hold, and after a quick good-bye, Mum and I went on board.

As I said it would definitely have been better if Tiny had remained indoors. I could see her straining as she tried to follow us. Unable to do so she began to howl: that pitiful cry found an echo in me, but my tears were silent."

Nan has become aware that, this time, Liam is holding her hand which she covers with her spare one. Eventually she is able to say, "Liam, it is my turn to say thank you for your persistence, and your love."

THE BURREN AND GALWAY BAY

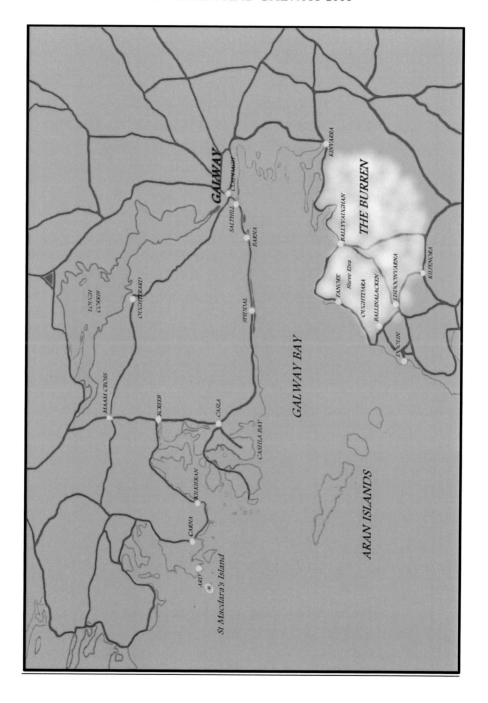

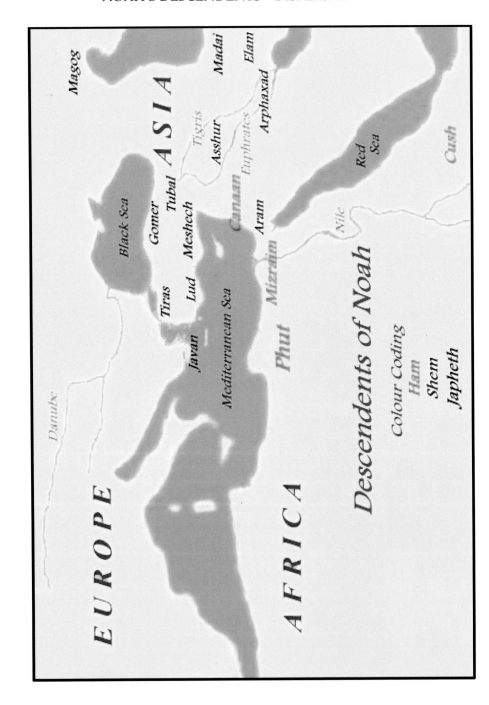

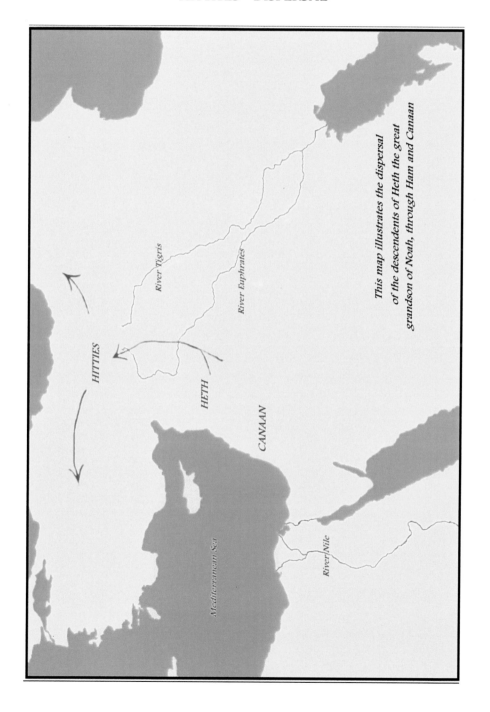

This map illustrates the dispersal of the descendents of Heth the great grandson of Noah, through Ham and Canaan

River Tigris

River Euphrates

HITTITES

HETH

CANAAN

Mediterranean Sea

River Nile

GENEALOGY LISTS

ADAM – EVE

DESCENDENTS

CAIN	ABEL	SETH
ENOCH		ENOSH
IRAD		CAINAN
MEHUJAEL		MAHALALEL
METHUSAEL		JARED
LAMECH		ENOCH
JUBAL		**METHUSELAH**
		LAMECH
		NOAH

LAMECH (Cain's descendent)

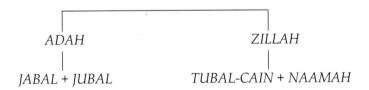

ADAH	ZILLAH
JABAL + JUBAL	TUBAL-CAIN + NAAMAH

JAPHETH	HAM	SHEM
GOMER	CUSH	ELAM
MAGOG	MIZRAIM	ASSHUR
MADAI	PHUT	ARPHAXAD
JAVAN	*CANAAN*	LUD
TUBAL		ARAM
MESSHECH		
TIRAS		

NOAH'S SONS AND GRANDSONS ACCORDING TO JOSEPHUS

The Bible names of the sons and grandsons of Noah, with descriptions of the migrations according to Josephus, in the Antiquities of the Jews Book 1, Ch.6.1,2. See also Genesis Chapters 10 and 11.

JAPHETH AND SONS

Gomer *'those whom the Greeks now call Galatians, [Galls], but were then called Gomerites.'*

Magog *'Magogites, but who are by the Greeks called Scythians.'*

Madai *'from Madai came the Madeans, who are called Medes by the Greeks.'*

Javan *'from Javan, Ionia and all the Grecians are derived.'*

Tubal	*'Thobel founded the Thobelites, who are now called (Thobel) Iberes.'*
Meshech	*'the Mosocheni were founded by Mosoch; now they (Mosoch) are Cappadocians.'*
Tiras	*'Thiras also called those whom he ruled over (Thiras) Thirasians, but the Greeks changed the name intoThracians.'*

HAM AND SONS

Cush	*'Chus; for the Ethopians over whom he reigned, are (Chus) even at this day, both by themselves and by all men in Asia called Chusites.'*
Egypt (Mestre)	*'The memory also of the Mesraites is preserved in their name; for all we who inhabit this country [of Judea] call Egypt Mestre, and the Egyptians Mestreans.'*
Put (Phut)	*'Phut also was the founder of Libya, and called the (Phut) inhabitants Phutites.'*
<u>Canaan</u>	*'inhabited the country of Judea, and called it from his own name Canaan.'*

SHEM AND SONS

Elam	*'Elam left behind him the Elamites, the ancestors of the Persians.'*
Asshur (Ashur)	*'Ashur lived at the city Nineve; and named his subjects (Ashur) Assyrians, who became the most fortunate nation, beyond others.'*
Arpachsad	*Arphaxad named the Arphaxadites, who are now called*

(Arphaxad) Chaldeans.'

Aram   *'Aram had the Aramites, which the Greeks call Syrians.'*

Lud   *'Laud founded the Laudites, which are now called
(Laud) Lydians.'*